RECURRENT

ELECTRICAL TRANSIENTS

PRENTICE-HALL ELECTRICAL ENGINEERING SERIES

W. L. EVERITT, *Editor*

RECURRENT

ELECTRICAL TRANSIENTS

By

L. W. VON TERSCH

Department of Electrical Engineering
Iowa State College

and

A. W. SWAGO

PRENTICE-HALL, INC.   New York

Library of Congress Card Catalog
Number: 52-14161.

First Printing . . . . *January, 1953*
Second Printing . . . . *August, 1954*
Third Printing . . . . *March, 1955*

PREFACE

This volume is not intended to be a reference book on wave-shaping circuits: several excellent works of this type are available and are listed often in the selected references following the respective chapters. The authors believe, however, that many of these references do not serve well as texts, and they have attempted to design this book primarily to teach a technique of analysis, while acquainting the reader with representative types of circuits in which the steady-state waveform may be considered as a series of recurring transients. Because such circuits may find applications in many places, including the fields of television, nuclear instrumentation, radar, computing devices, and industrial control, component circuits are emphasized but little attempt is made to consider over-all systems. The analysis stresses the time-constant concept in preference to frequency considerations. Rationalized mks units have been used. *Recurrent Electrical Transients* may be used as a textbook in a one-quarter or one-semester course on wave-shaping circuits, taught usually as part of an electrical engineering curriculum, or as elective material for physicists interested in those fields where specific electronic devices are extensively used.

Although many illustrative examples are included, they have been considered primarily as supplementary material. In many cases time limitations will preclude their use in regular classroom coverage. Solutions of the problems included at the end of the chapters are not, for the most part, possible by direct substitution in equations developed earlier. Though based on the fundamentals considered, most of the problems require original thought, and some may prove slightly difficult for undergraduate students. The subjects of pulse amplification and general transient analysis have been omitted from this volume because both are extensive in scope and are well treated in other sources. In addition to its primary value for understanding of theory, this volume may be useful to engineering graduates and technicians in helping them to become familiar with some of the circuits which have come into widespread use in recent years.

The authors wish to express their appreciation to Dean W. L. Everitt, the editor of this series, for his guidance and understanding; to Prof. M. S. Coover, Head of the Electrical Engineering Department, Iowa State College; to Dr. J. D. Ryder, Head of the Electrical Engineering Department, University of Illinois; and to the Staff of the Electrical Engineering Department of the Iowa State College, for suggestions and encouragement.

L. W. VON TERSCH

A. W. SWAGO

CONTENTS

CHAPTER ONE

FUNDAMENTAL CONCEPTS

A study of elementary electrical transients and their applications should begin with a discussion of the circuit elements which will be encountered. In general, these elements may be divided into two classes, active and passive.

The active elements can also be considered to exist in either of two forms, as current sources or as voltage sources. Both might

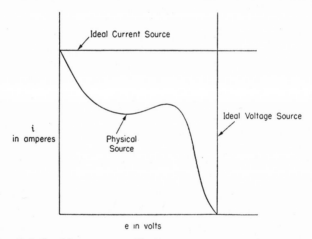

Fig. 1-1. Relationships among an ideal current source, an ideal voltage source and a physical source.

represent the same arrangement of physical elements, but certain mathematical operations might favor the use of one in preference to the other. In any practical system, the active elements will never exist alone but will appear in conjunction with some form of passive element. The general relationships between the two types of sources may be indicated by the volt-ampere characteristics of Fig. 1-1.

1

The terms *current source* and *voltage source* will apply equally well to time-varying or time-independent systems.

The passive elements which can appear in the networks to be studied will contain resistance, capacitance, inductance, or combinations of these. In a great number of examples, the circuit component can be specified as containing but one of these parameters, in which case the element will be called a resistor, a capacitor, or an inductor. In other instances, however, it may be impossible to define the component so simply.

1-1 Definition of Resistance

The resistors appearing in the circuits will, for the most part, be linear and bilateral, that is, over the operating range their resistance will be independent of the magnitude or the direction of their voltage and current, obeying the law

$$e = Ri \qquad (1\text{-}1)$$

However, the use of unilateral resistors (the term unilateral itself expressing a form of nonlinearity) is of great importance. These unilateral resistors will be represented primarily by contact-type rectifiers and gas or vacuum electron tubes. Usually a simple analytical expression relating the voltage and current for such an element will not be available; therefore recourse must be made to graphical or approximate analytical forms of solution. The given graphical relationship between the current and voltage may be capable of modification by the change in potential of other points in the circuit.

The volt-ampere characteristic of a resistor may be used to illustrate two resistance concepts. In one concept, the resistance value is given by the ratio of the voltage to the current at the point under consideration and the value so obtained is called the direct-current or static resistance. In the second concept, the resistance is given by the slope of the volt-ampere characteristic at the point in question and is called the dynamic or varying-current resistance. It should be emphasized that the latter concept of resistance has significance only for varying or changing current and voltage values. In the case of the linear resistor, the static and dynamic resistances become identical.

Consider the volt-ampere characteristic given by Fig. 1-2. The static resistance in the region between points O and A is nearly constant, and at point A has the value e_A/i_A. The static resistance at point B is greater than that of point A and is equal to e_B/i_B.

The dynamic resistance at point A is (de/di) $\rfloor_{i=i_A}$ and is a positive quantity whereas the dynamic resistance at point B, (de/di) $\rfloor_{i=i_B}$ is

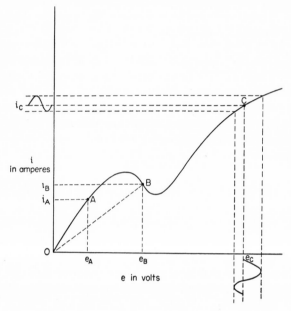

Fig. 1-2.   Indication of static and dynamic resistance.

a negative quantity.   Although physical systems can be arranged to produce a negative dynamic resistance, the static resistance of an element is usually considered to be positive.

Let the element, having the characteristics of Fig. 1-2 be placed in series with two sources of potential.   One of these sources will have a steady value equal to e_C and the other will be a varying voltage of small magnitude.   A current will then result which could be considered the sum of two currents.   One of these currents would be the direct current i_C, while the other would be equal to the applied varying voltage divided by the dynamic resistance at point C.

The static resistance of an element will be differentiated from the dynamic resistance by placing a bar over the top of the symbol for the static resistance. For example, the plate-cathode resistance of a high-vacuum triode will be written r_p for the dynamic plate resistance and $\bar{r}_p$ for the static plate resistance.

On some occasions it may be convenient to use the reciprocal of resistance. This is termed *conductance*; it is symbolized by g or $\bar{g}$.

1-2 Definition of Capacitance

The second element to be discussed is the capacitor. This term indicates an element which is not capable of dissipating energy, but only of storing it in an electric field. Any physical capacitor will also produce dissipation due to series resistance or to losses in the dielectric. In many cases this dissipation may be completely neglected. It is also possible for a capacitor to have a nonlinear dielectric, in which case the capacitance will be a function of the voltage across the capacitor. However, only linear capacitors will be considered here.

The capacitance of a capacitor is defined as the ratio of charge q to terminal voltage e, or

$$C = \frac{q}{e} \tag{1-2}$$

where C is the capacitance in farads, q is the charge in coulombs, e is the potential in volts. The current into a capacitor will be

$$i = \frac{dq}{dt} = \frac{d}{dt}(Ce) \tag{1-3}$$

For capacitors which have a linear dielectric (that is, the permittivity is not a function of charge or voltage) and a nonvarying physical shape, this becomes,

$$i = C\frac{de}{dt} \tag{1-4}$$

The charge on the capacitor is the time integral of the current into the capacitor or,

$$q = q_0 + \int_0^t i\,dt \tag{1-5}$$

The first term q_0 is the initial charge on the capacitor, while the integral term gives the charge that has been added during the period of interest, that is, the accumulation of charge from the time origin to the instant being considered. The quantity $\int_0^t i\, dt$ may actually add to, or subtract from, the original charge q_0. Since the voltage across the capacitor at any time is

$$e = \frac{q}{C} \tag{1-6}$$

Then $$e = \frac{1}{C}\left(q_0 + \int_0^t i\,dt\right) = e_0 + \frac{1}{C}\int_0^t i\,dt \tag{1-7}$$

The voltage e_0 is the original voltage on the capacitor corresponding to the charge q_0, that is

$$e_0 = \frac{q_0}{C} \tag{1-8}$$

One important fact is evident from Eq. (1-7). The voltage across the capacitor cannot be changed instantaneously, unless the integrand (i) is infinite. There is no similar restriction on the capacitor current. In capacitor circuits where switching is performed, the currents through the capacitors will usually be discontinuous unless inductive elements are also present.

Since most physical systems will contain a finite amount of resistance, infinite currents cannot be achieved. Therefore a physical capacitor will never have an instantaneous voltage change across its terminals. It may have a very high rate of change of voltage.

The reciprocal of capacitance $1/C$, called *elastance*, is designated by the symbol S.

1-3 Definition of Inductance

Self-inductance, the third element, is again a component which cannot dissipate energy, but which can only store energy in its associated magnetic field. Two inductors can mutually store energy in a magnetic field. The total energy may then be considered to be associated with the self-inductance of the first inductor, the self-inductance of the second inductor, and the mutual inductance between the two inductors. However, mutual inductance will not be considered a circuit element.

Any physical inductor will also introduce dissipation due to series resistance or to losses in the surrounding medium.

The inductance of an inductor will be defined as the ratio of the magnetic flux linkages λ to the current i, or

$$L = \frac{\lambda}{i} \tag{1-9}$$

where L is the inductance in henrys, λ is the magnetic flux linkages in weber-turns, i is the current in amperes. By Faraday's law, the induced voltage across the inductor will be equal to the time rate of change of magnetic flux linkages, or

$$e = \frac{d\lambda}{dt} = \frac{d}{dt}(Li) \tag{1-10}$$

where e is in volts, t is in seconds. If the permeability of the surrounding medium is not a function of current, and if the inductor is unchanged with time,

$$e = L\frac{di}{dt} \tag{1-11}$$

It must be remembered that the polarity of the induced voltage must be such as to oppose the change in current which is causing it. A negative sign is sometimes added to the previous equations to indicate this opposition.

The total number of magnetic flux linkages in an inductor is equal to the time integral of the voltage across the inductor, or

$$\lambda = \lambda_0 + \int_0^t e\,dt \tag{1-12}$$

Since the current through the inductor is

$$i = \frac{\lambda}{L} \tag{1-13}$$

then $$i = \frac{1}{L}\left(\lambda_0 + \int_0^t e\,dt\right) = i_0 + \frac{1}{L}\int_0^t e\,dt \tag{1-14}$$

The term i_0 is the initial current through the inductor, while the integral term gives the increment of current added or subtracted since the specified starting time.

The expression of Eq. (1-14) indicates that the current through the inductor cannot change instantaneously unless the applied voltage becomes infinite. The voltage across the inductor can be discontinuous.

Current and voltage expressions for the three passive elements are tabulated in Fig. 1-3. Note that since de_C/dt implies an increase

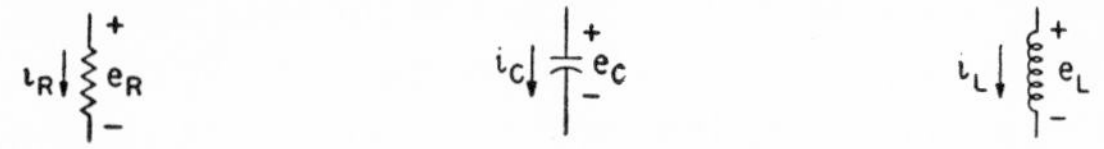

$$e_R = Ri_R \qquad e_C = e_0 + \frac{1}{C}\int_0^t i_C\,dt \qquad e_L = L\frac{di_L}{dt}$$

$$i_R = \frac{e_R}{R} \qquad i_C = C\frac{de_C}{dt} \qquad i_L = i_0 + \frac{1}{L}\int_0^t e_L\,dt$$

Fig. 1-3. Relationship between current and voltage for resistive, capacitive, and inductive elements.

in e_C, current will flow in the direction shown. Similarly for an increase in i_L, voltage will be induced across the inductor with the polarity shown. If the changes are decreases, the derivatives are negative, causing the capacitor current and the inductor voltage to be reversed.

1-4 Characteristics of Common Nonlinear Resistive Elements

Many nonlinear resistive elements will be used sufficiently in the following chapters to warrant a brief presentation of their characteristics.

One of the more important volt-ampere characteristics is of the form obtainable from a diode. Two general possibilities are available here; the diode may be either of the thermionic type or of the contact rectifier type.

A volt-ampere characteristic for the 6AL5 thermionic diode (one section) is shown in Fig. 1-4a. In Fig. 1-4b is shown an expanded view of the lower part of the curve. These curves do not pass throught the origin since many electrons leave the cathode with sufficient energy to reach the anode structure without the benefit of any accelerating potential.

For many types of problems, the accuracy introduced by the use of the exact nonlinear characteristic is not warranted by the extra labor involved. In such cases an acceptable approximate solution

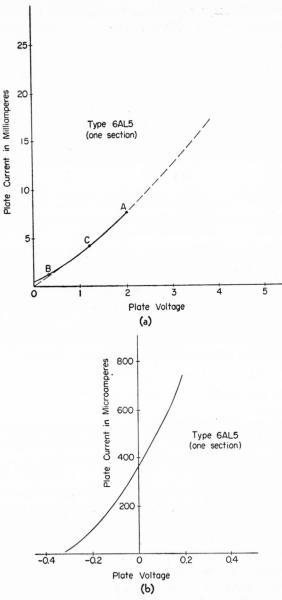

Fig. 1-4. (a) Volt-ampere characteristic for type 6AL5 thermionic diode (one section). (b) Expanded view of (a) around origin.

may be obtained by assumption of a constant static resistance in the positive region. In particular is this true if the diode is in series with a larger resistor.

If the diode of Fig. 1-4a is operated between point A and point B, it could be represented by a linear resistor having a resistance

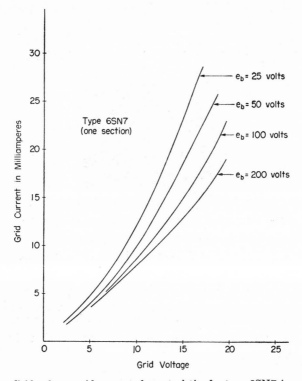

Fig. 1-5. Grid voltage-grid current characteristics for type 6SN7 (one section).

equal to the average static resistance between A and B. This resistance is given by the reciprocal of the slope of line OC.

A thermionic diode can also be obtained by using the grid and cathode elements of a triode or pentode tube. The characteristic obtained in this manner is similar to that obtained for the elementary diode. However the characteristic is not unique, in that a different grid-cathode characteristic exists for every value of plate voltage. Such a characteristic for the type 6SN7 tube (one section) is shown in Fig. 1-5.

The characteristic of a typical contact-type rectifier is shown in Fig. 1-6. Note that in Fig. 1-6a there is a scale change between the positive and negative ranges. Such rectifiers have several advantages with respect to thermionic diodes, among these being their small size, low shunt capacitance, and the lack of necessity for filament supply. In addition, there is no current flow for zero applied voltage as is the case for thermionic diodes. The chief disadvantage of the contact-type rectifier is the finite back resistance. For some applications, particularly those of clamping circuits and various

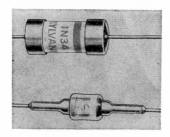

Fig. 1-7. Type 1N34 and 1N34A germanium diodes.
(Courtesy Sylvania, Inc.)

forms of step counters, the relatively low back resistance may offer some difficulty. Contact-type rectifiers also exhibit definite variation in characteristics with changes in temperature.

The concept of dynamic and static resistance as discussed in Sec. 1-1 is particularly applicable to triode or other multiple-element tubes. The plate current in a triode tube is a function of the plate voltage and the grid voltage, or

$$i_b = f(e_b, e_c) \tag{1-15}$$

where i_b is the total plate current. The grid voltage e_c is considered to be the total potential drop from grid to cathode, consisting of the sum of the d-c grid voltage and the changing grid voltage. Similarly, the plate voltage e_b is the sum of the d-c value and the changing plate voltage. The differential plate current can be written as

$$di_b = \frac{\partial i_b}{\partial e_b} de_b + \frac{\partial i_b}{\partial e_c} de_c \tag{1-16}$$

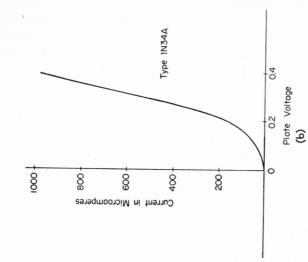

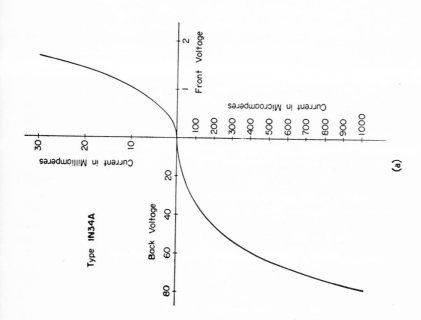

Fig. 1-6. (a) Volt-ampere characteristic for type 1N34A germanium diode. (b) Expanded view of (a) around origin.

The term $\partial i_b / \partial e_b$ is the reciprocal of the dynamic plate resistance and the term $\partial i_b / \partial e_c$ is defined as the transconductance of the tube with the symbol g_m. Then

$$di_b = \frac{1}{r_p} de_b + g_m de_c \qquad (1\text{-}17)$$

or

$$i_p = \frac{1}{r_p} e_p + g_m e_g \qquad (1\text{-}18)$$

where i_p, e_p, and e_g are the varying components of the plate current, plate voltage, and grid voltage, respectively. Rewriting Eq. (1-18) gives

$$\mu e_g = r_p i_p - e_p \qquad (1\text{-}19)$$

where

$$\mu = g_m r_p \qquad (1\text{-}20)$$

By examination of Eq. (1-19), an equivalent circuit can be devised which will describe the operation of the dynamic system. This circuit is shown in Fig. 1-8. The polarity signs indicate instantaneous values. It must be remembered that Eq. (1-19) and the circuit of Fig. 1-8 are applicable only to changing quantities. It has also been assumed that the range of operation is sufficiently small that the dynamic plate resistance and the transconductance are constant.

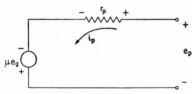

Fig. 1-8. Equivalent dynamic circuit for triode type tube.

For multiple-grid tubes in which the secondary grids are held at a fixed d-c potential, the analysis is identical to that for triodes.

In many types of problems involving triodes or multigrid tubes, the range of operation is too great to allow use of the dynamic plate resistance or transconductance. The problem can then be solved graphically, or in some cases an approximate value for the static resistance can be used.

The plate volt-ampere characteristics for the type 6J5 (similar to one section of the 6SN7), the type of 6C4 (similar to one section of the 12AU7), and the type 6CB6 are shown in Figs 1-9, 1-10, and 1-11, respectively.

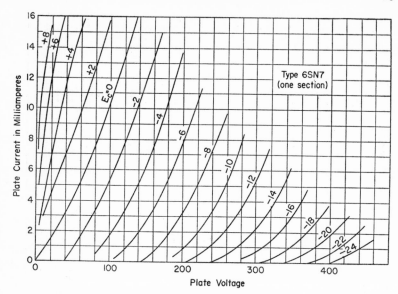

Fig. 1-9.   Plate characteristics for type 6SN7 (one section).

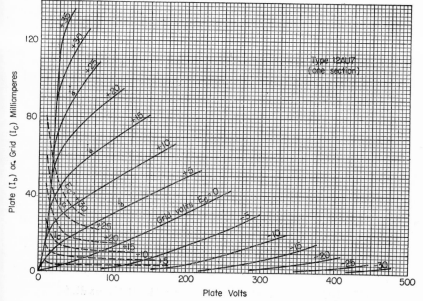

Fig. 1-10.   Plate characteristics for type 12AU7 (one section).

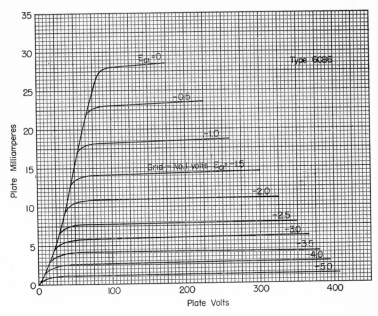

Fig. 1-11.   Plate characteristics for the type 6CB6.

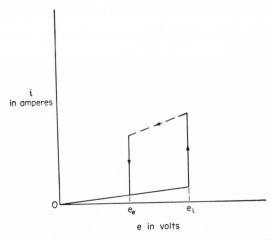

Fig. 1-12.   Idealized characteristics for cold-cathode gas diode.

A variety of volt-ampere characteristics are available from various forms of gas-tube discharge systems.   An idealized characteristic for a cold-cathode, gas-diode tube is shown in Fig. 1-12.   For low values of plate voltage only minute values of current are obtained, but as the plate voltage is increased to the ionization potential e_i the tube begins to conduct heavily.   If the plate voltage

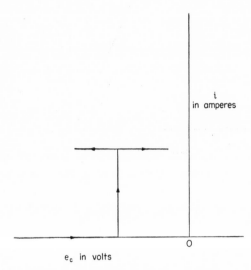

Fig. 1-13.   Idealized characteristics for gas triode.

is then decreased to the extinction potential e_e, the tube again becomes nonconducting.

If a grid structure is added to the gas diode, the value of the ionization potential can be made a function of the grid-cathode potential.   However, the grid in such a tube loses all control once the tube has started to conduct.   The only way in which the tube can be brought out of conduction is to lower the plate voltage below the extinction potential.   This type of operation is shown by the sketch of Fig. 1-13.

Also of interest is the relationship between the ignition potential and the grid voltage.   A typical curve of this type is shown in Fig. 1-14.

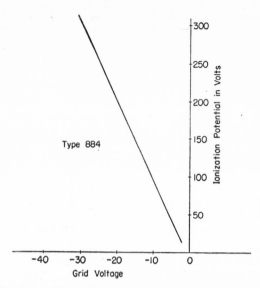

Fig. 1-14. Firing characteristic for type 884 gas triode.

REFERENCES

1. Boast, Warren B., *Principles of Electric and Magnetic Circuits*. New York: Harper and Brothers, 1950.
2. Chance, Britton; Hughes, Vernon; MacNichol, Edward F., Jr.; Sayre, David; and Williams, Frederick C., *Waveforms*. New York: McGraw-Hill Book Co., Inc., 1949.
3. Gardner, Murray F. and Barnes, John L., *Transients in Linear Systems*. New York: John Wiley and Sons, Inc., 1942.
4. M.I.T. Department of Electrical Engineering, *Applied Electronics*. New York: John Wiley and Sons, Inc., 1943.
5. Radio Corporation of America, *RCA Tube Handbook HB3*, Commercial Engineering, Tube Department, Radio Corporation of America, Harrison, New Jersey.
6. Ryder, John D., *Electronic Fundamentals and Applications*. New York: Prentice-Hall, Inc., 1950.

CHAPTER TWO

BASIC COMBINATIONS OF RESISTIVE, CAPACITIVE, AND INDUCTIVE ELEMENTS

This chapter is concerned with some of the more basic configurations which may be constructed from resistors, capacitors, and inductors. Many useful circuits each contain but one energy storage element, that is, either one inductor or one capacitor, and this type of circuit will be studied in detail. The transients in these circuits will be initiated by a switching process. Similar circuits which are being driven by voltages of various common wave forms will be discussed in Chapter 3.

Also to be considered in this chapter are simple forms of the series and parallel RLC circuits.

2-1 Single-Capacitor Linear RC Circuit

A restricted RC circuit will be considered first. This circuit will consist of but one capacitor and a two-terminal network which contains the switching system and any number of constant voltage sources, constant current sources, and linear resistors.

Regardless of the manner in which the capacitor is connected into the system, it can be represented as shown in Fig. 2-1. For any particular condition, the two-terminal network can be replaced by a constant voltage source in series with a resistor. As given by Thevenin's theorem, this voltage source will have a magnitude and polarity equal to that of the open-circuit voltage of the two-terminal network. The series resistor will have a resistance equal to that looking back from the capacitor terminals when the voltage sources are short-circuited and the current sources are open-circuited.

17

Let the two-terminal network, before the switching operation takes place, be represented by E' and R' as shown in Fig. 2-2a. The network after switching is shown in Fig. 2-2b. When the circuits are switched at $t = 0$, the capacitor voltage is equal to E_0. This may or may not be equal to E' depending upon the duration of time the circuit of Fig. 2-2a has been in existence. The following

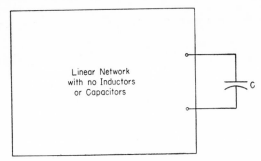

Fig. 2-1.   Restricted RC circuit.

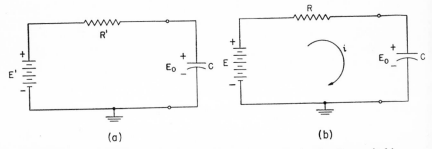

(a)   (b)

Fig. 2-2.   (a) RC circuit before switching.   (b) RC circuit after switching.

equation can be written from Fig. 2-2b, assuming the capacitor voltage at $t = 0$ to be E_0.

$$E = iR + \frac{1}{C} \int_0^t i\, dt + E_0 \qquad (2\text{-}1)$$

Differentiating all terms and dividing by R,

$$\frac{di}{dt} + \frac{i}{RC} = 0 \qquad (2\text{-}2)$$

or in D operator form,

$$\left(D + \frac{1}{RC}\right)i = 0 \qquad (2\text{-}3)$$

This has the solution

$$i = Ae^{-t/RC} \tag{2-4}$$

Evaluating Eq. (2-1) at $t = 0$ will give the required boundary condition.

$$E = Ri(0) + E_0 \quad \text{or} \quad i(0) = \frac{E - E_0}{R} \tag{2-5}$$

where $i(0)$ is the current at $t = 0$.

Therefore $A = (E - E_0)/R$ and

$$i = \frac{E - E_0}{R} e^{-t/RC} \tag{2-6}$$

The voltage across the capacitor

$$E_C = E_0 + \frac{1}{C} \int_0^t \frac{E - E_0}{R} e^{-t/RC} dt \tag{2-7}$$

$$= E_0 + (E - E_0)(1 - e^{-t/RC}) \tag{2-8}$$

Equation (2-8) is effective only so long as the circuit of Fig. 2-2b is unchanged. Further switching in the circuit can be accomodated by reapplying the technique above to the new equivalent circuits. The product RC which appears in Eqs. (2-4) and (2-8) is known as the *time constant* of the circuit; it must have the dimension of time and will be expressed in seconds if R has the units of ohms and C has the units of farads. Other combinations are shown in Fig. 2-3.

R	C	Time Constant
Megohms	Microfarads	Seconds
Ohms	Microfarads	Microseconds
Megohms	Micromicrofarads	Microseconds

Fig. 2-3. Time constant combinations for RC circuit.

The changing part of the capacitor voltage is seen to be $(E - E_0)(1 - e^{-t/RC})$, while the changing part of the capacitor current is $[(E - E_0)/R]e^{-t/RC}$. The terms $e^{-t/RC}$ and $1 - e^{-t/RC}$ appear in all single-capacitor RC transient problems.   The value of each of these expressions can be plotted as a function of t/RC to provide two very useful curves.   These curves are shown in Fig. 2-4.

From Fig. 2-4a it is apparent that after a period of time equal to one time constant, the voltage across the capacitor will have traversed 63 per cent of the total change which would be experienced

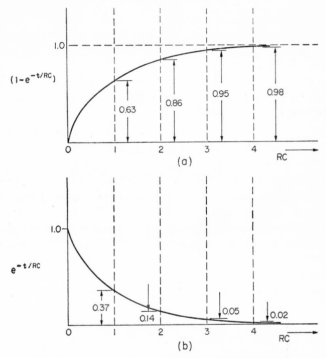

Fig. 2-4.   (a) Plot of $(i - e^{-t/RC})$.   (b) Plot of $e^{-t/RC}$.

if the circuit were indefinitely undisturbed.   Similarly, a check of the current equation and Fig. 2-4b shows that the current will also have changed 63 per cent of the total possible change during the same period of time.   Increments of 86 and 95 per cent are shown for elapsed time periods equal to two and three time constants, respectively.   For most practical applications, the transient can usually be assumed to have disappeared after a period of time equal to four time constants, since 98 per cent of the eventual change has taken place.

If the two-terminal network of Fig. 2-1 contains only constant voltage sources, constant current sources, and linear resistors, several general statements may be made. *All* voltage and current changes in the system will be of a general form similar to that of Eq. (2-8), that is,

$$e \text{ (or } i) = k_1 + k_2(1 - e^{-t/RC}) \qquad (2-9)$$

A form similar to that of Eq. (2-6) can be considered to be a specific case of the general form of Eq. (2-9). This equation is not restricted to representation of the voltage across, or the current through, a single element. For example, the equation might give the voltage across a particular series-parallel combination, or the total current through some other combination.

When, due to some switching operation, a sudden change takes place in the circuit, any desired voltage or current can be obtained by determining the constants k_1 and k_2 along with the time constant RC. Assume that in Fig. 2-1, some internal combination of resistors is to be switched at $t = 0$, and that some particular voltage is to be determined for the time interval following the switching.

The first step is to determine the voltage in question just after the switching has taken place ($t = 0^+$). The voltage across the capacitor cannot change instantaneously; therefore if the voltage on the capacitor is known just prior to the time of switching, it is known for the instant subsequent to the switching. Thus to find any voltage or current immediately after the switching, the capacitor can be replaced by a constant voltage source, symbolically a battery, equal to the capacitor voltage before the switching. The circuit is then solved as a simple d-c circuit. The magnitude of the voltage under consideration will be the k_1 of Eq. (2-9).

The second step is to find the voltage in question under the conditions which would exist if the transient were ever completed. This does not imply that the transient will be completed, but only that the terminal conditions are of interest in calculating the transient. The capacitor can be considered as an open circuit at this time, and the resulting circuit again solved for voltage relationships. The value of the voltage obtained in this way is the sum of k_1 and k_2. The two points which have just been found will then be connected by an exponential curve having the time constant RC.

EXAMPLE: The switch in Fig. 2-5 has been closed for a long time. It is then opened for 1000 microseconds, after which it is reclosed. The voltage from point A to ground shall be determined.

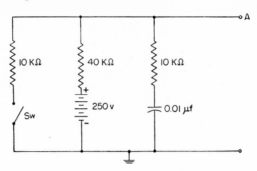

Fig. 2-5. RC circuit for example.

Since the switch has been closed for a long time, the original voltage across the capacitor may be found.

$$E_c = \frac{(10,000)(250)}{10,000 + 40,000} = 50 \text{ volts}$$

The switch will now be opened. To find the voltage from A to ground immediately following the switching operation, the capacitor will be replaced by a 50-volt battery as shown in Fig. 2-6. If the switch were to

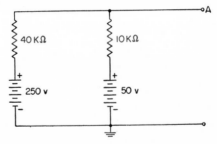

Fig. 2-6.   Equivalent circuit with switch open.

stay open for a long time, the capacitor voltage would become 250 volts. The time constant of the exponential curve which connects the 90- and 250-volt points is

$$= RC = (50)(10)^3(0.01)(10)^{-6}$$

$$= 500 \times 10^{-6} \text{ seconds} = 500 \text{ microseconds}$$

The voltage from A to ground is then of the form

$$e_A = k_1 + k_2(1 - e^{-t/RC})$$

where $k_1 = 90$ volts and $k_2 = 250 - 90 = 160$ volts. Then

$$e_A = 90 + 160(1 - e^{-t/RC})$$

This voltage is sketched in Fig. 2-7. The complete exponential between 90 and 250 volts would exist only if the switch remained open. Since the

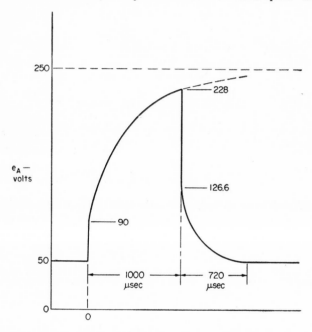

Fig. 2-7. Wave forms for circuit of Fig. 2-5.

switch is reclosed at $t = 1000$ microseconds, the potential at point A at this time will be

$$e_A = 90 + 160(1 - e^{-1000/500}) = 228 \text{ volts}$$

In order to solve the circuit again after the switch is reclosed, it is necessary to know the capacitor voltage at the time of closing. Summing the currents at node A gives

$$\frac{228 - E_C}{10,000} + \frac{228 - 250}{40,000} = 0 \qquad E_C = 222.5 \text{ volts}$$

Immediately after the switch is reclosed the circuit is that of Fig. 2-8.   The value of e_A will again be calculated.

$$\frac{e_A - 222.5}{10,000} + \frac{e_A}{10,000} + \frac{e_A - 250}{40,000} = 0 \qquad e_A = 126.6 \text{ volts}$$

A new exponential change will now occur.   The starting point is 126.6 volts.   At $t = \infty$, the voltage will have returned to the 50-volt value which

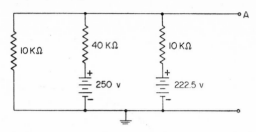

Fig. 2-8.   Equivalent circuit immediately after switch is opened.

existed before any switching occured.   Over this period of time, the exact equation is

$$e_A = 50 + (126.6 - 50)e^{-(t-1000\,\mu sec)/R'C}$$

It is usually easier to shift the time axis, that is, to pick a new time zero, than carry along the more complicated exponent of the previous equation. Rewriting the equation on this basis,

$$e_A = 50 + 76.6e^{-t/R'C}$$

The resistance in the time constant is marked with a prime to indicate that it is not the same resistance that was used in the original time constant. However R' is still the resistance looking into the circuit from the capacitor terminals, or

$$R' = \frac{(10,000)(40,000)}{50,000} + 10,000 = 18,000 \text{ ohms}$$

The voltage from A to ground will go through 98 per cent of the change to its final value (50 volts) in approximately four time constants, or 720 microseconds.

2-2 Single-Capacitor, Nonlinear RC Circuit

By conventional graphical methods any circuit containing one capacitor, any number of current sources, voltage sources, or linear and nonlinear resistors can be resolved into the circuit of Fig. 2-9. A completely general system would require the resistance R to be a function of i (or of the voltage e_R), and the capacitance C to be dependent upon the terminal voltage e_C (or the charge q on the capacitor). However, most low dielectric capacitors can be considered to be essentially linear devices, that is, C is independent of the terminal voltage or charge. As already indicated in Chapter 1, a great variety of nonlinear resistors may be encountered, particularly in the study of vacuum tubes and various forms of semiconductors.

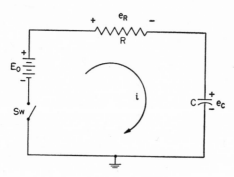

Fig. 2-9. Nonlinear RC circuit.

The nonlinear resistance R could be treated in a number of ways. One method might consider the voltage e_R as a power series in i or

$$e_R = a_0 + a_1 i + a_2 i^2 + \cdots \tag{2-10}$$

For the particular case of the linear resistor,

$$a_0 = a_2 = a_3 = \cdots = a_n = 0, \quad \text{and} \quad e_R = a_1 i$$

It is also possible to use a Fourier series to represent the volt-ampere characteristic. However, both of these methods result in cumbersome and difficult differential equations, particularly when discontinuities appear in the derivative of the volt-ampere characteristic. For these reasons, an approximate graphical method is favored.

The resistor R in Fig. 2-9 is described by the volt-ampere characteristic shown in Fig. 2-10. The switch is closed at $t = 0$. Let Δt_1 be an increment of time following the switching. If Δt_1 is taken to be very small, it can be assumed that the current during the Δt_1 period is essentially constant at Δi_1. If there is no initial

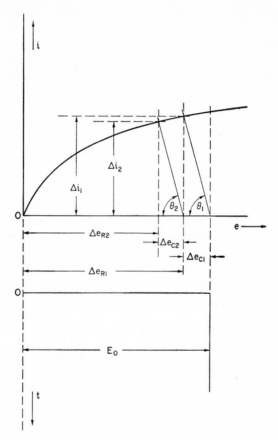

Fig. 2-10.   Graphical construction for nonlinear RC circuit.

charge on the capacitor, the capacitor voltage at the end of Δt_1 will be

$$\Delta e_{C1} = \frac{\Delta t_1 \, \Delta i_1}{C} \qquad (2\text{-}11)$$

Also at this time,

$$E_0 = \Delta e_{C1} + \Delta e_{R1} \qquad (2\text{-}12)$$

With reference to Fig. 2-10,

$$\tan \theta_1 = \frac{\Delta i_1}{\Delta e_{c1}} = \frac{\Delta i_1 C}{\Delta t_1 \, \Delta i_1} = \frac{C}{\Delta t_1} \tag{2-13}$$

Thus for any chosen increment of time, Δt_1, the current Δi_1 can be found by calculating $\tan \theta_1$, and then laying off a line from E_0 making an angle θ_1 with the base line.

To find the second increment of current, the effective supply voltage can be considered to be $E_0 - e_{c1}$. If equal increments are used, $\theta_1 = \theta_2$, and θ_2 can be laid off from the $E_0 - e_{c1}$ point.

The process is now continued until the current and voltage increments become arbitrarily small. Values of i, e_R and e_C can be plotted as functions of time. The accuracy of the system will depend upon the size of the time increments which are used. It is not necessary to use equal increments, although this usually simplifies the solution.

If the magnitude of the supply voltage is an arbitrary function of time, instead of remaining constant as was assumed above, the same technique can still be used.

EXAMPLE: The current and voltage in the circuit of Fig. 2-11 will be found by the graphical process which has been discussed.

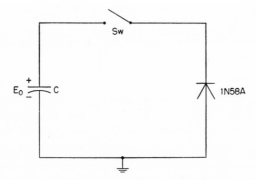

Fig. 2-11. Nonlinear RC circuit for example.

The capacitor has an initial voltage of 100 volts. The switch is closed at $t = 0$. Although the capacitor is discharging through the back resistance of the diode, this resistance is sufficiently low to allow the capacitor to be discharged in less than 1000 microseconds.

The diode characteristic is shown in Fig. 2-12, while the current and voltage are plotted in Fig. 2-13. For comparison, an exponential curve having a time constant of 150 microseconds is also shown.

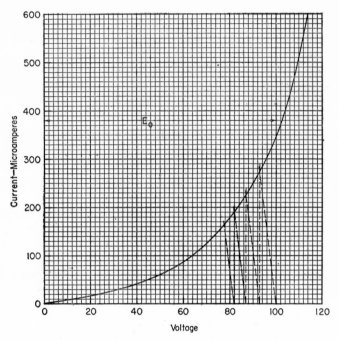

Fig. 2-12. Graphical construction for example.

2-3 Single-Inductor Linear RL Circuit

The application of RL circuits is not so general as that of RC circuits, but a study of such circuits is still quite justified. It is exceedingly difficult to obtain a physical inductor without distributed capacitance and with low series resistance, whereas capacitors with negligible inductance and resistance can be built more easily. Thus circuits with resistance and capacitance can be reproduced physically with some expectation that the desired theoretical results will be achieved practically. A circuit which would provide the same indicated results could probably be constructed with inductors and resistors, but considerable trial and error might be necessary before these results could be obtained. Another possi-

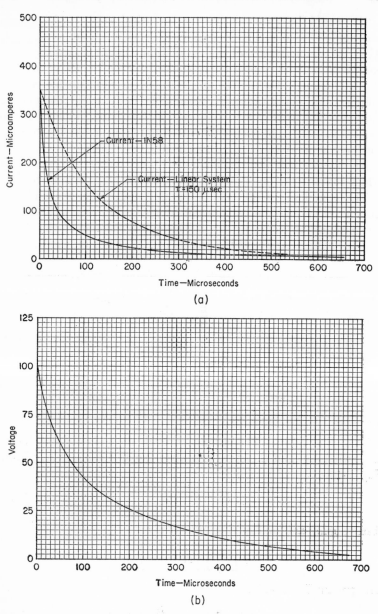

Fig. 2-13. (a) Current wave form in nonlinear RC circuit. (b) Capacitor voltage in nonlinear RC circuit.

bility would be an extensive mathematical study which would account for the unavoidable series resistance and shunt capacitance. Also, the elements of cost and availability might necessarily be a consideration with respect to the choice between the RL circuit and the RC circuit. Capacitors are available in wide ranges of both voltage and capacitance at reasonable cost, while commercial inductors are usually available only in restricted inductance and current values. The cost of the latter units is generally higher than for the comparative RC circuit elements.

An analysis will again be made for a very restricted system, one which contains but one storage element, in this case the inductor.

The complete circuit containing the single inductor and any number of voltage sources, current sources, and linear resistors can be simplified as before by use of Thevenin's theorem to the circuit of Fig. 2-14a. At $t = 0$ the circuit of Fig. 2-14a is switched into

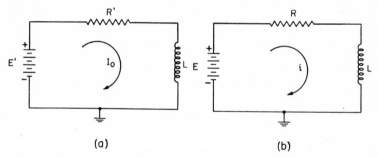

(a)   (b)

Fig. 2-14.   (a) RL circuit before switching.   (b) RL circuit after switching.

that of Fig. 2-14b. The current through the inductor just before the switching, and therefore just after the switching, is I_0. From Fig. 2-14b,

$$E = Ri + L\frac{di}{dt} \tag{2-14}$$

Rearranging and multiplying by $-R$ gives

$$-\frac{R}{E - Ri}\, di = -\frac{R}{L}\, dt \tag{2-15}$$

Integrating Eq. (2-15),

$$\ln (E - Ri) = -\frac{Rt}{L} + \ln A \tag{2-16}$$

Since $i = I_0$ when $t = 0$, $A = E - RI_0$. Then

$$i = I_0 + \left(\frac{E}{R} - I_0\right)(1 - e^{-Rt/L}) \qquad (2\text{-}17)$$

The same type of terms appear in Eq. (2-17) as were found in the solution of the RC circuit, with L/R now being the time constant. If L has the units of henrys and R the units of ohms, the time constant will be measured in seconds. Other combinations are given in Fig. 2-15.

Voltages and currents in the restricted RL circuit (any number of resistors and sources but only one inductor) can be found by

R	L	Time Constant
Ohms	Millihenrys	Milliseconds
Ohms	Microhenrys	Microseconds
Megohms	Microhenrys	Seconds

Fig. 2-15.   Time constant combinations for RL circuit.

using the same general technique as was described for the RC circuit, that is, all currents and voltages are still of the form

$$e \text{ (or } i) = k_1 + k_2(1 - e^{-Rt/L}) \qquad (2\text{-}18)$$

The only difference between Eq. (2-18) and Eq. (2-9) is in the form of the time constant.   It can also be seen that the voltage across the series resistor in the RC circuit is of the same form as the voltage across the inductor in the RL circuit.   The other pair of voltages is similarly reversed.

The usual RL circuit problem is determination of a particular voltage or current for a period of time following a switching operation.   First, the voltage or current in question shall be determined just after the switching has taken place.   This voltage or current shall then be found after a very long time has passed.   The term *long time* will still be loosely used as a period of time appreciably greater than four time constants.

The two points which have been determined, can then be connected with an exponential curve which has the time constant L/R. The resistance R is the resistance looking back into the circuit from the inductor terminals. Physically, this may consist in part of the coil resistance.

If the current through the inductor can be determined just prior to the switching, it is also known immediately after the switching. The voltage or current of interest can then be found just after the switching by solving the resulting d-c circuit. The voltage after a long time can be found by the same method, the inductor now being considered a short circuit.

EXAMPLE: Consider the circuit of Fig. 2-16. The switch has been open for a long time. It is closed for 50 microseconds, after which it is reopened.

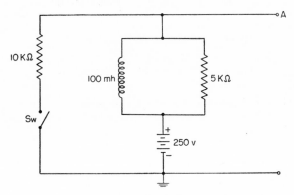

Fig. 2-16.   *RL* circuit for example.

The inductor current and the voltage from point A to ground are to be determined.

If the switch has been open for a long time, at $t = 0$ the inductor current is zero, and the output voltage is 250 volts. The inductor current then is zero at $t = 0^+$, after the switch is closed. Since there is no inductor current, the inductor may be treated as an open circuit. At this time e_A is

$$e_A = \frac{10,000}{15,000} (250) = 166.7 \text{ volts}$$

If the switch were to remain closed for a long time, the transient would disappear, and there would be no voltage across the inductor. Thus, at $t = \infty$, the inductor would be considered at short circuit, giving $e_A = 250$ volts.

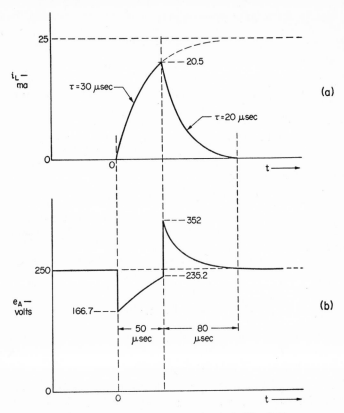

Fig. 2-17. Wave forms for circuit in Fig. 2-16.

The coil current is initially zero, and would rise exponentially to a value of

$$i_L = \frac{250}{(10)(10)^3} = 25 \times 10^{-3} \text{ ampere} = 25 \text{ milliamperes}$$

The time constant of this exponential curve is

$$\tau = \frac{L}{R} = \frac{(100)(10)^{-3}(15)}{(5)(10)^3(10)} = 30 \times 10^{-6} \text{ second} = 30 \text{ microseconds}$$

The general expression for e_A is

$$e_A = 166.7 + (250 - 166.7)(1 - e^{-Rt/L})$$
$$= 166.7 + 83.3(1 - e^{-t/30 \times 10^{-6}})$$

The voltage at $t = 50 \times 10^{-6}$ second is

$$e_A = 235.2 \text{ volts}$$

The current through the 10,000-ohm resistor at this time is

$$i_{10,000\Omega} = \frac{235.2}{(10)(10)^3} = 23.5 \times 10^{-3} \text{ amperes} = 23.5 \text{ milliamperes}$$

The current through the 5000-ohm resistor is

$$i_{5000\Omega} = \frac{250 - 235.2}{(5)(10)^3} = 2.96 \times 10^{-3} \text{ ampere} = 2.96 \text{ milliamperes}$$

The inductor current is then

$$i_L = 23.5 - 2.96 = 20.5 \text{ milliamperes}$$

The switch is now reopened. The inductor current must instantaneously remain at 20.5 milliamperes, and therefore the potential from point A to ground becomes

$$e_A = 250 + 5(20.5) = 352 \text{ volts}$$

This voltage will decay back to 250 volts in four time constants, or

$$4\tau = \frac{(4)(10)(10)^{-3}}{(5)(10)^3} = 80 \times 10^{-6} \text{ second} = 80 \text{ microseconds}$$

During this time the inductor current will exponentially approach zero.

2-4 Single-Inductor, Nonlinear RL Circuits

The circuit of Fig. 2-18 contains a nonlinear resistor R, having a known volt-ampere characteristic. The inductor is assumed to be

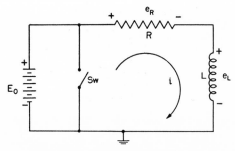

Fig. 2-18.   Nonlinear RL circuit.

linear. The circuit will be solved using a method very similar to that of Sec. 2-2. At all times after the switch is opened,

$$E_0 = e_R + e_L \tag{2-19}$$

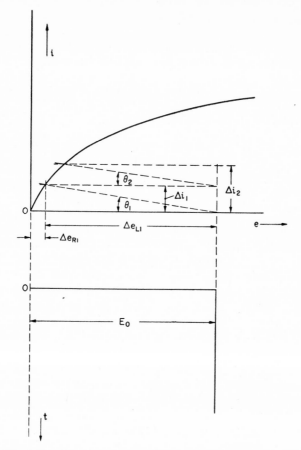

Fig. 2-19.   Graphical construction for nonlinear RL circuit.

Since

$$e_L = L \frac{di}{dt} \tag{2-20}$$

the approximate voltage across the inductor will be

$$e_L = L \frac{\Delta i}{\Delta t} \tag{2-21}$$

With reference to Fig. 2-19

$$\tan \theta_1 = \frac{\Delta i_1}{e_{L1}} = \frac{\Delta i_1 \, \Delta t_1}{L \, \Delta i_1} = \frac{\Delta t_1}{L} \tag{2-22}$$

The first increment of current can now be found by calculating tan θ_1 and setting off the correct angle from the voltage base line. To find the second increment of current the process is repeated, except that the angle $\theta_1 = \theta_2$ is set off from a horizontal line at the value of Δt_1. The same method is then used to find all further increments of current. The values of i, e_R, and e_L can then be plotted as functions of time.

The accuracy of the calculations will be increased if smaller values of time increments are used, since the analysis assumes that the change of current during an increment of time is linear, giving a constant $L(di/dt)$ drop.

2-5 Linear Isolated Series-Parallel RLC Circuit

An isolated, series-parallel RLC circuit is shown in Fig. 2-20. Node D will be used as a reference node. Summing currents at

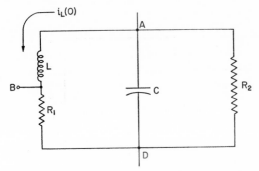

Fig. 2-20.   Isolated series-parallel RLC circuit.

node A and node B gives

$$C \frac{de_A}{dt} + \frac{e_A}{R_2} + \frac{1}{L} \int_0^t (e_A - e_B)\, dt + i_L(0) = 0 \qquad (2\text{-}23)$$

$$\frac{e_B}{R_1} + \frac{1}{L} \int_0^t (e_B - e_A)\, dt - i_L(0) = 0 \qquad (2\text{-}24)$$

Differentiating both equations with respect to time gives

$$C \frac{d^2 e_A}{dt^2} + \frac{1}{R_2} \frac{de_A}{dt} + \frac{1}{L} e_A - \frac{1}{L} e_B = 0 \qquad (2\text{-}25)$$

$$\frac{1}{R_1} \frac{de_B}{dt} + \frac{1}{L} e_B - \frac{1}{L} e_A = 0 \qquad (2\text{-}26)$$

From Eq. (2-25)

$$e_B = LC \frac{d^2e_A}{dt^2} + \frac{L}{R_2} \frac{de_A}{dt} + e_A \qquad (2\text{-}27)$$

Differentiating again,

$$\frac{de_B}{dt} = LC \frac{d^3e_A}{dt^3} + \frac{L}{R_2} \frac{d^2e_A}{dt^2} + \frac{de_A}{dt} \qquad (2\text{-}28)$$

Substituting Eq. (2-27) and Eq. (2-28) into Eq. (2-26) and rearranging,

$$\frac{d^3e_A}{dt^3} + \frac{d^2e_A}{dt^2} \left(\frac{L + R_1R_2C}{LR_2C} \right) + \frac{de_A}{dt} \left(\frac{R_1 + R_2}{R_2LC} \right) = 0 \qquad (2\text{-}29)$$

The general solution of Eq. (2-29) is

$$e_A = e^{-\alpha t}(a'e^{\beta t} + b'e^{-\beta t}) + k_0 \qquad (2\text{-}30)$$

where

$$\alpha = \frac{R_1R_2C + L}{2LCR_2} \qquad (2\text{-}31)$$

$$\beta = \sqrt{\left(\frac{R_1R_2C + L}{2LCR_2} \right)^2 - \frac{R_1 + R_2}{LCR_2}} \qquad (2\text{-}32)$$

To change to hyperbolic form, let

$$a' = \frac{A' + B'}{2} \quad \text{and} \quad b' = \frac{A' - B'}{2} \qquad (2\text{-}33)$$

Then

$$e_A = e^{-\alpha t}(A' \cosh \beta t + B' \sinh \beta t) + k_0 \qquad (2\text{-}34)$$

Since there can be no energy in the system at $t = \infty$, the constant k_0 must be zero.   Then

$$e_A = e^{-\alpha t}(A' \cosh \beta t + B' \sinh \beta t) \qquad (2\text{-}35)$$

If $e_A = e_A(0)$ when $t = 0$,

$$A' = e_A(0) \qquad (2\text{-}36)$$

Evaluating Eq. (2-23) at $t = 0$ gives

$$\frac{de_A}{dt} \bigg|_{t=0} = \frac{1}{C} \left(-i_L(0) - \frac{1}{R_2} e_A(0) \right) \qquad (2\text{-}37)$$

The constant B' can be found by differentiating Eq. (2-25) and substituing Eq. (2-37).

$$B' = \frac{1}{\beta}\left[e_A(0)\left(\alpha - \frac{1}{R_2C}\right) - \frac{i_L(0)}{C}\right] \qquad (2\text{-}38)$$

There are three possibilities for solution, depending upon whether β is real, imaginary, or zero. The circuit is said to be overdamped when β is real or

$$\frac{(CR_1R_2 + L)^2}{4LCR_2} > R_1 + R_2 \qquad (2\text{-}39)$$

When

$$\frac{(CR_1R_2 + L)^2}{4LCR_2} < R_1 + R_2 \qquad (2\text{-}40)$$

β is imaginary. Then

$$\beta = \sqrt{-1}\sqrt{\frac{R_1 + R_2}{LCR_2} - \left(\frac{R_1R_2C + L}{2LCR_2}\right)^2} = j\omega \qquad (2\text{-}41)$$

where

$$\omega = \sqrt{\frac{R_1 + R_2}{LCR_2} - \left(\frac{R_1R_2C + L}{2LCR_2}\right)^2} \qquad (2\text{-}42)$$

and ω is a real number. In this case it is probably simpler to write e_A in terms of trigonometric functions, or

$$e_A = e^{-\alpha t}(A' \cos \omega t + jB' \sin \omega t) \qquad (2\text{-}43)$$

The circuit is now said to be oscillatory with a frequency of

$$f = \frac{1}{2\pi}\sqrt{\frac{R_1 + R_2}{LCR_2} - \left(\frac{CR_1R_2 + L}{2LCR_2}\right)^2} \qquad (2\text{-}44)$$

If $\beta = 0$, that is

$$\frac{(CR_1R_2 + L)^2}{4LCR_2} = R_1 + R_2 \qquad (2\text{-}45)$$

the solution of the original equation is

$$e_A = \left\{e_A(0) + \left[e_A(0)\left(\alpha - \frac{1}{CR_2}\right) - \frac{i_L(0)}{C}\right]t\right\}e^{-\alpha t} \qquad (2\text{-}46)$$

The circuit is now said to be critically damped.

Simpler but still useful circuits are found in the particular cases where R_1 can be assumed to be very small or R_2 very large.

If $R_1 \to 0$,

$$\alpha = \frac{1}{2CR_2} \tag{2-47}$$

and

$$\beta = \sqrt{\frac{1}{4R_2^2 C^2} - \frac{1}{LC}} \tag{2-48}$$

If $R_2 \to \infty$,

$$\alpha = \frac{R_1}{2L} \tag{2-49}$$

and

$$\beta = \sqrt{\frac{R_1^2}{4L^2} - \frac{1}{LC}} \tag{2-50}$$

PROBLEMS

2-1 What voltage wave form must be applied to an inductor of 30 millihenrys inductance and 1000 ohms resistance in order to obtain the current wave shape shown?   Sketch the voltage in the proper time relationship with respect to the given current.   Label completely.

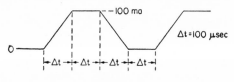

Prob. 2-1.

2-2 The switch has been open for a long time.   It is closed for two time constants (the time constant effective when the switch is closed) and then reopened.   (a) Sketch the voltage from A to ground, labeling all important time intervals and voltages.   (b) Calculate the energy output of each battery and show where all the energy has been dissipated.

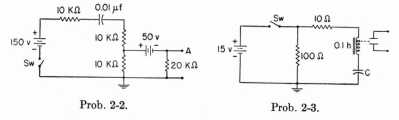

Prob. 2-2.   Prob. 2-3.

2-3 The relay shown has an inductance of 0.1 henry and a resistance of 10 ohms.   It will pull in at a current of 100 milliamperes and drop out at

80 milliamperes.   (a) What should be the value of C if the contacts are to close for a period of 250 microseconds when the switch Sw is closed?   (b) How long after the switch Sw is closed do the relay contacts close?

2-4 The switch has been open for a long time, and is closed at $t = 0$. Find the value of the current in the coil at $t = 20$ microseconds.

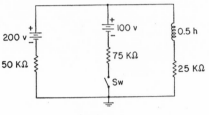

Prob. 2-4.

2-5 The switch has been closed for a long time and is opened for 100 microseconds and then reclosed. What is the maximum voltage from point A to ground and when does it occur?

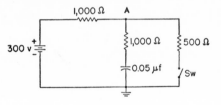

Prob. 2-5.

2-6 The switch has been open for a long time and is closed at $t = 0$. (a) Write an expression for the switch current as a function of time. (b) If the switch is again opened after steady-state conditions have been reached, write an expression for the voltage across the switch.

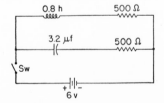

Prob. 2-6.

2-7 The switch has been in position 1 for a long time. It is moved instantaneously to position 2, held there for 60 microseconds, and then moved instantaneously back to position 1. Sketch the voltage from A to ground, labeling all important time intervals and voltages.

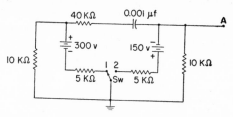

Prob. 2-7.

2-8 The capacitor is originally uncharged. If the switch is closed at $t = 0$, sketch and label the potential drop from A to ground.

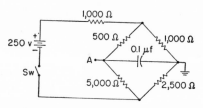

Prob. 2-8.

2-9 Find the frequency of oscillation of the buzzer shown. The pull-in current is 100 milliamperes, while the drop-out current is 80 milliamperes.

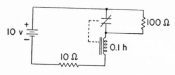

Prob. 2-9.

2-10 The switch has been open for a long time. If the switch is closed at $t = 0$, calculate the total energy dissipated in the 5000-ohm resistor. Assume an ideal characteristic for the diode.

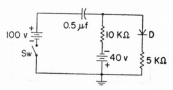

Prob. 2-10.

2-11 By graphical means find the drop in potential of point A resulting from a sudden increase of the input voltage from 0 to +0.5 volt. Compare with the result obtained by a linear dynamic analysis. If the input voltage rises from 0 to +0.5 volt and then stays constant at the latter value, how much time will elapse before the potential of A is halfway back to its quiescent value?

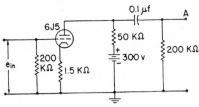

Prob. 2-11.

2-12 Using a graphical approach, find the current in the circuit of Fig. 2-2 if the switching occurs at $t = 0$ and the initial charge on the capacitor is zero. The resistor and capacitor are linear. Show that this current agrees with the known analytical value.

2-13 Repeat problem 2-12 for the current in the circuit of Fig. 2-14 if the switching occurs at $t = 0$ and the initial inductor current is zero.

2-14 The switch has been open for a long time and is closed at $t = 0$. (a) Find the energy dissipated in the 500-ohm resistor during the interval between switching and the instant the capacitor voltage reaches the first

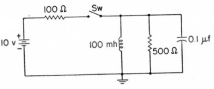

Prob. 2-14.

maximum. (b) Find the energy dissipated in the 500-ohm resistor from the instant of the first maximum voltage until an infinite time has passed.

2-15 The switch has been open for a long time. If the switch is closed at $t = 0$, sketch and label the coil current and the voltage across the coil.

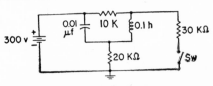

Prob. 2-15.

CHAPTER THREE

RESPONSE OF BASIC CIRCUITS TO SIMPLE WAVE FORMS

The solution of a linear circuit which is being driven by a current or a voltage of known analytical form can usually be found by a routine, although sometimes tedious, procedure. The generally accepted method is to write sufficient numbers of differential equations, either of the nodal or loop variety, change these differential equations to algebraic equations by a suitable transformation, and then solve simultaneously these algebraic equations. The inverse transformations can then be made, giving the desired solutions.

A number of current and voltage forms appear frequently in electronic applications. A few of these special forms will be applied to some simple circuits. The results which will be found can then be used directly in many problems.

Other important circuits are those which are essentially nonlinear because switching is taking place in the system. Examples of this type are among the several circuits treated at the end of the chapter.

3-1 Sine Wave Voltage Applied to the Series RLC Circuit

One of the more important forms of voltage or current that may be encountered is, of course, the sine wave. A sine wave of voltage will be used to excite a series RLC circuit. This problem is partially analogous to that of Sec. 2-5 in that the previous solution will be the complementary portion of the total solution to be obtained here.

The circuit to be solved is shown in Fig. 3-1a. The switch is moved instantaneously from position 1 to position 2 at $t = 0$. Variation in the angle θ will allow the driving signal to be connected to the circuit at any time during the cycle. From Fig. 3-1a

$$E_m \sin (\omega t + \theta) = L\frac{di_T}{dt} + Ri_T + \frac{1}{C}\int_0^t i_T \, dt + e_C(0) \quad (3\text{-}1)$$

It is possible to alter the form of the driving function in order to simplify the process of solution. Let a new driving function be

$$E_m e^{j(\omega t+\theta)} = E_m \cos (\omega t + \theta) + jE_m \sin (\omega t + \theta) \quad (3\text{-}2)$$

By the principle of superposition two answers will now be obtained, one of which will be real, while the other will be imaginary. The

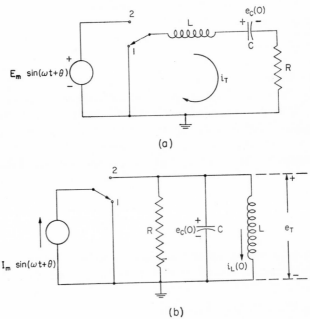

(a)

(b)

Fig. 3-1. (a) Sine-wave voltage source exciting RLC series circuit. (b) Sine-wave current source exciting RLC parallel circuit.

real part of the solution will be that which would have been obtained had $E_m \cos (\omega t + \theta)$ been the complete driving function, while the imaginary part will be that due to $jE_m \sin (\omega t + \theta)$. In the present problem, the imaginary part of the solution will be the desired answer. Substituting the driving function of Eq. (3-2) in place of the sine function of Eq. (3-1),

$$L \frac{di_T}{dt} + Ri_T + \frac{1}{C} \int_0^t i_T \, dt + e_C(0) = E_m e^{j(\omega t + \theta)} \quad (3\text{-}3)$$

Differentiating all terms and writing in operator form,

$$\left(D^2 + \frac{R}{L} D + \frac{1}{LC} \right) i_T = \frac{j\omega}{L} E_m e^{j(\omega t + \theta)} \quad (3\text{-}4)$$

The complete solution is given by the sum of the complementary and particular solutions. The form of the complementary solution is the same as that given in Sec. 2-5, and is subject to the same restrictions with regard to damping and oscillation.

The particular solution is given by

$$(i_T)_P = \frac{1}{D^2 + (R/L)D + (1/LC)} \frac{j\omega E_m}{L} e^{j(\omega t + \theta)} \quad (3\text{-}5)$$

$$= E_m \frac{R - j(\omega L - 1/\omega C)}{R^2 + (\omega L - 1/\omega C)^2} e^{j(\omega t + \theta)} \quad (3\text{-}6)$$

The imaginary part of Eq. (3-6) is

$$(i_T)_P = E_m \frac{\sin(\omega t + \theta - \psi)}{\sqrt{R^2 + (\omega L - 1/\omega C)^2}} \quad (3\text{-}7)$$

where

$$\psi = \arctan \frac{\omega L - 1/\omega C}{R} \quad (3\text{-}8)$$

The complete solution is

$$i_T = e^{-Rt/2L}$$

$$[a' e^{(\sqrt{R^2/4L^2 - 1/LC})t} + b' e^{-(\sqrt{R^2/4L^2 - 1/LC})t}] + \frac{E_m \sin(\omega t + \theta - \psi)}{\sqrt{R^2 + (\omega L - 1/\omega C)^2}} \quad (3\text{-}9)$$

For purposes of demonstration the solution will be considered to be overdamped in form. Rewriting Eq. (3-9)

$$i_T = e^{-Rt/2L}$$

$$\left[A' \cosh \left(\sqrt{\frac{R^2}{4L^2} - \frac{1}{LC}} \right) t + B' \sinh \left(\sqrt{\frac{R^2}{4L^2} - \frac{1}{LC}} \right) t \right]$$

$$+ \frac{E_m \sin(\omega t + \theta - \psi)}{\sqrt{R^2 + (\omega L - 1/\omega C)^2}} \quad (3\text{-}10)$$

In order to evaluate the constants A' and B', two boundary conditions are necessary. The first is $i_T = i_T(0)$ at $t = 0$, and the second is obtained by evaluating di_T/dt at $t = 0$ in Eq. (3-1). This gives

$$\frac{di_T}{dt}\bigg|_{t=0} = \frac{E_m \sin\theta - Ri_T(0) - e_c(0)}{L} \tag{3-11}$$

Applying these two conditions gives

$$A' = i_T(0) - \frac{E_m \sin(\theta - \psi)}{\sqrt{R^2 + (\omega L - 1/\omega C)^2}} \tag{3-12}$$

$$B' = \frac{1}{\sqrt{1/4R^2C^2 - 1/LC}}$$
$$\left[\frac{E_m \sin\theta - Ri_T(0) - e_c(0)}{L} + \frac{RA'}{2L} - \frac{\omega E_m \cos(\theta - \psi)}{\sqrt{R^2 + (\omega L - 1/\omega C)^2}}\right] \tag{3-13}$$

A system quite similar to the one just described is shown in Fig. 3-1b. The solution for this circuit, assuming heavy damping, is

$$e_T = e^{-\frac{t}{2RC}}\left\{\left[e_T(0) - \frac{I_m \sin(\theta - \psi)}{\sqrt{1/R^2 + (\omega C - 1/\omega L)^2}}\right]\right.$$
$$\cosh\left(\sqrt{1/4R^2C^2 - 1/LC}\,\right)t + \left[\frac{I_m \sin\theta - e_T(0)/R - i_L(0)}{C\sqrt{1/4R^2C^2 - 1/LC}}\right.$$
$$+ \frac{e_T(0) - \dfrac{I_m \sin(\theta - \psi)}{\sqrt{1/R^2 + (\omega C - 1/\omega L^2)}}}{2RC\sqrt{1/4R^2C^2 - 1/LC}}$$
$$\left.- \frac{\omega I_m \cos(\theta - \psi)}{\sqrt{1/4R^2C^2 - 1/LC}\,\sqrt{1/R^2 + (\omega C - 1/\omega L)^2}}\right]$$
$$\sinh\left(\sqrt{1/4R^2C^2 - 1/LC}\,\right)t\Bigg\} + \frac{I_m \sin(\omega t + \theta - \psi)}{\sqrt{1/R^2 + (\omega C - 1/\omega L)^2}} \tag{3-14}$$

3-2 Periodic Signal Applied to Two-Element Circuits

Four common two-element circuits are shown in Fig. 3-2. A periodic voltage wave form will be applied to each of these combinations and the average output voltage determined for the steady-state operating condition.

The average value of the steady-state output voltage for these circuits can be found by summing the area under the output voltage curve for a complete cycle, and dividing by the period. If the system is in steady-state, the charge on the capacitor in the circuit of Fig. 3-2a will have the same value at corresponding points in successive cycles.

$$\int_{\Delta t} i \, dt = 0 \tag{3-15}$$

where Δt is the period of the driving voltage. Since the output voltage of this circuit is also iR,

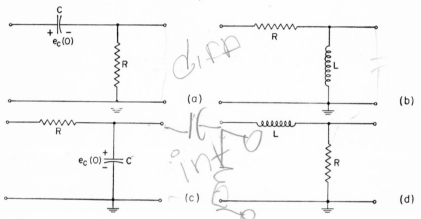

Fig. 3-2. (a) Resistive output RC circuit. (b) Inductive output RL circuit. (c) Capacitive output RC circuit. (d) Resistive output RL circuit.

$$(e_0)_{\text{av}} = \frac{1}{\Delta t} \int_{\Delta t} e_0 \, dt = \frac{1}{\Delta t} \int_{\Delta t} iR \, dt = 0 \tag{3-16}$$

For the circuit of Fig. 3-2b, the output voltage is given by $L(di/dt)$. If the area under the output voltage is summed for a complete cycle,

$$(e_0)_{\text{av}} = \frac{1}{\Delta t} \int_{\Delta t} e_0 \, dt = \frac{1}{\Delta t} \int_{\Delta t} L \frac{di}{dt} \, dt \tag{3-17}$$

The final integral is merely the time integral of di. When the limits are changed to i values, the initial and final limits must be the same if the system is to be in steady state. Thus

$$(e_0)_{\text{av}} = \frac{L}{\Delta t} \int_{i_0}^{i_0} di = 0 \tag{3-18}$$

Since the circuit of Fig. 3-2c is similar to that of Fig. 3-2a, except that the output voltage is taken across the capacitor instead of the resistor, no further calculations need be made. The average value of the voltage across the resistor has been shown to be zero, therefore the average value of the voltage across the capacitor is equal to the average value of the input signal. Similarly, the average value of the voltage across the resistor in the circuit of Fig. 3-2d is equal to the average value of the input signal.

All the previous proofs and statements have been dependent upon one assumption, that all the elements in the circuit have been linear

3-3 Square Wave Applied to Two-Element Circuit

A square wave of voltage will be applied to each combination shown in Fig. 3-2. Let the square wave have the form of Fig. 3-3.

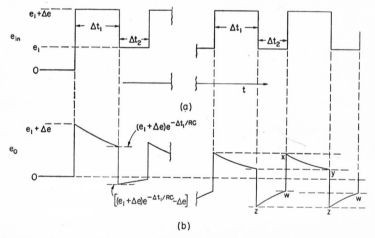

Fig. 3-3. Output voltage for the circuits of Fig. 3-2(a) and (b) with square-wave input voltage.

The circuit of Fig. 3-2a will be treated first. If the input waveform is applied at the time $t = 0$, the output voltage will jump instantaneously to a value of $e_1 + \Delta e$. The output voltage will then decay toward zero to a value of $(e_1 + \Delta e)e^{-\Delta t_1/RC}$ at the end of the first period. When the input voltage then drops by an amount Δe, the output voltage will become $(e_1 + \Delta e)e^{-\Delta t_1/RC} - \Delta e$. This will decay to a value of $[(e_1 + \Delta e)e^{-\Delta t_1/RC} - \Delta e]e^{-\Delta t_2/RC}$ at the end of the Δt_2 period. The above process can be carried on indefinitely, and after a few cycles it will be found that adjacent positive (and negative) excursions will have the same value, that is, the output voltage will have reached a steady-state, periodic condition. It is quite possible to work a numerical problem in this step-by-step manner, but a solution of the problem in general terms is rather involved. However, the steady-state values can be found by a simpler method. The general appearance of the steady-state output is shown in Fig. 3-3b. Let x, y, z, and w represent the values of the output voltage at the indicated points. The following equations can then be written

$$x - w = \Delta e \qquad \text{(a)}$$

$$y - z = \Delta e \qquad \text{(b)}$$

$$y = xe^{-\Delta t_1/RC} \qquad \text{(c)} \qquad\qquad (3\text{-}19)$$

$$w = ze^{-\Delta t_2/RC} \qquad \text{(d)}$$

The simultaneous solution of these equations gives

$$x = \Delta e \, \frac{(1 - e^{-\Delta t_2/RC})}{1 - e^{-(1/RC)(\Delta t_1 + \Delta t_2)}} \qquad \text{(a)}$$

$$y = \Delta e \, \frac{e^{-\Delta t_1/RC}(1 - e^{-\Delta t_2/RC})}{1 - e^{-(1/RC)(\Delta t_1 + \Delta t_2)}} \qquad \text{(b)}$$

$$(3\text{-}20)$$

$$z = \Delta e \, \frac{(e^{-\Delta t_1/RC} - 1)}{1 - e^{-(1/RC)(\Delta t_1 + \Delta t_2)}} \qquad \text{(c)}$$

$$w = \Delta e \, \frac{e^{-\Delta t_2/RC}(e^{-\Delta t_1/RC} - 1)}{1 - e^{-(1/RC)(\Delta t_1 + \Delta t_2)}} \qquad \text{(d)}$$

The values of x and y will be positive, while z and w will be negative.

The circuit of Fig. 3-2b can be substituted for that of Fig. 3-2a without modifying the previous analysis. The only change will be substitution of the new time constant L/R in place of the previous time constant RC.

If the general square wave of Fig. 3-3a is applied to the circuits of Fig. 3-2c and Fig. 3-2d, the output voltages may be most easily found by substituting the values calculated from the input values. The general shape of the outputs from these circuits is shown in Fig. 3-4.

3-4 Linear Input Voltage Applied to Two-Element Circuits

The previous section treated the RC circuit and the RL circuit for the case of square wave input voltages. Theoretically it is impossible, however, to produce instantaneous changes of voltage, since any physical system will always contain small amounts of shunt capacitance. Quite often under these conditions, a given voltage may, over a limited range, approach a linear function of time. The circuits of Fig. 3-2 will be solved, using such an input voltage. It will be assumed that $e_{in} = kt$, or in other words, the input voltage will increase at the rate of k volts per second. The value of k may be either positive or negative.

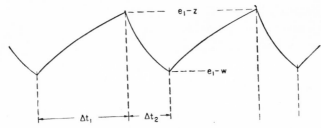

Fig. 3-4. Output voltage for the circuit of Fig. 3-2(c) and (d) with square-wave input voltage.

For the circuit of Fig. 3-2a, the voltage on the capacitor at the time $t = 0$ will be $e_C(0)$ with a polarity as shown. Then

$$e_{in} = Ri + \frac{1}{C} \int_0^t i \, dt + e_C(0) = kt \qquad (3\text{-}21)$$

Differentiating all terms, dividing by R, and using the D operator form,

$$\left(D + \frac{1}{RC}\right) i = \frac{k}{R} \qquad (3\text{-}22)$$

or

$$i = A e^{-t/RC} + kC \qquad (3\text{-}23)$$

The constant A may be evaluated by using the initial condition of

$$i(0) = \frac{-e_C(0)}{R} \qquad (3\text{-}24)$$

where $i(0)$ is the current at $t = 0$. Then

$$A = \frac{-e_C(0)}{R} - kC \qquad (3\text{-}25)$$

The current will be

$$i = -\left(\frac{e_C(0)}{R} + kC\right) e^{-t/RC} + kC \qquad (3\text{-}26)$$

and

$$e_0 = -e_C(0) + (kRC + e_C(0))(1 - e^{-t/RC}) \qquad (3\text{-}27)$$

If the linear input voltage were applied to the circuit of Fig. 3-2b, a result very similar to that of Eq. (3-27) would be realized. By substituting L/R for RC the following equation is obtained.

$$e_0 = \frac{kL}{R} (1 - e^{-Rt/L}) \qquad (3\text{-}28)$$

The additional condition that the initial output voltage (or the output current) is zero, has been applied in the latter case.

The input voltage and the output voltage as indicated by Eq. (3-27) are sketched in Fig. 3-5.

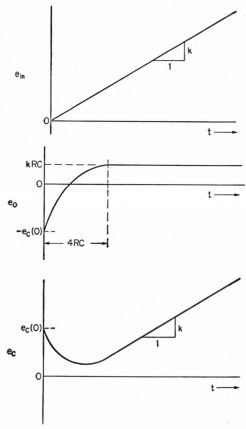

Fig. 3-5.   Wave forms for RC circuit with linear input voltage.

A linear input signal to the circuit of Fig. 3-2a will provide a constant value of kRC volts after a long time (longer than four time constants) has elapsed. If the original voltage on the capacitor were negative (opposite in polarity to that indicated in Fig. 3-2a) and equal to kRC, then the output voltage would also be equal to kRC at zero and all times past zero.

The output voltage as given by Eq. (3-27) also fits the general form for the exponential curve as given in Chapter 2. That is, the voltage across the output resistor can be found by finding the original voltage, the final voltage, and then connecting them by an exponential curve of the proper time constant.

The voltage across the capacitor in Fig. 3-2c or the resistor in Fig. 3-2d can again be found by direct subtraction. A linear input voltage $e_{in} = kt$, applied to the circuit of Fig. 3-2c, would give an output

$$e_0 = kt + e_C(0) - (kRC - e_C(0))(1 - e^{-t/RC}) \qquad (3\text{-}29)$$

For the circuit of Fig. 3-2d, Eq. (3-29) can be modified by letting $e_C(0) = 0$, and changing the time constant RC to L/R. It should be noticed that these equations are not exponential in form.

EXAMPLE: The circuit of Fig. 3-2a is being driven by a sawtooth voltage as shown in Fig. 3-6a. It is required to find the steady-state output voltage

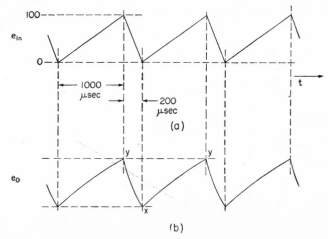

Fig. 3-6.   Output voltage for the circuit of Fig. 3-2(a) with sawtooth input voltage.

when the time constant of the circuit is 500 microseconds.   From the previous discussion, the general shape of the output voltage may be sketched as shown in Fig. 3-6b. The values of x and y must then be determined.   If

$t = 0$ at the start of the 1000-microsecond period, Eq. (3-27) may be written

$$y = x + \left\{ \frac{(100)(500)(10)^{-6}}{(1000)(10)^{-6}} - x \right\} \{1 - e^{-1000/500}\}$$

$$= 0.135x + 43.25$$

Repeating the process for the 200-microsecond period gives

$$x = y - \left[y + \frac{(100)(500)(10)^{-6}}{(200)(10)^{-6}} \right] (1 - e^{-200/500})$$

$$= 0.67y + 82.5$$

The simultaneous solution of these two equations in x and y gives

$$y = 35.35 \text{ volts} \quad x = -58.85 \text{ volts}$$

3-5 Exponential Voltage Applied to Two-Element Circuits

Let an input voltage $e_{\text{in}} = E_m e^{-\alpha t}$ be applied to the circuit of Fig. 3-2a. Then

$$E_m e^{-\alpha t} = Ri + \frac{1}{C} \int_0^t i \, dt + e_C(0) \tag{3-30}$$

or

$$\left(D + \frac{1}{RC} \right) i = \frac{\alpha E_m}{R} e^{-\alpha t} \tag{3-31}$$

This equation has the solution

$$i = A e^{-t/RC} + \frac{\alpha E_m}{R(\alpha - 1/RC)} e^{-\alpha t} \tag{3-32}$$

At $t = 0$,

$$i(0) = \frac{E_m - e_C(0)}{R} \tag{3-33}$$

so that

$$A = \frac{E_m - e_C(0)}{R} - \frac{\alpha E_m}{R(\alpha - 1/RC)} \tag{3-34}$$

Then

$$i = \left(\frac{E_m - e_C(0)}{R} - \frac{\alpha E_m}{R(\alpha - 1/RC)} \right) e^{-t/RC} + \frac{\alpha E_m}{R(\alpha - 1/RC)} e^{-\alpha t} \tag{3-35}$$

$$e_0 = \left(E_m - e_C(0) - \frac{\alpha E_m}{\alpha - 1/RC} \right) e^{-t/RC} + \frac{\alpha E_m}{\alpha - 1/RC} e^{-\alpha t} \tag{3-36}$$

An interesting case arises when $\alpha = 1/RC$. Under this condition

$$e_0 = (E_m - e_C(0) - \alpha t E_m) e^{-\alpha t} \tag{3-37}$$

If the input voltage $e_{\text{in}} = E_m e^{-\alpha t}$ is applied to the circuit of Fig. 3-2b, the output voltage will be of the form:

$$e_0 = \frac{E_m}{\alpha - R/L} \left(\alpha e^{-\alpha t} - R/L\, e^{-Rt/L} \right) \tag{3-38}$$

Again it has been assumed that the inductor current at $t = 0$ is zero.

To find the output voltages of the circuits of Fig. 3-2c and Fig. 3-2d the values already obtained can be subtracted from the input voltages.

If an input voltage $e_{\text{in}} = E_m(1 - e^{-\alpha t})$ is used, the output of the circuit of Fig. 3-2a will be

$$e_0 = \left(\frac{\alpha E_m}{\alpha - 1/RC} - e_C(0) \right) e^{-t/RC} - \frac{\alpha E_m}{\alpha - 1/RC} e^{-\alpha t} \tag{3-39}$$

For the circuit of Fig. 3-2b with $i(0) = 0$ the output will be

$$e_0 = E_m \left(1 + \frac{R/L}{\alpha - R/L} \right) e^{-Rt/L} - \frac{\alpha E_m}{\alpha - R/L} e^{-\alpha t} \tag{3-40}$$

3-6 Differentiating Circuits

Assume the initial capacitor voltage, $e_C(0)$, is zero in the circuit of Fig. 3-2a. Then

$$e_{\text{in}} = \frac{1}{C} \int_0^t i\, dt + iR \tag{3-41}$$

If the time constant RC is made very small, the integral term may become large with respect to the proportional term. The input voltage is then approximately equal to the capacitor voltage, or

$$e_{\text{in}} \approx \frac{1}{C} \int_0^t i\, dt \tag{3-42}$$

The current in the circuit is

$$i \approx C \frac{de_{\text{in}}}{dt} \tag{3-43}$$

while the output voltage becomes

$$e_0 \approx RC \frac{de_{\text{in}}}{dt} \tag{3-44}$$

Thus with a low time constant circuit, the output voltage will be approximately proportional to the derivative of the input signal.

The circuit of Fig. 3-2a, *with this restriction on the time constant*, is known as a differentiating circuit.

The circuit of Fig. 3-2b can also be considered to be a differentiating circuit if the time constant L/R is small with respect to the smallest time interval in the input signal.

For this circuit

$$e_{\text{in}} = Ri + L\frac{di}{dt} \tag{3-45}$$

$$e_0 = L\frac{di}{dt} \tag{3-46}$$

If L/R is small,

$$i \approx \frac{1}{R}e_{\text{in}} \tag{3-47}$$

or

$$e_0 \approx \frac{L}{R}\frac{de_{\text{in}}}{dt} \tag{3-48}$$

Let a square wave be applied to the circuits of Fig. 3-2a and Fig. 3-2b, for which the time constants are very small with respect to the period of the square wave. This input voltage and the resulting output voltage are shown in Fig. 3-7.

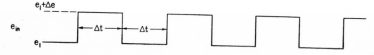

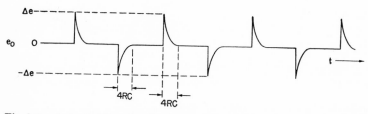

Fig. 3-7.　Output voltage for the circuit of Fig. 3-2(a) with square-wave input voltage.　Time constant of circuit is small with respect to half period of square wave.

The true derivative of the input signal would be a series of alternative positive and negative pulses which are infinite in height and zero in width. The output of the physical differentiating circuit cannot have an infinite magnitude, but as the time constant of the circuit is decreased, the output pulses will become narrower. The smaller the time constant, the more nearly will the output voltage approach the true derivative. However, the magnitude of the output pulses will always be equal to the instantaneous change in voltage, in this case, Δe.

A second example is sketched in Fig. 3-8.

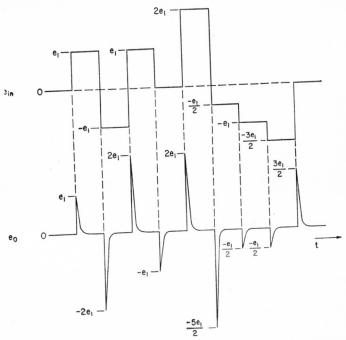

Fig. 3-8. Output voltage for the circuit of Fig. 3-2(a) with input voltage as shown. Time constant of the circuit is small with respect to time intervals in input signal.

The approximate differentiating effect also occurs if the circuit is used with sinusoids. If a sine wave were applied to a differentiating circuit, a steady-state analysis would indicate that the output voltage would be much smaller than the input voltage, and that there would be nearly a 90-degree phase shift between the input and output voltages. The approximate expression for the output voltage would provide nearly the same results.

$$e_0 \approx RC \frac{de_{\text{in}}}{dt} = RC \frac{d}{dt} (\sin \omega t) = \omega RC \cos (\omega t) \qquad (3\text{-}49)$$

An RL differentiating circuit which contains an inductor with appreciable resistance, but with negligible capacitance, is shown in Fig. 3-9. Since $L/(R + R_L)$ is assumed to be small, $e_{\text{in}} \approx (R + R_L)i$

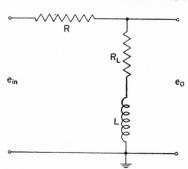

and $e_0 \approx \dfrac{R_L}{R + R_L} e_{\text{in}} + \dfrac{L}{R + R_L} \dfrac{de_{\text{in}}}{dt}$

$$\approx k_1 e_{\text{in}} + k_2 \frac{de_{\text{in}}}{dt} \qquad (3\text{-}50)$$

If a square wave of peak-to-peak amplitude Δe is applied to the circuit, the steady-state output voltage will be as sketched in Fig. 3-10.

Fig. 3-9. Inductive output RL circuit in which inductor has appreciable resistance. Time constant of circuit is small with respect to time intervals in the input signal.

When a linear input voltage is applied to an RC differentiating circuit which has zero initial capacitor voltage, the output voltage

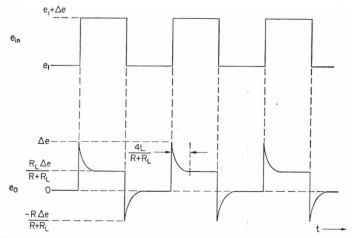

Fig. 3-10.   Output voltage for the circuit of Fig. 3-9 with square-wave input voltage.   Time constant of the circuit is small with respect to the half period of the square wave.

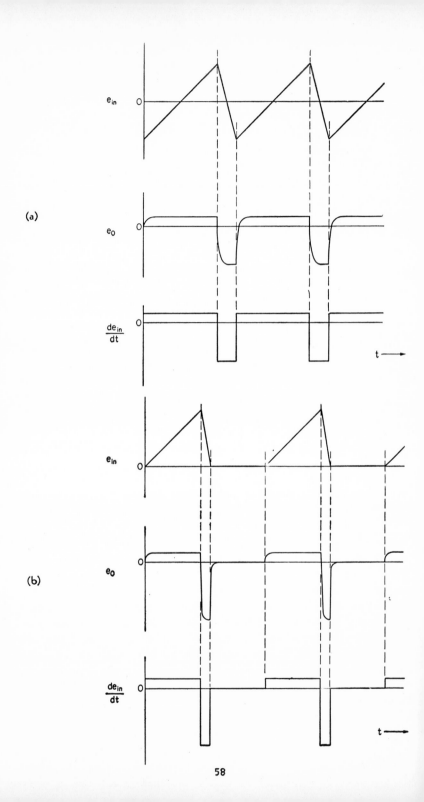

(a)

e_{in}

e_0

$\dfrac{de_{in}}{dt}$

$t \longrightarrow$

(b)

e_{in}

e_0

$\dfrac{de_{in}}{dt}$

$t \longrightarrow$

58

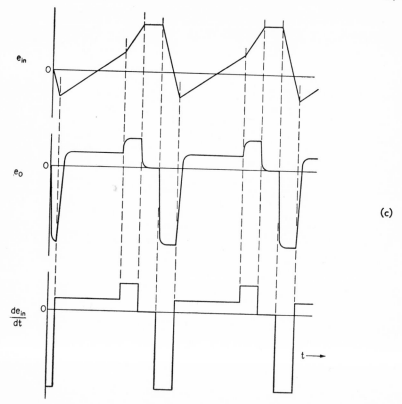

Fig. 3-11. Output voltage of differentiating circuit as compared to the true derivative for (a) sawtooth input voltage; (b) discontinuous sawtooth input voltage; (c) two-section sawtooth input voltage.

follows the input voltage for a short period of time. However, as more time elapses, the output voltage approaches a constant. The same general effect can be obtained by making the time constant smaller, in which case the output voltage becomes more nearly the derivative of the input voltage. The sketches of Fig. 3-11 compare the output of a differentiating circuit to the time derivative for three different input wave forms. Fig. 3-12 shows the effect of changing the circuit time constant. As the time constant becomes small with respect to the smallest time interval in the input signal, the output voltage looks more and more like the derivative of the input signal.

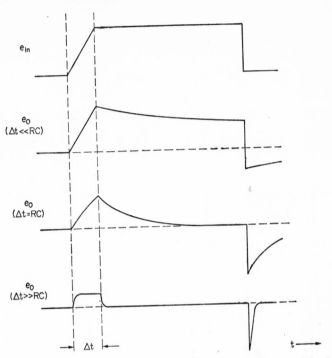

Fig. 3-12.   Effect of increasing the time constant in the circuit of Fig. 3-2(a).

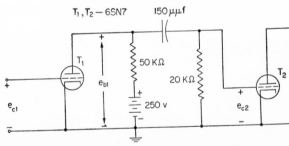

Fig. 3-13.   Differentiating circuit as coupling element between amplifiers.

EXAMPLE: The circuit shown in Fig. 3-13 could be classified as a differentiating circuit if the effective time constant is small with respect to the corresponding period of the square wave.

The input square wave with the corresponding voltage wave forms at the plate of T_1 and the grid of T_2 are shown in Fig. 3-14.

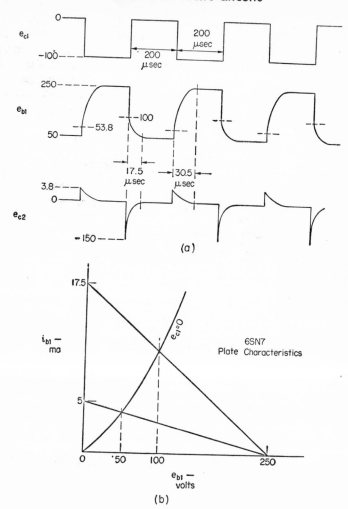

Fig. 3-14.   (a) Voltage wave forms for the circuit of Fig. 3-13.   (b) Graphical solution for the circuit of Fig. 3-13.

If T_1 is cut off and the system is in steady state, e_{b1} will be 250 volts, and e_{c2} will be zero.   The capacitor will be charged to a value of 250 volts. When T_1 first comes on, the intersection of the effective load line and the e_{c1} curve is at $e_{b1} = 100$ volts.   The effective load line is found by taking the Thevenin equivalent of the supply voltage, the load resistor, the charged capacitor, and the grid resistor.

Since the plate of T_1 has dropped instantaneously by 150 volts, the grid of T_2 will drop by the same amount. If sufficient time is now available, the capacitor will discharge until the plate voltage of T_1 reaches 50 volts, and e_{c2} again reaches zero. During this time the static plate resistance of T_1 is varying from approximately 12,500 to 9700 ohms. By averaging these values, a resistance can be obtained with which the approximate time constant can be calculated. This time constant is

$$\tau = \left[\frac{(11.1)(50)}{11.1 + 50} + 20\right] [(10)^3(150)(10)^{-12}]$$

$$= 4.36 \times 10^{-6} \text{ second} = 4.36 \text{ microseconds}$$

Thus it will take 17.5 microseconds to complete the transient. Since the capacitor voltage was 50 volts just before the square wave turned off T_1, the grid of T_2 will be driven positive when this occurs. A conducting resistance of 1000 ohms will then be assumed to be present between the grid and cathode of T_2. The grid of T_2 will be driven positive by an amount

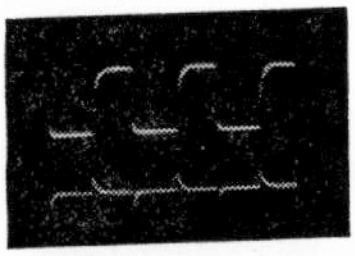

$$e_{c2} = \frac{\frac{20}{21}}{50 + \frac{20}{21}} (250 - 50) = 3.8 \text{ volts}$$

Fig. 3-15. Photographs of e_{b1}, (top) and e_{c2} (bottom) for the circuit of Fig. 3-13.

and will decay toward zero with a time constant

$$\tau = (50 + \tfrac{20}{21})(10)^3(150)(10)^{-6}$$

$$= 7.62 \times 10^{-6} \text{ second} = 7.62 \text{ microseconds}$$

The plate voltage of T_1 and the grid voltage of T_2 are again shown in the photographs of Fig. 3-15.

3-7 Integrating Circuits

The circuits of Fig. 3-2c and Fig. 3-2d under certain conditions can produce an output voltage which is the approximate integral of the input signal. Consider first the circuit of Fig. 3-2c, where the initial capacitor voltage is zero.

$$e_{in} = Ri + \frac{1}{C}\int_0^t i\, dt \tag{3-51}$$

$$e_0 = \frac{1}{C}\int_0^t i\, dt \tag{3-52}$$

If the time constant is very large with respect to the longest time interval in the input signal,

$$Ri \gg \frac{1}{C} \int_0^t i \, dt \tag{3-53}$$

and
$$i \approx \frac{e_{\text{in}}}{R} \tag{3-54}$$

$$e_0 \approx \frac{1}{Rc} \int_0^t e_{\text{in}} \, dt \tag{3-55}$$

The circuit of Fig. 3-2d, under long time constant conditions, can give the following equations.

$$e_{\text{in}} = Ri + L\frac{di}{dt} \tag{3-56}$$

$$e_0 = Ri \tag{3-57}$$

For a large value of L/R,

$$e_{\text{in}} \approx L\frac{di}{dt} \tag{3-58}$$

or
$$i \approx \frac{1}{L} \int_0^t e_{\text{in}} \, dt + i_L(0) \tag{3-59}$$

If the initial value of the inductor current is zero,

$$e_0 = Ri \approx \frac{1}{L/R} \int_0^t e_{\text{in}} \, dt \tag{3-60}$$

Basically, the integrating circuit and the differentiating circuit are both simple RC or RL series circuits. There are, however, several important differences. The time constant of the differentiating circuit is very low with respect to the shortest time interval in the input signal, while the time constant of the integrating circuit is long in comparison to the longest time interval. The output of the RC differentiating circuit is taken from the resistor, while the output of the RC integrating circuit is from the capacitor. Similar relations hold for the RL circuits. The output of the differentiating circuit is independent of the d-c level of the input signal, but the output of the integrating circuit is quite dependent upon the input level, having an average value exactly equal to the average value of the input signal. The true integral of any wave shape depends, of necessity, on the original starting time. For true integration, the summation of voltages would begin with the starting time of the voltage wave. The useful application of a voltage integral usually involves the integral of the wave over only limited time periods. The integrating circuit provides some approach to such applications, but the steady-state output of an integrating circuit would approach the true integral only if the average value of the input signal were zero.

For the case of square waves which are being applied to the integrating circuit, the output wave forms can be found by the method discussed in Sec. 3-3. When linear or sawtooth voltages are applied to the circuit, the output can most easily be found by first determining the voltage across the resistor and then subtracting this voltage from the input voltage.

3-8 Coupling Circuits

The square wave of Fig. 3-3 will be applied to the RC circuit of Fig. 3-2a under the following conditions. First, the time constant RC will be assumed to be very large. Second, the ratio of Δt_1, to Δt_2 will be specified as A, that is, $\Delta t_1 = A \Delta t_2$. The values of x, y, z, and w will then be determined. If the time constant becomes large, $\Delta t_2/RC \to 0$ and

$$x = \lim_{\Delta t_2/RC \to 0} \Delta e \frac{(1 - e^{-\Delta t_2/RC})}{1 - e^{-(\Delta t_2/RC)(1+A)}} = \frac{\Delta e}{1 + A} \quad \text{(a)}$$

$$y = \lim_{\Delta t_2/RC \to 0} \Delta e \frac{e^{-A\Delta t_2/RC}(1 - e^{-\Delta t_2/RC})}{1 - e^{-(\Delta t_2/RC)(1+A)}} = \frac{\Delta e}{1 + A} \quad \text{(b)}$$

$$z = \lim_{\Delta t_2/RC \to 0} \Delta e \frac{(e^{-A\Delta t_2/RC} - 1)}{1 - e^{-(\Delta t_2/RC)(1+A)}} = \frac{-A\Delta e}{1 + A} \quad \text{(c)}$$

$$w = \lim_{\Delta t_2/RC \to 0} \Delta e \frac{e^{-\Delta t_2/RC}(e^{-A\Delta t_2/RC} - 1)}{1 - e^{-(\Delta t_2/RC)(1+A)}} = \frac{-A\Delta e}{1 + A} \quad \text{(d)}$$

$$(3\text{-}61)$$

These results could have been obtained without recourse to Eq. (3-20). Since the time constant is assumed to be very large, the voltage across the capacitor cannot follow the changes in the input voltage, and the output voltage must be similar in shape to the input voltage. The output voltage must also have zero average value; therefore the results of Eq. (3-61) could be obtained directly.

The circuit of Fig. 3-2a, under the restriction that the time constant is large with respect to the period of the input signal, is called a *coupling circuit*. The circuit of Fig. 3-2b could also be included in this classification, but it is not so valuable as the first circuit because the inductor will always have a finite resistance and shunt capacitance.

The use of coupling circuits is, of course, not restricted to square wave voltages, but is applicable to any wave shape where the restriction on the time constant can be observed.

Perhaps the most common use of the coupling circuit is **as** the connecting system between the plate circuit of one amplifier stage and the grid circuit of the following amplifier, as shown in Fig. 3-16. The capacitor in this case is called a blocking capacitor in

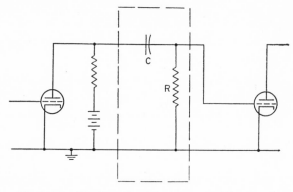

Fig. 3-16.   Coupling circuit between amplifier stages.

that it blocks out the d-c component of the input signal. Since the resistor is the grid return resistor of a vacuum tube, its magnitude must be limited or operation will become unstable. Thus the largest possible capacitor will be used. Care must be taken however that an excessive amount of shunt resistance is not present in the coupling capacitor or bias considerations in the following stage may be disturbed. The voltage rating of the capacitor must be sufficiently great to withstand the supply voltage of the driving stage. Although in normal operation only the average value of the input signal appears across the capacitor, the total supply voltage may appear when the system is turned on or off.

In the design of coupling circuits for amplifiers, considered from the sine wave point of view, it is quite often stated that the reactance of the capacitor at the lowest frequency to be used should be equal to, or less than, one-tenth of the value of the resistance. To obtain some idea of what this means in terms of the time constant, a symmetrical square wave will be applied to a *coupling circuit*.

The output voltage will be calculated by Eq. (3-20) and will be plotted for several different values of time constant.

The fundamental or lowest frequency in the input signal is

$$f = \frac{1}{\Delta t} \tag{3-62}$$

where Δt is the period of the square wave. If

$$X_c = \frac{1}{2\pi f C} = \frac{R}{10} \tag{3-63}$$

then

$$\frac{\Delta t}{RC} = \frac{\pi}{5} \tag{3-64}$$

The steady-state output voltage is shown in Fig. 3-17 along with the results for several other values of $\Delta t/RC$.

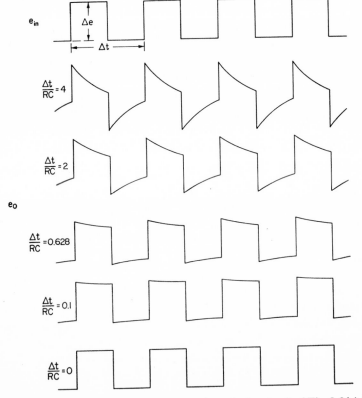

Fig. 3-17. Effect of increasing the time constant in the circuit of Fig. 3-2(a) for a square-wave input voltage.

The quality of the output signal may also be expressed by the amount the voltage decays from its maximum positive or negative value during the time $\Delta t/2$. For a symmetrical square wave, the percentage decay as a function of X_c/R may be found, where X_c is always calculated at the fundamental frequency. In accordance with the previous notation,

$$y = xe^{-\Delta t/2RC} = xe^{-\pi X_c/R} \qquad (3\text{-}65)$$

$$\% \text{ decay} = \frac{100(x-y)}{x} = 100(1 - e^{-\pi X_c/R}) \qquad (3\text{-}66)$$

This expression is plotted in Fig. 3-18.

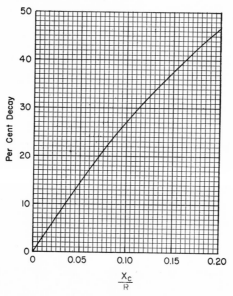

Fig. 3-18.   Plot of decay as a function of X_c/R for the circuit of Fig. 3-2(a) with a symmetrical square-wave input voltage.

It must be noted that whenever the time constant of the coupling circuit is made long in order to improve the response, the duration of the transient period is also increased. This may prove to be of importance where the input signal is not periodic.

3-9 Use of Differentiating and Integrating Circuits in Television Receivers

Differentiating and integrating circuits find an important application in the synchronizing systems of some television receivers. The problem here involves separation of wide pulses from narrow pulses of the same magnitude. The wide pulses must be made to produce a signal which will eventually control the vertical sweep circuits, while the narrow pulses operate the horizontal system.

The video signal in the receiver will normally consist of the synchronizing pulses and the picture signal. By the use of suitable clipping circuits, the synchronizing pulses can be separated from the composite signal. This process is discussed in Chapter 5. The synchronizing pulses can then be applied to the parallel combination of an integrating circuit and a differentiating circuit. The differentiating circuit will act upon any steep input wave form to

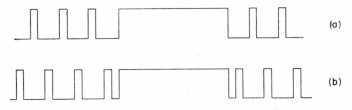

Fig. 3-19.   Television synchronizing signal (no equalizing pulses).

produce output pulses with which to control the horizontal sweep system. The integrating circuit will very nearly ignore the narrow pulses and will produce a sloping front output pulse for the vertical system.

Actually, the problem is more complicated for two reasons. In the first place, the wide pulses are very nearly the length of three horizontal sweep periods. Therefore the long vertical synchronizing pulse must be broken up into sharp wave fronts in order that control of the horizontal system shall not be lost during this time. These breaks can be very short in duration, so that the output capacitor of the integrating circuit will not have enough time to lose any appreciable charge.

The second complication arises from the fact that an interlaced scan is used with a pattern having an odd number of lines. Interlacing is obtained by ending the first vertical sweep when a horizontal sweep is only half finished. All the vertical sweeps are of the same amplitude, and the second vertical sweep starts with the horizontal deflection at mid-point. The region around two successive vertical synchronizing pulses, neglecting the breakup of the vertical synchronizing pulses, is shown in Fig. 3-19. Since the time intervals between the last horizontal synchronizing pulse and the vertical synchronizing pulse are different for the two cases pictured in Fig. 3-19, the output voltages of the integrating circuit will not be the same.   The vertical sweep system depends upon the output of the integrating circuit; therefore two successive vertical sweeps may be different.   However, for the type of interlaced scan to be used, the vertical sweeps should all be identical.   To accomplish this, the synchronizing pulses of Fig. 3-19 must be modified. This is done by providing the horizontal synchronizing pulses at

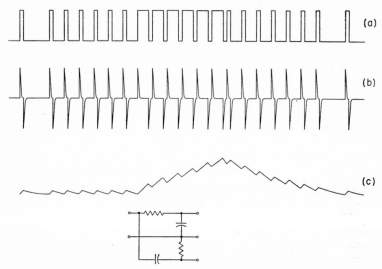

Fig. 3-20.   (a) Television synchronizing signal.   (b) Output voltage of differentiating circuit.   (c) Output voltage of integrating circuit.

a doubled frequency in the neighborhood of a vertical synchronizing pulse, thus making the regions around successive vertical pulses the same.   These double frequency pulses are known as equalizing pulses.   The horizontal sweep system is constructed so that it will not respond to pulses of doubled frequency, but will continue to be synchronized at the original rate.   The complete synchronizing signal and the output of the separating circuit are shown in Fig. 3-20.

REFERENCES

1. Allen B. DuMont Lab., Inc., "Notes on Attenuator Distortion," *The Oscillographer*, July–August, 1946, Vol. 8.

2. Brainerd, J. G.; Reich, H. J.; Koehler, G.; and Woodruff, L. F., *Ultra-High Frequency Techniques*. New York: D. Van Nostrand Company, Inc., 1942.

3. Cameron, W. M., "Pulse-Sine Wave Generator," *Electronics*, March, 1949, Vol. 22, p. 174.

4. Chance, Britton; Hughes, Vernon; MacNichol, Edward F., Jr.; Sayre, David; and Williams, Frederick C., *Waveforms*. New York: McGraw-Hill Book Co., Inc., 1949.

5. Cherry, Colin, *Pulses and Transients in Communication Circuits*. London: Chapman and Hall, Ltd., 1949.

6. Cruft Laboratory Electronics Training Staff, *Electronic Circuits and Tubes*. New York: McGraw-Hill Book Co., Inc., 1947.

7. Deeter, E. L. and Dau, W. K., "Interval Timer," *Electronics*, July, 1947, Vol. 20, p. 86.

8. Easton, A. and Odessey, P. H., "Counter Circuits for Television," *Electronics*, May, 1948, Vol. 21, p. 120.

9. Frank, Ernest, *Pulsed Linear Networks*. New York: McGraw-Hill Book Co., Inc., 1945.

10. Fritz, W. H., "Portable Repeating Flash Unit," *Electronics*, March, 1949, Vol. 22, p. 74.

11. Frost-Smith, E. H., "An Experimental Method of Determining the Relationship Between Current and Time in an Inductive Circuit," *J. Sci. Instruments*, July, 1949, Vol. 26, p. 241.

12. Fundingsland, O. T. and Wheeler, G. J., "Constant Current Circuits," *Electronics*, November, 1946, Vol. 19, p. 130.

13. General Radio Co., "F-M Monitor For Broadcast and Television Service," *General Radio Experimenter*, October, 1947, Vol. 22.

14. Hallmark, C. E., "An Improved Counter-Timer for Television," *Radio News-Electronic Engr. Supplement*, July, 1947, Vol. 38, p. 8.

15. Hoadley, George B. and Lynch, Wm. A., "Transients in Coupling Circuits," *Communications*, June, 1943, Vol. 23, p. 32.

16. Kurtz, Edwin B. and Corcoran, George F., *Introduction to Electric Transients*. New York: John Wiley and Sons, Inc., 1935.

17. Lorenz, Egon; Weikel, Joanne; and Norton, Sue Gray, "Counting Rate and Frequency Meter," *Rev. Sci. Instruments*, July, 1946, Vol. 17, p. 276.

18. Marchand, N., "The Response of Electrical Networks to Non-Sinusoidal Periodic Waves," *Proc. IRE*, June, 1941, Vol. 29, p. 330.

19. M.I.T. Radar School Staff, *Principles of Radar*. New York: McGraw-Hill Book Co., Inc., 1946.

20. Nolle, R. A., "Electronic Circuit Has Logarithmic Response," *Electronics*, September, 1948, Vol. 21, p. 166.

21. Preisman, Albert, *Graphical Construction for Vacuum Tube Circuits.* New York: McGraw-Hill Book Co., Inc., 1943.

22. Schultz, M. A., "Linear Amplifiers," *Proc. IRE*, May, 1950, Vol. 38, p. 475.

23. Wald, Sidney, "Precision Interval Timer," *Electronics*, December, 1948, Vol. 21, p. 89.

24. Winkler, Marion, "Instantaneous Deviation Control," *Electronics*, September, 1949, Vol. 22, p. 97.

PROBLEMS

3-1 The switch has been open for a long time. When it is closed the capacitor has a potential of 100 volts, with the polarity shown. If the circuit is to go immediately into the steady-state condition, what is the magnitude of the sine wave driving voltage, and at what time during the cycle should the switch be closed?

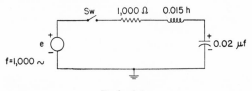

Prob. 3-1.

3-2 Let the voltage of Fig. 3-3a be applied to the circuit of Fig. 3-2a where $e_1 = 0$, $R = 50,000$ ohms, and $C = 1.0$ microfarad. The maximum value of the energy stored in the circuit is 10 per cent of the total energy supplied to the circuit in one cycle. What is the ratio of Δt_1 to Δt_2? Assume the maximum energy point occurs during the Δt_1 period.

3-3 The nonrepetitive wave form shown is applied to the circuit of Fig. 3-2b where $L = 800$ millihenrys, $R = 5000$ ohms, and $\Delta t = 100$ microseconds. Sketch and label the output voltage.

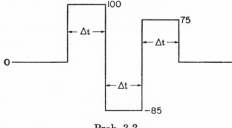

Prob. 3-3.

3-4 Let the given wave form be applied to the circuit of Fig. 3-2a. Sketch and label the steady-state voltages across the resistor and the capacitor. The time constant of the circuit is 700 microseconds.

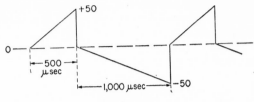

Prob. 3-4.

3-5 In the circuit of Fig. 3-2a, $C = 100$ micromicrofarads and $R = 100,000$ ohms. Sketch and label the output voltage for the given input voltage.

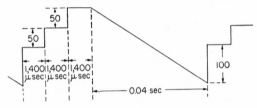

Prob. 3-5.

3-6 Sketch and label the steady-state output voltage from the circuit of Fig. 3-2a for the given input voltage. $R = 150,000$ ohms $C = 0.001$ microfarad.

Prob. 3-6.

3-7 Let the voltage shown be applied to the circuit of Fig. 3-2a. Sketch and label a generalized steady-state output voltage.

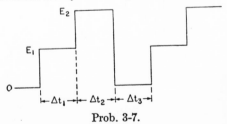

Prob. 3-7.

3-8 Alter the circuit of Fig. 3-13 by placing a 5000-ohm resistor in the cathode circuit of T_1.   Rework the example of Sec. 3-6.

3-9 Alter the circuit of Fig. 3-13 by placing a 250,000-ohm resistor in series with the grid of T_2.   Rework the example of Sec. 3-6.

3-10 If the switch is closed at $t = 0$, and $e = E_m \sin (\omega t + \theta)$, find the steady-state voltage across the capacitor.

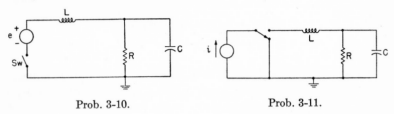

Prob. 3-10.   Prob. 3-11.

3-11 If the current $i = I_m \sin (\omega t + \theta)$ is switched into the system at $t = 0$, in the circuit shown, find the steady-state capacitor voltage.

3-12 The voltage $e = E_m \sin (\omega t + \theta)$ is switched into the given system at $t = 0$.   Calculate the steady-state output voltage.

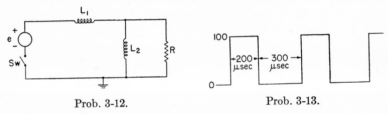

Prob. 3-12.   Prob. 3-13.

3-13 The wave form shown is applied to a series RLC circuit.   Sketch and label the steady-state current in the circuit.

CHAPTER FOUR

CLAMPING CIRCUITS

In many types of circuits, it is necessary that the voltage appearing at a given location have some point on its wave form at a particular potential. For any given wave form, the first way of approaching this problem might be to add a d-c voltage until the desired potential is reached. However, this scheme has a severe disadvantage. Usually most circuits contain some form of capacitive coupling; therefore if the wave shape is changed, the magnitude of the d-c voltage which was originally added will be incorrect.

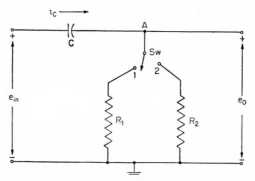

Fig. 4-1. Switched RC circuit.

A more suitable solution to the problem is to use a circuit which will maintain some point on the wave form, usually a positive or a negative maximum, at the desired potential, independent of the wave shape. Such circuits will be discussed in this chapter.

4-1 Use of Variable Time Constant to Control d-c Level in RC Circuits

The circuit shown in Fig. 4-1 is a more generalized version of the circuit shown in Fig. 3-2a. It will be assumed that the switch is

74

either in position 1 or in position 2, and that it can make the change from one position to the other instantaneously.

The switch can, in general, be controlled in two ways. It may be activated by the voltage appearing at point A. For instance, when A is positive with respect to ground, the switch may be in position 1, while when A is negative, the switch will be in position 2. It should be realized that if this method of operation is used, the circuit becomes nonlinear if $R_1 \neq R_2$.

The second method of control is that of remote operation. In this case the position of the switch is determined by a control voltage; that is, a third voltage, not necessarily e_{in} or e_0, operates the switch.

Let an arbitrary periodic wave form of voltage be applied to the circuit, and let the voltage from A to ground be the controlling voltage on the switch, as previously discussed. During the part of the cycle when point A is positive with respect to ground, the switch is in position 1. The output voltage during this time is,

$$(e_0)_1 = i_c R_1 \qquad (4\text{-}1)$$

During the time that A is negative,

$$(e_0)_2 = i_c R_2 \qquad (4\text{-}2)$$

The area A_1 as represented in Fig. 4-2 can be expressed as

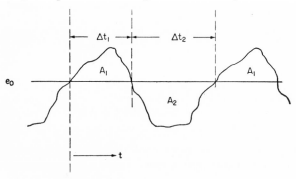

Fig. 4-2. Generalized input voltage to the circuit of Fig. 4-1.

$$A_1 = \int_{\Delta t_1} i_c R_1 \, dt \qquad (4\text{-}3)$$

while

$$A_2 = \int_{\Delta t_2} i_c R_2 \, dt \qquad (4\text{-}4)$$

If the system is in steady state, there is just as much charge added to the capacitor during the Δt_1 period as is removed during the Δt_2 time. Thus

$$\int_{\Delta t_1} i_C \, dt + \int_{\Delta t_2} i_C \, dt = 0 \qquad (4\text{-}5)$$

Taking the ratio of A_1 to A_2,

$$\frac{A_1}{A_2} = \frac{\displaystyle\int_{\Delta t_1} i_C R_1 \, dt}{\displaystyle\int_{\Delta t_2} i_C R_2 \, dt} = -\frac{R_1}{R_2} \qquad (4\text{-}6)$$

The d-c value of the output voltage will be

$$(e_0)_{av} = \frac{A_1 + A_2}{\Delta t_1 + \Delta t_2} = \frac{A_2(1 - R_1/R_2)}{\Delta t_1 + \Delta t_2} \qquad (4\text{-}7)$$

Thus it is possible to make the average value of the output voltage either positive or negative by variation of the two resistors. When the resistors are equal the circuit becomes linear, with zero d-c output voltage.

The square wave of Fig. 3-3 will now be applied to the circuit of Fig. 4-1, with the controlling voltage the same as before. It is not necessary to rework the problem completely, since Eq. (3-20) can be modified to provide the correct results. Using the same nomenclature as before, these equations are:

$$x = \Delta e \, \frac{(1 - e^{-\Delta t_2/R_2 C})}{1 - e^{-(1/C)(\Delta t_1/R_1 + \Delta t_2/R_2)}} \qquad (a)$$

$$y = \Delta e \, \frac{e^{-\Delta t_1/R_1 C}(1 - e^{-\Delta t_2/R_2 C})}{1 - e^{-(1/C)(\Delta t_1/R_1 + \Delta t_2/R_2)}} \qquad (b)$$

$$z = \Delta e \, \frac{(e^{-\Delta t_1/R_1 C} - 1)}{1 - e^{-(1/C)(\Delta t_1/R_1 + \Delta t_2/R_2)}} \qquad (c) \qquad (4\text{-}8)$$

$$w = \Delta e \, \frac{e^{-\Delta t_2/R_2 C}(e^{-\Delta t_1/R_1 C} - 1)}{1 - e^{-(1/C)(\Delta t_1/R_1 + \Delta t_2/R_2)}} \qquad (d)$$

If the time constants $R_1 C$ and $R_2 C$ are large with respect to Δt_1 and Δt_2, respectively, the system will be a good coupling circuit and the output voltage will look essentially like the input voltage. However, the d-c level of the output voltage will depend upon the ratio of R_1 to R_2.

An interesting and very useful circuit appears when one of the time constants is very large and the other is quite small. By Eq.

(4-6), all the output voltage must then appear either above zero or below zero. This can also be seen from Eq. (4-8). For example, let $R_1 = 0$ and $R_2 = \infty$. For finite values of Δt_1 and Δt_2,

$$\frac{\Delta t_1}{R_1 C} = \infty \quad \text{and} \quad e^{-\Delta t_1/R_1 C} = 0 \tag{4-9}$$

$$\frac{\Delta t_2}{R_2 C} = 0 \quad \text{and} \quad e^{-\Delta t_2/R_2 C} = 1 \tag{4-10}$$

Then $\quad x = 0, \quad y = 0, \quad z = -\Delta e, \quad \text{and} \quad w = -\Delta e \tag{4-11}$

If the ratio of R_1 to R_2 were made large, all the output voltage would appear above zero instead of below zero.

When one time constant is very much larger than the other, the extreme values of the output voltage are independent of the time intervals. In addition, one extreme value will be zero, independent of the amplitude or average value of the input voltage. By the judicious use of applied d-c voltages, this fixed value can be made other than zero.

A circuit which acts in the manner stated is quite often called a *clamping circuit*, in that either the positive or the negative extremes can be held at a given fixed potential. Such possibilities also give rise to other names for the circuit, such as *d-c restoring circuit* or *d-c reinsertion circuit*, since any desired d-c voltage can be inserted into a voltage wave form by the use of the system.

4-2 Simple Diode Clamping Circuit

One of the simplest clamping circuits can be physically produced by the use of an RC coupling circuit and a diode. The diode may be

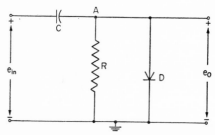

Fig. 4-3.   Diode clamping circuit.

either a high-vacuum diode or a crystal diode having a high back resistance. When point A is positive with respect to ground the diode will conduct heavily, when it is negative the diode will conduct but slightly. In terms of the R_1 and R_2 of Fig. 4-1,

$$R_1 = \frac{\bar{r}_f R}{\bar{r}_f + R} \tag{4-12}$$

$$R_2 = \frac{\bar{r}_r R}{\bar{r}_r + R} \tag{4-13}$$

where $\bar{r}_f$ is the static forward resistance of the diode and $\bar{r}_r$ is the static reverse resistance. In the case of the high-vacuum diode, $\bar{r}_r$ will be infinite in magnitude. Actually the diode resistances are not linear in either direction, but usually $\bar{r}_f$ will be sufficiently small and $\bar{r}_r$ sufficiently large so that R_2/R_1 will be quite large.

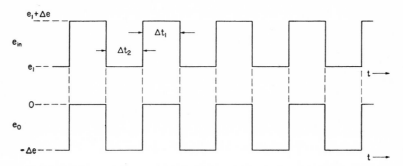

Fig. 4-4. Input and output voltages for the circuit of Fig. 4-3.

If the square wave voltage is applied to the circuit, the steady-state output voltage will be as given by Fig. 4-4.

Practically, there may be two deviations from the wave forms shown in Fig. 4-4. First, the time constant during the negative part of the square wave is not infinite, therefore the bottom portion of the wave form may not be perfectly horizontal but may actually decay an appreciable amount toward zero. Second, if the negative portion of the wave form does decay an appreciable amount toward zero, the output voltage will becomes slightly positive when the input voltage increases by the amount Δe. The diode will immediately conduct heavily to restore the lost charge to the capacitor, since in steady state the diode will conduct just enough to allow the capacitor to regain the charge it lost during the negative half of the cycle. Excessive diode conduction will becomes noticeable by the appearance of a positive narrow pulse on the leading edge of the output square wave.

The circuit of Fig. 4-3 will work well on most periodic signals for which R and C alone would form a good coupling circuit. For cases where the positive portion of the voltage is very short in duration, the capacitor may not have sufficient time to charge fully; therefore the positive peaks will not be at zero but will be slightly above zero.

4-3 Modifications of Single Diode Clamping Circuit

The diode clamping circuit of Fig. 4-3 may be modified slightly in several ways. The chief purpose of these modifications is to allow the extreme of a voltage wave form to be clamped at a potential other than zero. It will be assumed in this section that the reverse resistance of the diode is very high, and the term *conduction* will indicate current flow in the forward direction.

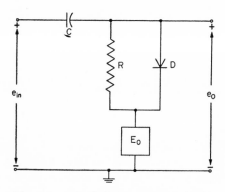

Fig. 4-5.   Biased diode clamping circuit.

For the first change, let the cathode-resistor junction in Fig. 4-3 be returned to a given potential other than zero, with respect to ground. This potential, E_0, may be either positive or negative. For purposes of explanation, the fixed voltage E_0 may temporarily be considered part of the input voltage, and the output e'_0 considered to be across the resistor. This is shown in Fig. 4-6. The previous study has shown that the positive peaks of e'_0 are clamped at zero

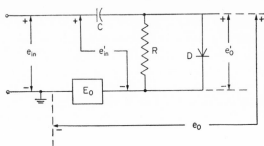

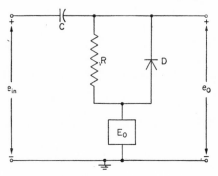

Fig. 4-6. Solution of biased diode clamping circuit.

Fig. 4-7. Biased diode clamping circuit with diode inverted.

regardless of the average value of the input voltage. Thus e_{in} and e'_{in} will produce the same e'_0. Since the positive peaks of e'_0 are clamped at zero, e_0 must have the positive peaks clamped at E_0.

Fig. 4-8. Photographs of the output voltage of the circuit of Fig. 4-7 for several different values of square-wave input voltage.

As shown in Sec. 4-1, the diode can be reversed in position to allow the negative peaks to be clamped. A general circuit of this nature is shown in Fig. 4-7, where E_0 can again be positive or negative. The negative peaks of the output signal will be fixed at a potential E_0 volts from ground.

The wave forms of Fig. 4-8 are examples of this type of clamping. The output of a circuit similar to that of Fig. 4-7 is shown for several different values of square wave input voltage.

A further modification takes place when the resistor in the basic circuit is returned to ground while the diode is returned to a fixed potential. A case of this kind is shown in Fig. 4-9. If the cathode of the diode is held positive there is the possibility that the diode may never conduct, in which case the device is not a clamping circuit but is a coupling circuit. If the cathode is held negative with respect to ground, the diode will always conduct for some part of the cycle and the circuit will clamp the positive peaks at E_0. Similarly, the diode may never conduct if it is reversed with the anode held at a negative voltage. With the diode in the reversed position,

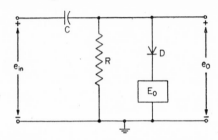

Fig. 4-9.   Modification of biased diode clamping circuit.

and the anode held at a positive voltage, the circuit will clamp the negative peaks at the reference potential.

A more careful examination of the clamping circuits which have been discussed shows several general rules governing their operation. (1) The output voltage of a clamping circuit will have essentially the same shape as the input voltage if the greater time constant is much larger than the time intervals in the input signal. (2) If the cathode voltage of the diode is fixed, the positive extremes of the output voltage will be clamped at the cathode voltage. (3) If the anode voltage of the diode is fixed, the negative extremes of the output voltage will be clamped at the anode voltage. (4) Before the second or third rule can be applied, it must be definitely ascertained whether or not the circuit is a clamping circuit.

Clamping in all cases is characterized by conduction of the diode over at least a small part of the cycle. To determine if the diode will ever conduct, the diode can be temporarily removed from the circuit and the steady-state voltage across the diode terminals noted under this condition. If this voltage is such as to cause the diode to conduct, were it in the circuit, the circuit is a clamping circuit. The circuit of Fig. 4-9 will be used to demonstrate this point. The cathode of the diode will be made positive with respect to ground as shown in Fig. 4-10a. The input voltage is given in Fig. 4-10b.

If the diode is temporarily taken from the circuit, the output voltage will be as sketched in Fig. 4-10c. Without the diode the

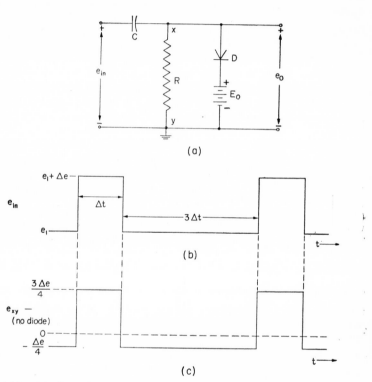

Fig. 4-10. (a) Clamping circuit. (b) Input to the circuit of (a). (c) Output of the circuit of (a) with no diode.

system becomes a linear coupling circuit with an output voltage having zero average value. The most positive voltage at the output is $3\Delta e/4$. If $3\Delta e/4$ is greater than E_0, the voltage across the diode socket is such as to make the diode conduct, were it in place. Thus the circuit is a clamping circuit. If $3\Delta e/4$ is less than E_0, the circuit is a coupling circuit with or without the diode in place, since the diode would never conduct anyway.

4-4 Miscellaneous Considerations in Simple Diode Clamping Circuits

It has been shown that for best operation of the clamping circuit, the ratio of the reverse to the forward resistance should be very high. In this respect then, the high-vacuum diode will prove to be superior to the crystal diode, since the crystal has a finite reverse resistance. In the forward direction, both high-vacuum and crystal diodes have nonlinear characteristics. The form of this non-linearity is such that the conducting resistance is decreased as the voltage across the diode is increased. Thus best results will be obtained when the signal applied to the clamping circuit is as large as possible.

When signals of approximately the same shape but of different magnitudes are applied to the clamping circuit, operation may take

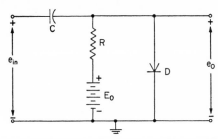

Fig. 4-11.   Circuit to decrease effective conducting resistance of diode.

place on different portions of the diode characteristic resulting in different values of resistance.   On certain wave shapes, particularly narrow pulses, the output voltages may then become quite different. This effect can be partially eliminated by insertion of a positive bias voltage as shown in Fig. 4-11.   The total d-c voltage developed across the resistor in Fig. 4-11 is the sum of the bias voltage and the signal-developed voltage. If the bias voltage is made large as compared to the signal-developed potential, the average current through the resistance will not change appreciably with changes in magnitude of the input voltage.   Since there is no average current through the capacitor, the average diode current will also remain relatively constant. This can be shown by assuming the diode resistance to be very small with respect to the resistor R. If $E_0 = 0$, the average diode current will be equal to $\Delta e/2R$.   Changing the magnitude of Δe without changing the duty cycle will change the average diode current and peak diode current by the same percentage.   When the battery E_0 is added to the circuit, the average diode current becomes $(E_0 + \Delta e/2)/R$.   Thus if E_0 is large with respect to Δe, the average and peak diode currents will not change very much with changes in Δe.

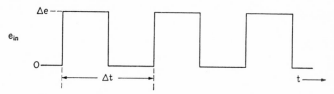

Fig. 4-12.   Input voltage to the circuit of Fig. 4-11.

The above reasoning is correct as long as the diode resistance is much less than the resistance R.   If the diode resistance becomes appreciable in size as compared to R, the analysis is not correct and it is possible that the diode will conduct during the entire cycle.

4-5 Multielement Tubes in Clamping Circuits

A multielement tube such as a triode, tetrode, or pentode can also be used to form a clamping circuit.   The grid-cathode circuit of such a tube has the same characteristic as does a diode, that is, grid current will result when the grid is driven positive with respect to the cathode.   As in the case for a high-vacuum diode, grid current will also flow when the grid voltage is near zero but still slightly negative, due to high-energy electrons being emitted from the cathode.   There is one further complication in that the grid-cathode characteristic is dependent upon the potential of the other elements in the tube.   For example, in a triode with a constant positive grid-cathode potential, the grid current will decrease with increases in the plate voltage.

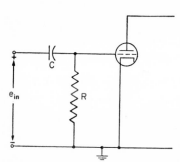

Fig. 4-13.   Triode clamping circuit.

The simplest possible triode clamping circuit is shown in Fig. 4-13.   The same restrictions as to time constant which were discussed in Sec. 4-1 and Sec. 4-2 are applicable to this circuit.

If the resistor is placed in parallel with the capacitor instead of being returned to ground, the operation of the system is not altered appreciably. In this new form, shown in Fig. 4-14, the circuit is quite often used as a self-bias system for a Class C amplifier or as a grid-leak detecting system.

The circuits of both Fig. 4-13 and Fig. 4-14 are unique in one respect. In steady-state operation it is impossible to drive the grids very positive. Assume that the input signal is a sine wave which is being slowly increased in amplitude. The grid will be driven just positive enough to allow the capacitor to stay charged to the peak value of the input signal. The grid-cathode voltage is thus clamped with the positive peak at approximately zero, as shown in Fig. 4-15.

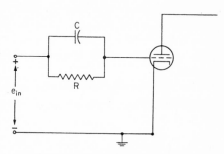

Fig. 4-14. Triode clamping circuit, R and C in parallel.

Maximum plate dissipation will occur when the input signal is zero. In order to limit this dissipation to a safe value if the input signal remains at zero for an appreciable length of time, some form of fixed bias is usually used. A battery may be inserted into the system in one of the ways shown in Sec. 4-3. A

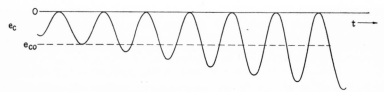

Fig. 4-15. Grid voltage for the circuits of Fig. 4-13 and Fig. 4-14.

cathode resistance can also be used, but it tends to destroy the effectiveness of the clamping action. When the grid is driven positive, increased plate current flows through the cathode resistance, and the grid-cathode voltage is decreased. This forces operation at a lower grid current and correspondingly high grid-cathode resistance.

4-6 Clamped Triode as a Switch

A triode can be used as a switch if a square wave voltage of correct amplitude is applied to the grid circuit. Actually, the equivalent circuit should consist not of a switch alone, but of a switch in series with the static plate resistance of the triode. When the grid-cathode voltage is brought above the cutoff potential, the switch is effectively shut; when the grid-cathode voltage is below cutoff, the switch is open. If an input circuit similar to Fig. 4-13 is used, the positive peaks of the input square wave will be clamped at zero, tending to make the static conducting resistance the same every time the switch is closed. The square wave must have a peak-to-peak amplitude which is greater than the magnitude of the cutoff potential.

The value of the resistance in series with the switch is sometimes very difficult to determine, as it is in general nonlinear and depend-

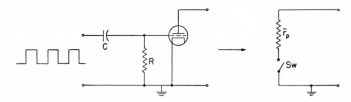

Fig. 4-16. Clamped triode as a switch.

ent upon the plate voltage of the tube. One method of estimating this resistance is to average, over the operating range, the static resistance given by the plate characteristic for zero grid voltage. If the increased labor is warranted by more accurate results, the nonlinear procedures of Chapter 2 may be used.

It is sometimes preferable to use, in the grid circuit, controlling voltages which do not have instantaneous changes of magnitude. If the interelectrode capacitances are appreciable in value, and square waves are used, a differentiated form of the input signal may appear in the plate circuit. Sloping the sides of the input square wave will usually eliminate this problem but may introduce other errors if accurate timing is to be obtained. A pentode with its lower grid-plate capacitance will also tend to alleviate the difficulty.

The system of Fig. 4-16 is widely used for different types of sweep circuits, and will be further discussed in that connection. It also has applications in many other types of switched circuits, one of which will be treated in the following section.

4-7 Ringing Circuit

A circuit which demonstrates the use of a triode as a switch is the *ringing circuit*. Two of the forms which this circuit can take are shown in Fig. 4-17.

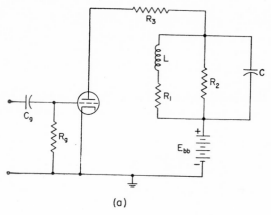

(a)

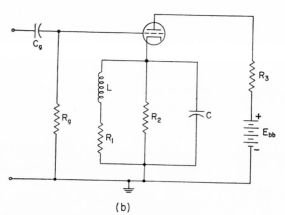

(b)

Fig. 4-17. (a) Ringing circuit, plate output. (b) Ringing circuit, cathode output.

The input signal to each circuit shall be a square wave with amplitude greater than the cutoff potential of the tube. This cut-off potential must be determined for each circuit independently. The C_g, R_g, $\bar{r}_g$ combination will serve as a clamping circuit to clamp the positive peaks of the square wave at zero. When the tube is cut off by the negative portion of the input square wave, there will be a transient in the L, R_1, R_2, C circuit. When the grid voltage returns to zero, a second transient will take place. This transient will in general be much shorter in duration due to the shunting effect of the conducting tube.

The conditions just after cutoff can be represented by the circuit of Fig. 2-20, which is shown again in Fig. 4-18. Using D as a reference, the voltage across this circuit (except for the special case of critical damping), was given by Eq. (2-35) as

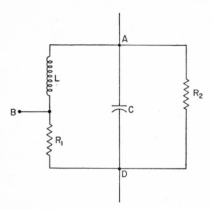

$$e_A = e^{-\alpha t}\{A' \cosh \beta t + B' \sinh \beta t\} \quad (4\text{--}14)$$

$$\text{where} \quad \alpha = \frac{R_1 R_2 C + L}{2 L C R_2} \quad (4\text{-}15)$$

$$\beta = \sqrt{\left(\frac{R_1 R_2 C + L}{2 L C R_2}\right)^2 - \frac{R_1 + R_2}{R_2 L C}} \quad (4\text{-}16)$$

Fig. 4-18. Series-parallel RLC circuit.

$$A' = e_A(0) \quad (4\text{-}17)$$

$$B' = \frac{e_A(0)(\alpha - 1/R_2 C) - i_L(0)/C}{\beta} \quad (4\text{-}18)$$

Let $i(0)$ be the current through the tube just before the grid voltage drops below the cutoff value. If the grid voltage had been at zero sufficiently long for steady-state conditions to be reached, $i(0)$ could be found by the intersection of the load line and the zero grid voltage plate characteristic. This load line is drawn using a resistance of $R_3 + (R_1 R_2)/(R_1 + R_2)$. The following substitutions can then be made for A' and B' in the general equations.

$$A' = e_A(0) = \frac{i(0) R_1 R_2}{R_1 + R_2} \quad (4\text{-}19)$$

$$B' = \frac{i(0) R_1 R_2}{\beta(R_1 + R_2)} \left(\alpha - \frac{1}{R_2 C} + \frac{1}{R_1 C}\right) \quad (4\text{-}20)$$

The voltage across the circuit may, as before, take three forms. It may be oscillatory, critically damped, or overdamped, depending

upon the relationship between the terms $(R_1R_2C + L)^2/(2LCR_2)^2$
and $(R_1 + R_2)/(R_2LC)$. The circuit will be oscillatory with a
frequency of

$$f = \frac{1}{2\pi} \sqrt{\frac{(R_1 + R_2)}{LCR_2} - \left(\frac{R_1R_2C + L}{2LCR_2}\right)^2} \qquad (4\text{-}21)$$

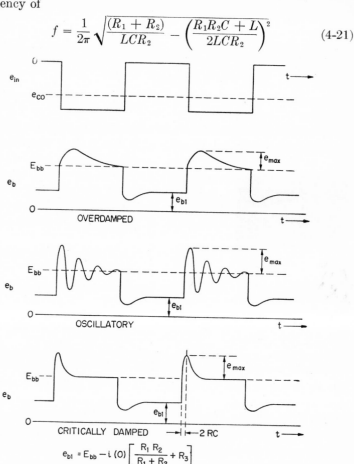

$$e_{b1} = E_{bb} - i(0)\left[\frac{R_1 R_2}{R_1 + R_2} + R_3\right]$$

Fig. 4-19.   Wave forms for the circuit of Fig. 4-17(a).

when
$$R_1 + R_2 > \frac{(R_1R_2C + L)^2}{4LCR_2} \qquad (4\text{-}22)$$

The circuit will be critically damped when

$$R_1 + R_2 = \frac{(R_1R_2C + L)^2}{4LCR_2} \qquad (4\text{-}23)$$

and overdamped when

$$R_1 + R_2 < \frac{(R_1R_2C + L)^2}{4LCR_2} \qquad (4\text{-}24)$$

If the RLC combination is connected in the plate circuit of the tube as shown in Fig. 4-17a, the wave forms of Fig. 4-19 will be applicable. The wave forms of Fig. 4-20 also show the voltage across the parallel circuit under oscillatory conditions.

In order to find the required amplitude of the input square wave, the value of the cutoff potential must be known.   Since it has been assumed that the tube remains cut off during the negative portion of the input signal, the cutoff potential is that voltage which will hold the tube nonconducting at the maximum value of plate voltage which may exist during that time.   For the circuits of Fig. 4-17, this maximum plate voltage will be the sum of the supply voltage and the maximum voltage across the RLC circuit. This can be found rigorously by finding the maximum value of e_A in Eq. (4-14).   If the circuit is oscillatory with little loss (that is, R_1 is small and R_2 is large) the maximum value of the voltage across the RLC circuit can be approximated.   Just as the tube is cut off, most of the stored energy will be in the magnetic field of the inductor.   A quarter of a cycle later, this energy will have been transferred to the electric field of the capacitor.   Equating these two quantities,

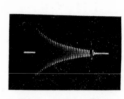

Fig. 4-20. Photograph of the voltage across the RLC circuit under oscillatory conditions.

$$\tfrac{1}{2}Li_L{}^2(0) = \tfrac{1}{2}Ce_T{}^2 \qquad (4\text{-}25)$$

where e_T is the voltage due to the energy transferred to the capacitor from the inductor.   The maximum value of capacitor voltage will then be

$$e_{\max} = e_T + e_A(0) = \frac{R_2 i(0)}{R_1 + R_2}\left(\sqrt{\frac{L}{C}} + R_1\right) \qquad (4\text{-}26)$$

The value of $e_{\max}$ as given by Eq. (4-26) is the highest possible value for the capacitor voltage.   If the grid voltage is sufficient to keep the tube cut off at a plate voltage of $E_{bb} + e_{\max}$, it is assured that proper operation will take place regardless of whether the circuit is critically damped, overdamped, or oscillatory.

When the system is oscillatory, the frequency of oscillation is very nearly independent of the tube characteristics. Changes in emission and plate supply voltage will affect the amplitude but will not change the frequency of the output wave form. Changes in the output capacitance of the tube will change the total capacitance of the circuit. If the square wave driving frequency is the same as the frequency of oscillation, the circuit very closely resembles that of a Class C amplifier.

The voltage across the RLC combination can be made an excellent source of time markers, since the frequency is stable, and the ampli-

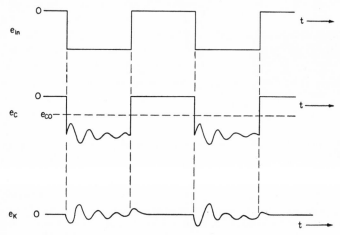

Fig. 4-21. Wave forms for the circuit of Fig. 4-17(b).

tude can be made uniform by clipping the output at a preset level. If the clipped sine waves are then differentiated, very sharp markers can be obtained. The first marker in each set will always lag the start of the negative portion of the input square wave by the same amount.

The circuit of Fig. 4-17b has many features in common with that of Fig. 4-17a. For the same components and d-c applied voltages, the induced voltage will be the same as before. However, the input square wave will now have to be of greater magnitude than in the previous case. The maximum plate-to-cathode voltage has not changed, but the induced voltage now also appears in the grid-cathode circuit. The peak-to-peak voltage which will be required to cut the tube off will be equal to the voltage required for the circuit of Fig. 4-17a plus the maximum induced voltage. Possible wave forms for the oscillatory case are shown in Fig. 4-21.

Each circuit of Fig. 4-17 will also have a transient when the tube is brought back into conduction. In the first case, a resistance equal to $R_3 + \bar{r}_p$ is added in parallel to R_2. This will increase the damping in the system. In the circuit of Fig. 4-17b, the system will be damped more heavily when the tube returns to conduction, since the cathode output resistance is much less than the plate output resistance.

4-8 Use of Clamping Circuits in Television Receivers

If the video sections of a number of television receivers were examined, a considerable variety of clamping circuits would be found. Before discussing the form of these clamping circuits, an investigation into their need will be undertaken.

The output signal of the video amplifier in a television receiver contains a great amount of information since it includes the picture components, the horizontal and vertical synchronizing pulses, the equalizing pulses, and the blanking pulses. The purpose of the blanking pulses is to make the grid-cathode voltage of the cathode-ray tube sufficiently negative to cut off the tube during the horizontal and vertical retrace times. A sketch of the video output signal over a period of several horizontal sweeps is shown in Fig. 4-22.

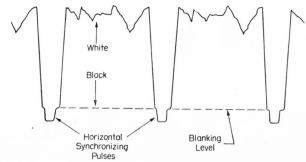

Fig. 4-22. Television video signal.

If the output of the video amplifier were applied directly to the grid-cathode circuit of the cathode-ray tube, the correct d-c value of the blanking level could be adjusted for any one set of picture components. However, since the video amplifier is most conveniently constructed with capacitive coupling circuits, any change in the picture components will change the average value of the composite signal, and thus change the potential difference between the average value and the blanking level. In other words, with capacitive coupling in the preceding amplifiers, the absolute potential of some point on the output wave form has little meaning. Probably the best example of this problem is to let three successive sets of picture components represent a white scene, a light gray scene, and a dark gray scene, respectively.

The white scene could be represented by a series of pulses, one of which is shown in the left sketch of Fig. 4-23. The light gray

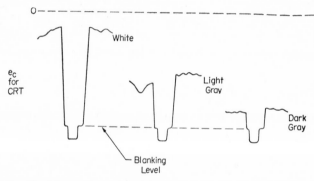

Fig. 4-23. Blanking and synchronizing pulses for a white, light gray, and a dark gray scene.

scene is represented by the middle sketch of this figure, and the dark gray scene by the right sketch. For correct operation the peaks of the blanking pulses, as applied to the cathode-ray tube grid, should all be at the same d-c level, regardless of the intensity of the scene being viewed. If the wave forms of Fig. 4-23 were passed through a video amplifier which utilized RC coupling circuits, the output voltage might appear as in Fig. 4-24. The average value or d-c value of this new signal is zero. If this signal were applied to the grid-cathode circuit of the cathode-ray tube, two major difficulties would immediately be realized: (1) regardless of the intensity of the scene being viewed, the average illumination would always be the same, (2) if the fixed grid bias for the cathode-ray tube is set such that the retraces are blanked for some scenes, they may not be blanked for others.

The foregoing discussion shows that some method must be devised to fix a certain value on the wave form at a definite potential

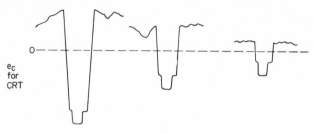

Fig. 4-24. Blanking and synchronizing pulses after passing through capacitive coupled amplifiers.

regardless of the shape or average value. Such requirements immediately indicate the need for some form of clamping circuit.

4-9 Synchronized or Keyed Clamping Circuits

In order to follow more easily the discussion of forms of operation not hitherto considered, the circuit of Fig. 4-1 is shown again in

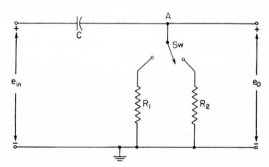

Fig. 4-25. Switched RC circuit.

Fig. 4-25. The past sections have discussed circuits in which the switch is controlled by the potential existing at point A. It was stated in Sec. 4-1, however, that it is possible to control the switch by application of a separate voltage, which is not the input or output voltage of the circuit.

The circuit of Fig. 4-26 is an example of this second type of operation. The ratio $R/(R' + \bar{r}_f)$ is large, where $\bar{r}_f$ is the forward resistance of the diode. The control voltage has a value of e_m until it is desired to make the diode conduct. At this time the control voltage is brought to zero, so that if the signal potential of point A is greater than zero, current will flow from the capacitor into the diode. Between control voltage pulses, the capacitor can

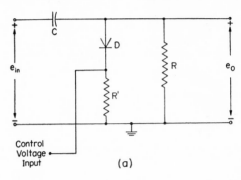

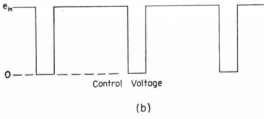

Fig. 4-26.   (a) One-way synchronized clamping circuit.   (b) Control voltage for (a).

charge or discharge only through a long time constant circuit; thus the level of some chosen point on the signal wave form has been brought to zero. Care must be taken that the magnitude of the positive excursions of the output signal voltage are always less than e_m or the diode will conduct between control voltage pulses. This type of clamping circuit is known as a one-way clamping circuit, in that current can flow through the diode or switching system in but one direction.

Sometimes it becomes convenient to have a two-way clamping circuit, that is, a system in which the capacitor can gain or lose charge during the keying process. Consider the wave form of Fig. 4-27. It is necessary to clamp the positive peaks of this wave form at zero. Therefore the coupling capacitor must be able to both charge and discharge into the switching system. It must charge first in order that the positive peaks of the No. 1 pulses be at zero, but it must then be able to discharge slightly or the positive peaks of the succeeding pulses will be below zero. The normal time constant cannot be decreased to let the capacitor discharge between pulses, or excessive distortion will result. The synchronized two-way clamping circuit will allow the above operation to take place.

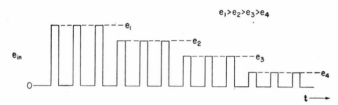

Fig. 4-27. Wave form showing the necessity for a two-way clamping circuit.

The circuit of Fig. 4-26 will be modified to allow conduction in both directions through the keying system. Two control signals in time synchronism will be needed as shown in Fig. 4-28. The control input to the R_2D_2 combination is the same as for the circuit of Fig. 4-26, while the input to the R_1D_1 set is a series of positive pulses as given in Fig. 4-28b. If the signal voltage is above zero at the clamping time, current will flow into D_2, if it is below, through D_1.

A two-way system which will allow clamping at an arbitrary level, and one which is not so critical with respect to the d-c level of the control voltage, is shown in Fig. 4-29.

Whenever it is necessary to set the level of the output signal voltage, a positive pulse is applied to F and a negative pulse to G. These pulses force the diodes to conduct, and during the conduction time, points A, B, and D are approximately at the same potential if the conducting resistance of the diodes is small. This potential is the reference or clamping potential.

Let the positive and negative control pulses have magnitudes of e_1 and e_2 respectively. The capacitors C_1 and C_2 will then gain a

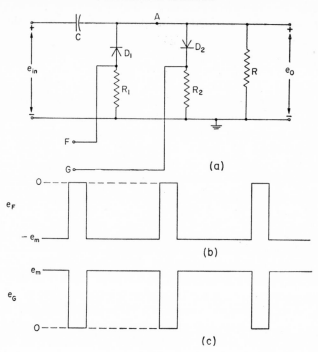

Fig. 4-28. (a) Two-way synchronized clamping circuit. (b) and (c) Control pulses for (a).

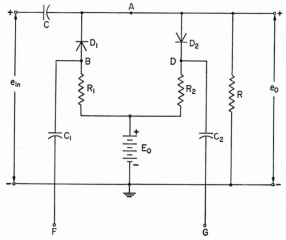

Fig. 4-29. Biased two-way synchronized clamping circuit.

voltage of e_1 plus e_2 during the pulses. After the pulses these capacitors will start to discharge with an initial current of

$$i_d = \frac{e_1 + e_2}{R_1 + R_2} \tag{4-27}$$

If the time constants R_1C_1 and R_2C_2 are made very large, the current i_d will not have changed appreciably by the time of the next pulse. The potential at point B just before a pulse could then be written as

$$e_B = E_0 - R_1 i_d = E_0 - \frac{R_1(e_1 + e_2)}{R_1 + R_2} \tag{4-28}$$

When the pulse occurs, e_B will rise by a value of e_1 volts, and the new value of e_B is the clamping potential e_{C1}.

$$e_{C1} = e_1 + E_0 - \frac{R_1(e_1 + e_2)}{R_1 + R_2} \tag{4-29}$$

$$= E_0 + \frac{R_2 e_1 - R_1 e_2}{R_1 + R_2} \tag{4-30}$$

If $R_2 e_1 = R_1 e_2$ (probably most easily done by making $R_1 = R_2$ and $e_1 = e_2$), the reference or clamping potential will be equal to E_0. When the resistors are unbalanced, there is a tendency for the pulse voltages to appear in the output.

A double triode circuit can also be used to serve as a two-way clamping circuit. Consider the circuit of Fig. 4-30.

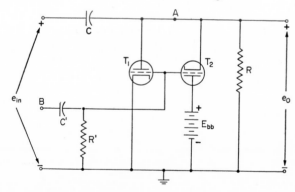

Fig. 4-30.   Double-triode, two-way clamping circuit.

The tubes T_1 and T_2 are in series with the supply voltage. A series of positive pulses will be applied to point B, with the positive peaks of these pulses clamped at zero. The amplitude of the peaks is great enough so that T_1 is cut off between pulses. When the grid-cathode voltage of T_1 is zero, the plate voltage of T_1 becomes the grid-cathode voltage of T_2. When T_1 is cut off by the input square wave, the current in T_2 must also be zero, since the tubes are in series. Thus as long as the grid of T_1 is below cutoff, the output voltage is free to take any value. When the grid of T_1 comes to zero, the potential of A becomes fixed by the ratio of the static resistances of the two tubes.

EXAMPLE: An example pertaining to the circuit of Fig. 4-30 will be shown. Let T_1 and T_2 be 6J5 tubes with a supply voltage of 300 volts. For $e_{c1} = 0$, values of e_{b1} will be selected, from which i_{b1} can be found. Since $e_{b2} = 300 - e_{b1}$ and $e_{c2} = -e_{b1}$, corresponding values of i_{b2} may be determined. The point at which $i_{b1} = i_{b2}$ is the correct operating point. This occurs when the plate voltage of T_1 is approximately 14.6 volts. If the signal potential at point A rises higher than 14.6 volts, current will flow from C into the keying system; if the potential of A goes below 14.6 volts, current will flow from the keying system into the capacitor.

REFERENCES

1. Bell, D. A., "Double-Ended D-C Restorers," *Electronics*, July, 1949, Vol. 22, p. 162.

2. Chance, Britton; Hughes, Vernon; MacNichol, Edward F., Jr.; Sayre, David; and Williams, Frederick C., *Waveforms*. New York: McGraw-Hill Book Co., Inc., 1949.

3. Cruft Laboratory Electronics Training Staff, *Electronic Circuits and Tubes*. New York: McGraw-Hill Book Co., Inc., 1947.

4. Foster, D. E. and Rankin, J. A., "Video Output Systems," *RCA Review*, April, 1941, Vol. 4, p. 409.

5. Haughawout, John, "Improved Television Modulator," *Electronics*, February, 1950, Vol. 23, p. 86.

6. Kiver, Milton S., "Modern Television Receivers," *Radio News*, August, 1949, Vol. 42, p. 41; September, 1949, Vol. 42, p. 62; October, 1949, Vol. 42, p. 59.

7. Heiser, W., "Synch Separator Circuit Analysis," *Electronics*, July, 1950, Vol. 23, p. 108.

8. Lost, Emanuel, "Restorer Circuit Operation," *Electronics*, September, 1945, Vol. 18, p. 132.

9. Mather, Norman W., "Clipping and Clamping," *Electronics*, July, 1947, Vol. 20, p. 111.

10. Pollard, Ernest C. and Sturtevant, Julian M., *Microwaves and Radar Electronics*.   New York: John Wiley and Sons, Inc., 1948.

11. Roe, John H., "New Television Field-Pickup Equipment Employing the Image Orthicon," *Proc. IRE*, December, 1947, Vol. 35, p. 1532.

12. Schultz, J. L., "Television Stabilizing Amplifier," *Radio News—Electronic Engr. Supplement*, March, 1949, Vol. 41, p. 12.

13. Soller, J. Theodore; Starr, M. A.; and Valley, George E., Jr., *Cathode Ray Tube Displays*.   New York: McGraw-Hill Book Co., Inc., 1948.

14. Webb, R. C. and Morgan, J. M., "Simplified Television for Industry," *Electronics*, June, 1950, Vol. 23, p. 70.

15. Wendt, K. R., "Television D.C. Component," *RCA Review*, March, 1948, Vol. 9, p. 85.

16. Williams, F. C., "Introduction to Circuit Techniques for Radiolocation," *Proc. IEE*, Radiolocation Conv., No. 1, 1946, Vol. 93, p. 289.

PROBLEMS

4-1 The sawtooth output from a sweep generator varies from 10 to 80 volts.   It is desired to have the wave-form range from 15 to 85 volts. Show and explain a circuit to do this.

4-2 The circuit of Fig. 4-13 is altered by returning the grid resistor R to a negative 10 volts instead of to ground and by adding a plate circuit consisting of a 20,000-ohm resistor in series with a 250-volt supply.   A symmetrical square wave varying from 0 to 25 volts and having a frequency of 5000 cycles per second is applied to the circuit.   Sketch and label the plate voltage of the tube if $C = 0.1$ microfarad, $R = 100,000$ ohms, and the tube is a 6J5.

4-3 The given voltage is applied to the circuit of Fig. 4-13 in which a plate circuit consisting of a 40,000-ohm resistor in series with a 300-volt

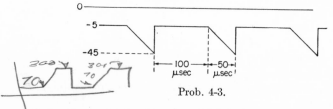

Prob. 4-3.

supply has been added.   Sketch and label the output voltage if $C = 10.$ microfarad, $R = 100,000$ ohms, and the tube type is a 6J5.

4-4 A symmetrical square wave having a frequency of 2000 cycles per second and varying from -75 volts to $+75$ volts is applied to the circuit

of Fig. 4-17b. The inductor has negligible series resistance and an i
tance of 0.4 henry. Also $C_g = 0.1$ microfarad, $R_2 = 10,000$ ohms, $R_g = 250,000$ ohms, $E_{bb} = 250$ volts, and the tube is a 6J5. The maximum
instantaneous output voltage is to be 100 volts. (a) Find the value of C
and R_3. (b) Find the time necessary for the output voltage to drop to
$1/e$ of its maximum value.

4-5 The wave form shown is applied to the circuit of Fig. 4-1. The
switch is in position 1 for the Δt_1 period, but is moved to position 2 for the
Δt_2 and Δt_3 periods. If Δt_1, Δt_2, and Δt_3 are all small as compared with

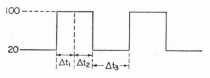

Prob. 4-5.

R_1C or R_2C, sketch and label the output voltage. $R_1 = 2R_2$, $\Delta t_3 = \Delta t_1 + \Delta t_2 = 2\Delta t_1$.

4-6 Let the wave form of Fig. 4-4 be applied to the circuit of Fig. 4-10.
Assume the diode has an infinite back resistance and a forward resistance
of $\bar{r}_p$. Sketch and label the generalized output voltage.

4-7 What effect will be noticed on the plate wave form of Fig. 4-17a if
the magnitude of the input square wave is not sufficiently great to keep
the tube cut off during the negative part of the cycle?

4-8 Using the input signal of Fig. 4-4, sketch and label the output voltage of the circuit shown. The time constant R_2C is much greater than the
period of the square wave. Consider the diode to have an infinite resistance in the back direction and a resistance of $\bar{r}_p$ in the forward direction.

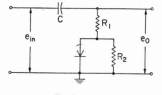

Prob. 4-8.

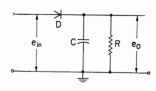

Prob. 4-9.

4-9 The wave form of Fig. 4-4 will be applied to the accompanying
circuit. Assuming the diode to have an ideal characteristic and $RC = \Delta t_1 + \Delta t_2$, calculate the output voltage.

4-10 Repeat problem 4-9 if $RC \gg \Delta t_1 = \Delta t_2$.

4-11 Repeat problem 4-9 where $RC \gg \Delta t_1 = \Delta t_2$ and the diode has a
front resistance of $\bar{r}_{p1}$ and a back resistance of $\bar{r}_{p2}$.

4-12 The wave form of Fig. 4-4 is to be applied to the given RL circuit. Could this circuit be operated in a fashion similar to that of Fig. 4-1? Explain, using any necessary sketches.

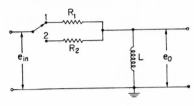

Prob. 4-12.

4-13 Sketch and explain a circuit using an inductive (instead of capacitive) element which will clamp the positive peaks of a square wave at a positive potential.

4-14 Sketch and explain a circuit which will clamp the positive peaks of a current at a given level.

CHAPTER FIVE

CLIPPING CIRCUITS

The preceding chapter was primarily concerned with a circuit in which the output wave form was similar in shape, but not equal in average value, to the input signal. This chapter deals with circuits which, although like clamping circuits in some respects, operate under vastly different conditions. These new circuits, which are definitely designed to alter the wave shape of the input signal, are called *clipping circuits*. The general characteristic of the clipping circuit will first be found, after which a study will be made of many circuits having this approximate characteristic.

5-1 General Clipping Characteristic

The circuit of Fig. 5-1 may be used as an introduction to a general clipping characteristic. This characteristic is not peculiar to this

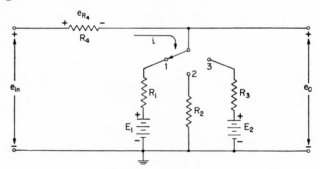

Fig. 5-1. Circuit to produce generalized clipping characteristic.

circuit alone, but may be found in a great number of widely different circuits.

The switch is connected to only one of the three positions at any time, but may switch instantaneously from one to another. The volt-

103

age E_1 is smaller than E_2.   The switching action is most commonly controlled by the instantaneous value of the input voltage, but it may possibly be controlled by a potential from some external circuit.

Let the switch connection be made to point 1 whenever the input voltage is less than E_1, to point 2 for all values of input signal between E_1 and E_2, and to point 3 when the input signal exceeds the value of E_2.

When the input signal is less than E_1, R_1 and R_4 are in series, giving an output voltage of

$$e_0 = E_1 + \left(\frac{R_1}{R_1 + R_4}\right)(e_{\text{in}} - E_1) \tag{5-1}$$

A sketch of output voltage as a function of input voltage for this condition then appears as in region 1 of Fig. 5-2.

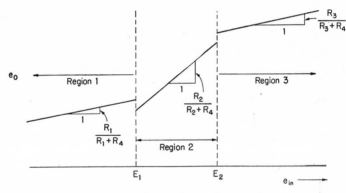

Fig. 5-2.   Generalized clipping characteristic.

When the switch is connected to R_2, the output voltage is

$$e_0 = \frac{R_2}{R_2 + R_4}\, e_{\text{in}} \tag{5-2}$$

A sketch of this equation is shown in region 2 of Fig. 5-2.

When the input signal exceeds E_2 and the switch is connected to point 3,

$$e_0 = E_2 + \frac{R_3}{R_3 + R_4}\,(e_{\text{in}} - E_2) \tag{5-3}$$

The results of Eq. (5-3) are shown in region 3 of Fig. 5-2.

The complete sketch of Fig. 5-2 is the generalized clipping characteristic.   In many cases this characteristic may be slightly modified by special relationships among the three resistors.   An interesting possibility is obtained when $R_2 \gg R_4 \gg R_1, R_3$.   Then

$$\frac{R_1}{R_1 + R_4} \approx 0, \quad \frac{R_2}{R_2 + R_4} \approx 1, \quad \frac{R_3}{R_3 + R_4} \approx 0$$

The resulting output voltage-input voltage characteristic is shown in Fig. 5-3a.   Since

$$e_{\text{in}} = e_{R_4} + e_0$$

the form of Fig. 5-3b may also be obtained.

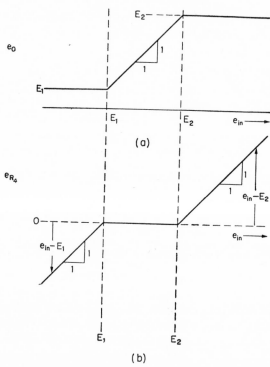

Fig. 5-3.   (a) Modified clipping characteristic.   (b) Modified characteristic for voltage across R_4.

The characteristic of Fig. 5-3a is perhaps the most useful, and again may have several modifications.   For example, either of the horizontal portions might be missing, with the unity-slope line continuing indefinitely toward that side.

Application of the input-signal wave form to the characteristic of Fig. 5-3a will give the output wave shape.   Examples given in

Fig. 5-4 show that operation around the value of E_1 results in removing or "clipping" the wave shape for all values below E_1, while operation around the value of E_2 clips all parts of the wave shape for which the input voltage is greater than E_2. However, the clipped portions appear across the series resistor R_4.

Although a circuit such as that shown in Fig. 5-1 might be physically constructed to give clipping action due to switching

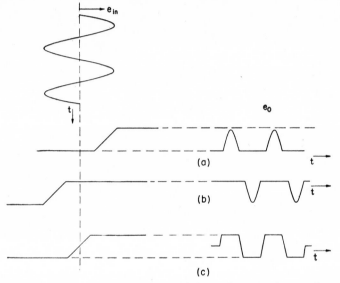

Fig. 5-4. Effect of modified characteristic on sine-wave input voltage.

between several circuit elements, other circuits are available which will give similar clipping action without resort to actual switching. *Any device which has a broken-line characteristic such as given by Fig. 5-3a may be operated to give clipping action.* The flatter the plateau regions, and the more abrupt the change in slope, the more nearly perfect will be the removal of undesired portions of the wave form.

5-2 Saturation-Type Clipping Circuits

If a device having a volt-ampere characteristic of the same general shape as that of Fig. 5-3a is placed in series with a resistor, the resistor voltage-input voltage characteristic will also be similar, and the over-all combination can then be used for clipping.

Volt-ampere characteristics of this type are exhibited by vacuum tubes operating under various types of saturation. This section will consider only the cases where plate current saturation occurs as

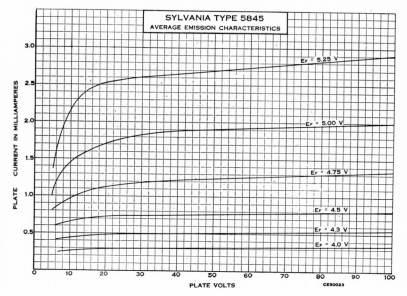

Fig. 5-5. Characteristic of the type 5845 emission saturated diode.

the plate voltage is varied. Probably the simplest device of this type is an emission-saturated diode. Since the rate of electron emission from a thermionic cathode is a function of the power supplied to the heater, variation of the filament supply voltage will also give a variation in the total emission. At some particular value of plate voltage for a given tube, almost all the emitted electrons are drawn to the plate, and the plate current remains almost constant for further increases of plate voltage. In this region, the tube is said to be emission-saturated. The characteristics of a tube designed especially for saturation use is shown in Fig. 5-5.

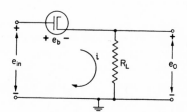

Fig. 5-6. Saturated diode clipping circuit.

For the emission-saturated diode circuit of Fig. 5-6, a graphical technique can be used to find the over-all output voltage-input voltage characteristic. Output wave forms are obtained from an example of this construction in Fig. 5-7, using a sinusoidal input voltage.

The output amplitude may be controlled by changing the filament voltage. Since the diode conducts in only one direction, control

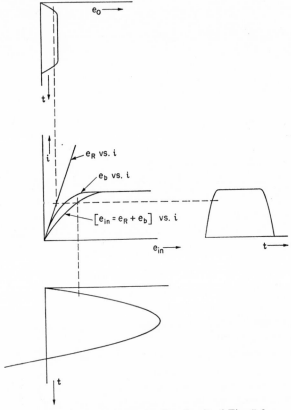

Fig. 5-7. Wave forms for the circuit of Fig. 5-6.

over either of the clipping levels can, for a given input wave, be obtained by placing a d-c voltage in series with the input signal source as in Fig. 5-8a. Clipping at both positive and negative voltage levels might also be obtained by use of two saturated elements as illustrated in the circuit of Fig. 5-8b.

Since in the saturated region of a diode there is some increase in current as the plate voltage rises, the clipped portions may

not be sufficiently flat for some applications.   Also, the saturation
level may be more readily controlled in some of the other devices
described in the following paragraphs.   For these reasons, the
saturated diode is seldom used for clipping purposes.

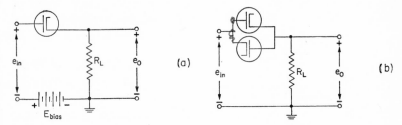

Fig. 5-8.   (a) Saturated diode clipping circuit in which clipping level can be
controlled.   (b) Circuit to clip both positive and negative peaks with saturated
diodes.

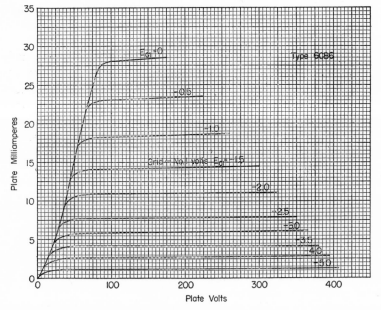

Fig. 5-9.   Plate characteristics for the type 6CB6 pentode tube.

A better approach to flatter clipping levels is found in the characteristic curves for pentodes.   The saturation level in this case is
determined by the bias voltage, giving ease of control.   Typical
curves for a pentode, shown in Fig. 5-9, indicate that the change to

the saturated region is not very abrupt, however, and considerable rounding of edges will occur.

The pentode circuit of Fig. 5-10 and the emission-saturated diode circuits of Figs. 5-6 and 5-8 require that the signal source supply the plate circuit power. This is another factor which tends to make saturation clipping circuits of these types impractical.

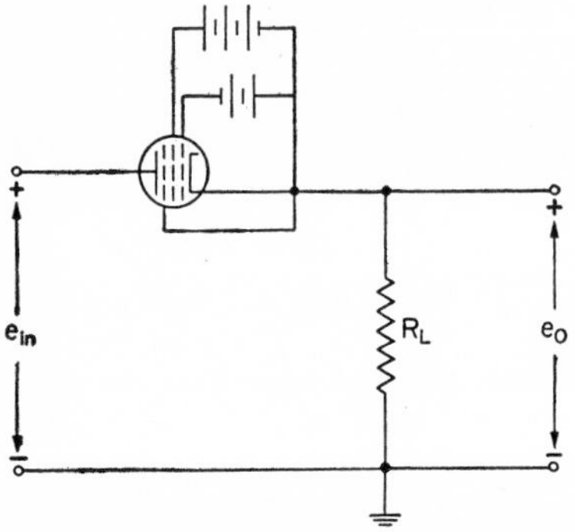

5-3 Clipping Circuits Using Single Diodes as Switching Elements

Among the clipping circuits more frequently used is that consisting of a diode, a series resistor, and a reference voltage source. One possible arrangement of such elements, using a conventional thermionic vacuum diode, is shown in Fig. 5-11.

Fig. 5-10. Clipping circuit utilizing the nonlinear characteristics of the pentode-type tube.

A circuit of this type usually serves satisfactorily at low frequencies, but difficulties due to capacitance effects may be present at high frequencies. Even at low frequencies, however, the stray capacitance causes rounding of sharp corners of the output wave form. The heater requirements are a disadvantage at all times.

Crystal diodes have much lower stray capacitance, are more rugged, and require no heating power. Their use therefore greatly improves circuit operation at all frequencies. Crystals, however, do allow some current flow with inverse voltage. The two types of diodes will be discussed in further detail at the conclusion of this section.

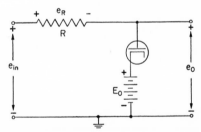

Fig. 5-11. Biased diode clipping circuit.

The circuit of Fig. 5-11 is very similar to that of Fig. 5-1, except that the branch with R_1 and E_1 is removed. The series resistor R is chosen much greater than the static plate resistance of the diode over the voltage range used. When the input voltage e_{in} exceeds the cathode potential, the diode serves as a switch connecting the battery E_0 to the output terminals. When e_{in} is less than E_0 however, the plate is at a lower potential than the cathode, and the diode is an open circuit, so that e_{in} is effectively transferred to the output terminals. The input-output characteristic operates around the upper discontinuity of the broken-line characteristic, as shown in Fig. 5-4b. With a sinusoidal input voltage, the voltages across the various parts of the circuit are shown in Fig. 5-12.

Reversal of the diode, as shown in Fig. 5-13, gives the circuit of Fig. 5-1 with the branch containing R_3 and E_2 removed. Whenever the input voltage is less than E_0, the diode conducts, and the output voltage remains very close to E_0 volts. For input voltages greater than E_0, the diode conduction ceases, and the input signal is transferred to the output terminals. This action corresponds to operation around the lower discontinuity, in the manner of Fig. 5-4a. The wave forms for a sinusoidal input voltage are shown in Fig. 5-13b.

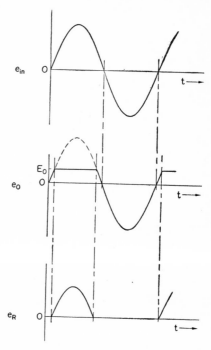

Fig. 5-12.   Wave forms for the circuit of Fig. 5-11.

Reversal of the polarity of the bias voltage E_0 as shown in Fig. 5-14, does not alter the basic clipping action, but the levels at which clipping occurs do change. The action of the simple shunt diode clipping circuit may thus be generalized: (1) If the cathode potential is fixed, all values greater than that potential are removed. (2) If the plate potential is fixed, all values less than that potential are removed.

It should be noted that the voltage across the resistor R in the circuit of Fig. 5-11 has the same wave shape as the output of the circuit of Fig. 5-13, but the voltage levels differ. A similar inter-

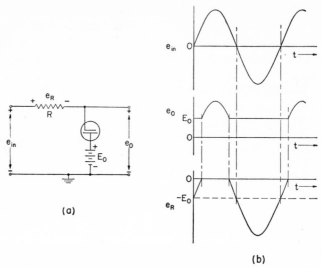

(a)

(b)

Fig. 5-13.   (a) Inverted biased diode clipping circuit.   (b) Wave forms for the circuit of (a).

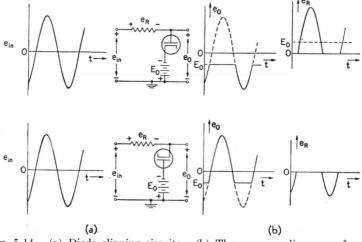

(a)   (b)

Fig. 5-14.   (a) Diode clipping circuits.   (b) The corresponding wave forms.

change of wave shapes occurs with the resistors and output terminals of the circuits shown in Fig. 5-14.   Since the resistor does not have a terminal at ground, little practical use is made of the resistor voltage, as the same wave shape may be obtained from the output terminals of some other combination.

The circuit elements may be rearranged as shown in Fig. 5-15 to give the indicated theoretical results. The voltage level at which clipping occurs does not appear in the output of Fig. 5-15b, although the output wave shape is the same as that of the circuit of Fig. 5-13a.

In applications where the cathode potential must vary with respect to ground, as in the circuits of Fig. 5-15, crystal diodes serve

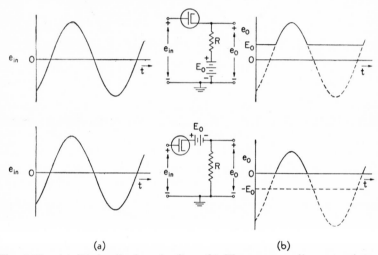

(a)   (b)

Fig. 5-15.   (a) Diode clipping circuits.   (b) The corresponding wave forms.

more satisfactorily than thermionic types because of their lower capacitance to ground.

5-4 Other Disadvantages of Diode Clipping Circuits

In the discussion of the shunt-diode clipper circuit, the assumption has been made that the input-output voltage characteristic is of the ideal type of Fig. 5-3a. This implies that the diode has the ideal characteristic shown in Fig. 5-16a.

A conventional vaccum diode has the characteristic shown in Fig. 5-16b. The current flow for small negative values of applied voltage is due to electrons emitted with high velocity from the cathode. Only until the plate sets up a sufficiently high negative field to repel these electrons does the plate current drop to zero. The clipping level therefore does not occur precisely at zero plate-cathode voltage, and the effect is to lower slightly the clipping level.

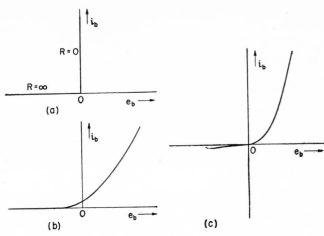

Fig. 5-16.   Characteristics of (a) ideal diode; (b) thermionic diode; (c) crystal diode.

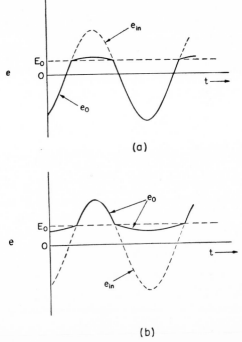

Fig. 5-17.   Wave forms when the diode resistance is appreciable: (a) for the circuit of Fig. 5-11; (b) for the circuit of Fig. 5-13.

Also, in all the cases previously considered, the value of R has been assumed so large as to render negligible the plate resistance of the diode.   When this is not the case, sufficient voltage divider action may occur between the two resistances to cause rounding of "flat" parts of the output wave forms previously shown.   Under

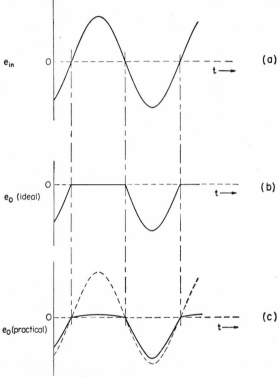

Fig. 5-18.   (a) Input voltage to the circuit of Fig. 5-11.   (b) Output voltage assuming an ideal diode.   (c) Output voltage with crystal diode.   ($E_0 = 0$. Applicable to parts a, b and c.)

such conditions, the output wave forms for the circuits of Figs. 5-11 and 5-13 become those shown in Fig. 5-17.   Due to the non-linear plate resistances of the diodes, the rounded portions deviate from sinusoidal form.

The characteristic for a typical crystal diode given in Fig. 5-16c shows that the crystal has a high, but finite, resistance in the inverse direction.   If this inverse resistance is not many times greater than the series resistance, the unclipped portion of the voltage wave is reduced in magnitude because of the voltage drop across the series resistor caused by the inverse current.   For the circuit of Fig. 5-11 with a crystal diode, and with the bias E_0 equal to zero, the ideal and practical wave forms for a sinusoidal input are shown in Fig. 5-18.

A similar reduction of magnitude may take place if the input impedance of the circuit following a diode clipper is not sufficiently high.   In all the circuits previously discussed, the output terminals have been shown open-circuited.

In summary, for flat clipping levels, the series resistance must be very large, but the shunt resistance during the period of non-conduction must be much greater than this series resistance.   In practice, it is often impossible to achieve these conditions, but because of economic considerations, the shunt diode clipper may be used, even though some loss of clipping quality will result.

5-5 Other Diode Clipping Circuits; External Control

The rounding of flat portions of the wave forms previously discussed is remedied by the circuits next described.   In general, the

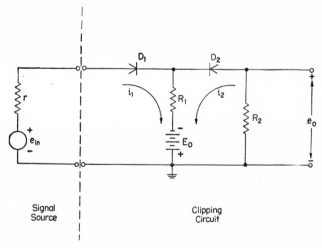

Fig. 5-19.   Clipping circuit utilizing two series diodes.

clipping is obtained by cutoff of a diode, with flat portions of the output wave forms corresponding to nonconduction periods.

A circuit of this type is shown in Fig. 5-19.   It will be assumed that at the time under consideration, both diodes are conducting.

Then, neglecting the conducting resistances of the diodes (assuming these are small with respect to the other circuit parameters), the voltage equations for each loop are:

$$e_{in} + E_0 = (r + R_1)i_1 + R_1 i_2$$
$$E_0 = R_1 i_1 + (R_1 + R_2)i_2 \tag{5-4}$$

Simultaneous solution of these equations gives

$$i_1 = \frac{e_{in}(R_1 + R_2) + E_0 R_2}{r(R_1 + R_2) + R_1 R_2}$$

and

$$i_2 = \frac{rE_0 - R_1 e_{in}}{r(R_1 + R_2) + R_1 R_2} \tag{5-5}$$

However, the diode action will not permit either current to reverse (have negative values in Eq. 5-5). The limits of operation may be found by setting each equation to zero.

$$i_1 = 0 \quad \text{if} \quad e_{in}(R_1 + R_2) = -E_0 R_2$$

or

$$e_{in} = \frac{-R_2 E_0}{R_1 + R_2} \tag{5-6}$$

For all signal voltages lower than this value, i_1 will remain zero.

Similarly, i_2 goes to zero when $rE_0 = R_1 e_{in}$ or

$$e_{in} = \frac{r}{R_1} E_0 \tag{5-7}$$

and remains so for all input signal voltages greater than this value.

When $i_1 = 0$, or during all periods of nonconduction of diode D_1,

$$i_2 = \frac{E_0}{R_1 + R_2} \tag{5-8}$$

and

$$e_0 = \frac{-R_2 E_0}{R_1 + R_2} \tag{5-9}$$

Since $e_0 = -i_2 R_2$ when diode D_2 is nonconducting, $e_0 = 0$. Between the limits found above, both diodes conduct, and

$$e_0 = \frac{R_1 R_2 e_{in} - r R_2 E_0}{r(R_1 + R_2) + R_1 R_2} \tag{5-10}$$

The input-output voltage characteristic is sketched in Fig. 5-20.

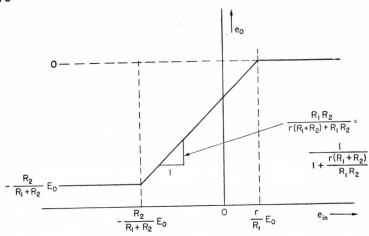

Fig. 5-20.   Clipping characteristics for the circuit of Fig. 5-19.

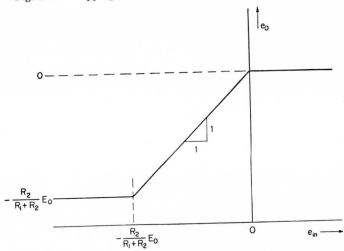

Fig. 5-21.   Clipping characteristic for the circuit of Fig. 5-19 assuming negligible source resistance.

If the internal resistance of the generator is quite small, r may be neglected in Eq. (5-10), and the input-output voltage characteristic becomes that of Fig. 5-21.   It may be noted that the entire positive portion of the input wave form is removed, as may be the negative peaks if the magnitude of the signal is sufficiently great. The remainder of the wave form is transferred to the output terminals with no attenuation (under the idealized diode assumptions previously made).

The resistance of diode D_1, however, may be considered part of the internal resistance of the generator r, while the resistance of diode D_2 and the resistor R_2 form a voltage divider. If the conducting resistance of the diodes is approximated, the diagram of Fig. 5-20 may be modified to give a result more closely approaching the actual case.

The circuit of Fig. 5-19 may be used as an externally controlled clipping circuit. To simplify the discussion, let it be assumed that

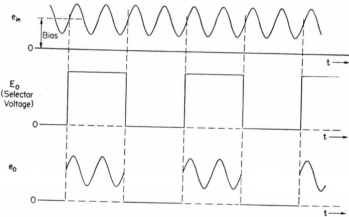

Fig. 5-22.   Wave forms for the circuit of Fig. 5-11, variable bias voltage used for control.

the internal resistance of the source r is quite small. One clipping limit will then be at zero signal voltage. If the battery E_0 is replaced by a variable source with a voltage high enough so that $R_2E_0/(R_1 + R_2)$ is greater than the maximum negative value of e_{in}, all negative portions of the input wave form will be retained. If the voltage of the external source is reduced, clipping of negative peaks may occur. If the external voltage goes to zero, none of the applied signal will pass through.

The input signal may be biased negatively to shift the entire signal range to total negative values. In this case, then, presence or absence of a sufficient voltage E_0 will give the effect of switching, so that the input signal will or will not be transmitted by the circuit. The system is especially adaptable for pulsed input signals.

In all cases, the resistance level of the parameters should be made considerably greater than the diode resistance in order to minimize the nonlinearity of the diode over its conducting range.

External control may be applied to some of the single diode clippers described earlier. For example, replacement of the battery E_0 by an external controlling source in the circuit of Fig. 5-11 gives similar selective clipping, as illustrated with a biased sinusoidal input and a square wave selector voltage in Fig. 5-22.

5-6 Vacuum Triodes as Switching Elements in Clipping Circuits

The broken-line characteristic necessary for clipping operation may be obtained by the use of triodes in a number of ways. Since the triode grid will draw current if driven positive with respect to the cathode, the grid-cathode combination may be used as the diode

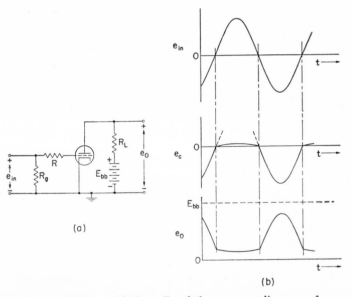

Fig. 5-23. Triode "grid clipper" and the corresponding wave forms.

in one type of clipping circuit previously discussed. In addition, however, the grid voltage may exercise control over the plate current, giving additional clipping possibilities. The gain obtained through the stage may also be advantageous in some applications.

When the grid is used as a diode plate, as in Fig. 5-23a, the circuit

is often termed a *grid clipper*. In conventional usage, the series
resistor R is chosen large as compared with the static resistance
which exists between grid and cathode during grid conduction. The
grid circuit forms a shunt-diode clipper, of the type shown in Fig.
5-11, with the bias voltage E_0 removed. The output voltage of
this circuit, however, is the input voltage to the amplifier portion of
the circuit. For a sine wave of small magnitude, the output voltage appears as in Fig. 5-23b.

Even though the grid cannot be driven very positive, slight
rounding of the grid voltage due to the finite grid-cathode resistance
must necessarily occur. This effect will also be noted in the plate
circuit due to this changing positive grid voltage.

Since only the grid-cathode capacitance shunts the clipper part
of the circuit, the requirement of high impedance following the

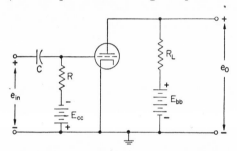

Fig. 5-24.   Biased triode clipping circuit.

clipper circuit is automatically met, except at frequencies so high
that the charging time of the interelectrode capacitance becomes an
appreciable part of the cycle.

Clipping circuits using the cutoff control of the grid are sometimes
called *cutoff clippers*. In one type of circuit using this principle, a
conventional amplifier is so biased as to bring the grid voltage to
cutoff when the input signal is at the level to be clipped. All
undesired portions of the wave form drive the grid beyond cutoff.
The combination of resistance and capacitance forms a good coupling circuit, but the input signal is kept small enough so that the
grid is never driven positive, and clamping does not occur. A
typical *biased-triode clipping circuit* is shown in Fig. 5-24.

Since cutoff effectively changes both the dynamic and d-c circuits
of the system, it is difficult to obtain a simple equivalent circuit,

as was done with the diode clipper.   Assuming that dynamic action
of the tube is linear, the dynamic characteristic for the system will be
similar to that shown in Fig. 5-25.   Since the grid will not be driven
positive, the characteristic is shown only for negative grid values.
The cutoff characteristic is of the broken-line type necessary for

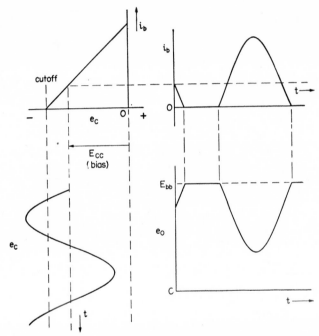

Fig. 5-25.   Wave forms for the circuit of Fig. 5-24.

clipping.   Typical steady-state grid and output wave forms are
also shown.
    If the bias voltage is removed, the input signal will be clamped
with the positive peaks at zero grid potential.   If the magnitude of
the input voltage can be adjusted so that the level at which clipping
is to occur coincides with cutoff, the undesired portions of the wave
form will not appear in the output circuit.   This circuit is termed a
signal-biased triode clipper.
    Since the cutoff voltage is a function of the plate supply voltage,
control of the clipping level for a given input signal may be achieved
by variation of the plate voltage.   This is usually inconvenient,

but offers a possibility where little control may be exercised over the input signal without clipping the desired portions of the wave form.

Although the clamped-signal circuit is preferable to the biased circuit of Fig. 5-24, since the necessity for the bias source is removed, the plate supply voltage must not be so large that the rated plate dissipation of the tube is exceeded when the input signal is removed.

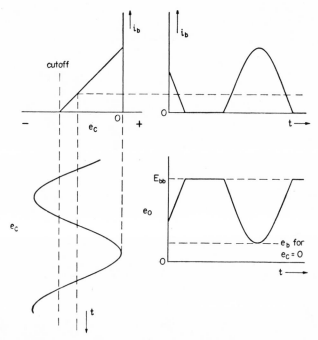

Fig. 5-26.   Wave forms for the circuit of Fig. 5-24 for $E_{cc} = 0$.

For comparison, wave forms for the signal-biased clipper are shown in Fig. 5-26, using the same dynamic characteristic of Fig. 5-25.

When cutoff clipping is used, it is not necessary that the input resistance of the stage following the clipper be made as high as in the shunt diode clipper.   The cutoff action is not dependent upon relative resistance magnitudes in the plate circuit, and the requirements become only those of the conventional amplifier circuit.   A distinct advantage of cutoff clipping is that, aside from the capacitance effects, the output wave form remains flat when the grid is driven beyond cutoff, since the plate voltage is then at the constant value of the supply source.

It should be noted, however, that interelectrode and other shunt capacitance will cause an effect at high frequencies. At such frequencies, the grid circuit input impedance may drop appreciably but there will be less effect on rounding of sudden wave form changes than in the plate circuit. In general, the charging time of the plate-to-ground capacitance is greater when the tube is driven from conduction to cutoff than when operation goes the other way, since at cutoff the capacitance must charge through the load resistor alone. When the tube returns to conduction, the capacitor discharges through a parallel combination of the tube and load resistor.

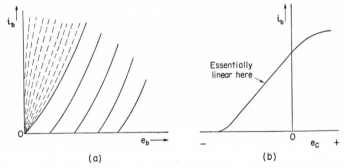

(a)   (b)

Fig. 5-27.   (a) Plate characteristics of typical triode.   (b) Dynamic characteristic of triode.

If the grid of a triode is driven into nonlinear positive regions, a characteristic of the shape required for clipping is obtained. A conventional triode amplifier with a large value of load resistance is used. As shown by the plate characteristics of Fig. 5-27a, driving the grid positive causes the plate voltage to drop to a low value. Little field exists to capture electrons from the space charge, and further increases in grid voltage do little to aid the plate in attracting more. The dynamic characteristic is then of the shape shown in Fig. 5-27b. If the input signal is sufficiently large, the tube may be driven to cutoff on the negative half cycle. Typical wave forms for both types of clipping are shown in Fig. 5-28.

This circuit requires, in general, a driving source capable of supplying comparatively high power at a large voltage level. The tube must be capable of dissipating this driving power in the grid circuit. Because of these requirements, and because the clipping level is not too flat, this method finds little use.

If degenerative feedback is used in a triode circuit, the slope of the dynamic characteristic is reduced because a greater signal volt-

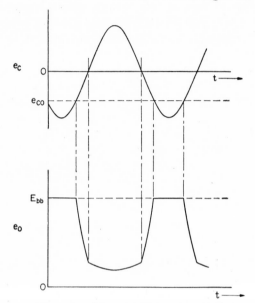

Fig. 5-28.   Wave forms for overdriven triode circuit.

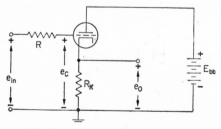

Fig. 5-29.   Cathode-follower clipping circuit.

age change is needed to produce a given change in plate current. In the case of the cathode follower, the signal range between cutoff and the positive grid region is greatly increased over that resulting when the same tube is used in a system with no negative feedback.

The dynamic characteristic for the stage may be found by graphical means. In the cathode follower circuit of Fig. 5-29, $e_c = e_{in} -$

i_bR_k. If the load line is drawn on the plate characteristics, corresponding values of i_b and e_c may be obtained as is usually done in obtaining the dynamic characteristic. Substitution of these values into the equation given will yield corresponding values of plate current and signal voltage, from which the characteristic may be plotted. A typical characteristic is plotted in Fig. 5-30, along with the dynamic characteristic for the same circuit with no feedback.

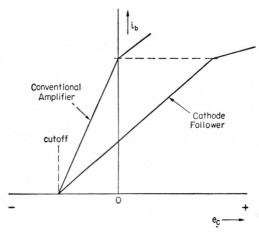

Fig. **5-30.** Dynamic characteristic for cathode follower compared with characteristic of similar circuit with no feedback.

Unless the plate voltage is very low, the input signal quite large, or external bias in the grid circuit is used, it is impossible that the grid will be driven positive. Since the signal range from zero to cutoff is much smaller than from zero to grid conduction, the circuit is usually operated as a cutoff clipper.

5-7 Self-Bias Clipping; Imperfect Clamping

In many applications, a parallel resistance-capacitance combination may be substituted for the bias sources labeled E_0 in the previously discussed clipping circuits. The required magnitudes of the resistances in the circuit may usually be determined analytically if the input wave can be expressed mathematically. In some cases where this cannot easily be done, an approximate expression for the input wave might yield resistor values of the proper range, after which final adjustment might be made experimentally. Several circuits will be considered, using simple input wave forms for examples. The technique to be used is much like that of Sec. 4-1.

In each of the circuits to be discussed, the discharge time of the capacitor will be assumed very much larger than the period of the input wave forms. Under these conditions, the capacitor voltage

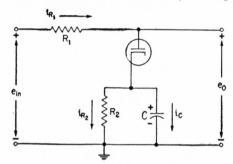

Fig. 5-31. Self-biased clipping circuit.

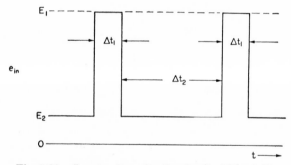

Fig. 5-32. Input voltage for the circuit of Fig. 5-31.

will not change appreciably during the cycle. To remain in the steady state, however, the net charge gained each cycle must be zero.

The circuit of Fig. 5-31 is similar to that of Fig. 5-11 except that the battery E_0 has been replaced by the combination R_2 and C. The input voltage will be the square wave of Fig. 5-32. If $R_2C \gg (\Delta t_1 + \Delta t_2)$, the capacitor voltage will remain essentially constant at E volts. During conduction of the diode,

$$i_C = \frac{E_1 - E}{R_1} - \frac{E}{R_2} \tag{5-11}$$

During the nonconducting period,

$$i_C = -\frac{E}{R_2} \qquad (5\text{-}12)$$

The net charge gained by the capacitor over a complete cycle is zero, or

$$\int_{\Delta t_1} \left(\frac{E_1 - E}{R_1} - \frac{E}{R_2}\right) dt + \int_{\Delta t_2} \left(-\frac{E}{R_2}\right) dt = 0 \qquad (5\text{-}13)$$

Carrying out the mathematical operations, and rearranging, gives

$$\frac{R_1}{R_2} = \left(\frac{E_1}{E} - 1\right)\left(\frac{\Delta t_1}{\Delta t_1 + \Delta t_2}\right) \qquad (5\text{-}14)$$

This equation is plotted in Fig. 5-33.

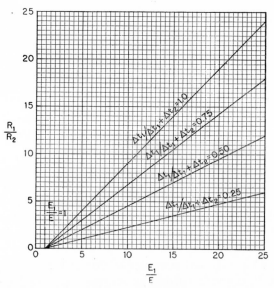

Fig. 5-33.   Plot of R_1/R_2 as a function of E_1/E for several values of $\Delta t_1/\Delta t_1 + \Delta t_2$.   (See Eq. 5-14.)

Another circuit which will give self-bias for clipping is shown in Fig. 5-34. The wave form of Fig. 5-32 will be applied to this circuit, and the assumption that $R_2C \gg (\Delta t_1 + \Delta t_2)$ will again be made.

The nearly constant capacitor voltage will be E. During diode conduction,

$$i_C = \left(\frac{E_1 - E}{R_1 R_2}\right)(R_1 + R_2) \tag{5-15}$$

During the nonconducting period of the diode,

$$i_C = \frac{E_2 - E}{R_2} \tag{5-16}$$

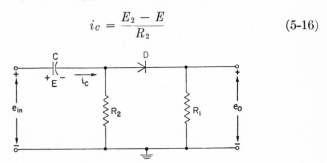

Fig. 5-34.   Modified self-biased clipping circuit.

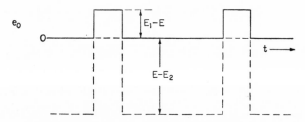

Fig. 5-35.   Output voltage for the circuit of Fig. 5-34.

Since, for the wave form of Fig. 5-32, diode conduction occurs only during the interval Δt_1, the equation for the capacitor charge is

$$\int_{\Delta t_1} \left(\frac{E_1 - E}{R_1 R_2}\right)(R_1 + R_2)\, dt + \int_{\Delta t_2} \left(\frac{E_2 - E}{R_2}\right) dt = 0 \quad (5\text{-}17)$$

The results of the integration may be rearranged to give

$$\frac{R_2}{R_1} = \left(\frac{E - E_2}{E_1 - E}\right)\left(\frac{\Delta t_2}{\Delta t_1}\right) - 1 \tag{5-18}$$

The output of the circuit is shown in Fig. 5-35.

Rearranging the circuit to the configuration of Fig. 5-36a will give the same relationship between circuit parameters, signal values, and

bias as expressed in Eq. (5-18).   The output voltage changes, however, and is that shown in Fig. 5-36b.

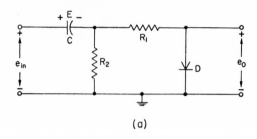

(a)

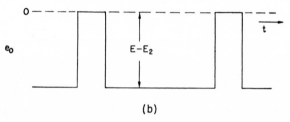

(b)

Fig. 5-36.   (a) Rearrangement of the circuit of Fig. 5-34.   (b) Output voltage
of (a).

If a sine wave $e_{in} = E_m \sin \omega t$ is applied to the circuit of Fig. 5-31,
the capacitor current during the interval of diode conduction is

$$i_C = i_{R_1} - i_{R_2} = \frac{E_m \sin \omega t - E}{R_1} - \frac{E}{R_2} \tag{5-19}$$

During the period in which the diode does not conduct,

$$i_C = -\frac{E}{R_2} \tag{5-20}$$

Again it has been assumed that the discharge time of the capacitor is
much larger than the period of the input signal.   The diode will
begin to conduct at $t = t_1$, when

$$E_m \sin \omega t_1 = E$$

or
$$t_1 = \frac{1}{\omega} \arcsin \frac{E}{E_m} \tag{5-21}$$

The diode will cease conduction at t_2, where

$$t_2 = \frac{T}{2} - t_1 = \frac{2\pi}{\omega} - \frac{1}{\omega} \text{ arc sin } \frac{E}{E_m} \qquad (5\text{-}22)$$

These points are shown in the diagram of Fig. 5-37. Since the net charge gained by the capacitor during the period is zero,

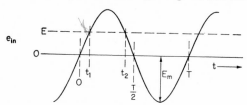

Fig. 5-37.   Sine-wave input signal to the circuit of Fig. 5-31.

$$\int_0^T i_C \, dt = \int_0^{t_1} \left(-\frac{E}{R_2} \right) dt + \int_{t_1}^{t_2} \left(\frac{E_m \sin \omega t - E}{R_1} - \frac{E}{R_2} \right) dt$$
$$+ \int_{t_2}^T \left(-\frac{E}{R_2} \right) dt = 0 \quad (5\text{-}23)$$

Rearranging gives

$$\int_0^T \left(-\frac{E}{R_2} \right) dt + \frac{1}{\omega} \int_{\omega t_1}^{\omega t_2} \left(\frac{E_m \sin \omega t - E}{R_1} \right) d(\omega t) = 0 \quad (5\text{-}24)$$

Carrying out the integration of Eq. (5-24) gives

$$-\frac{ET}{R_2} + \frac{1}{\omega R_1} [E_m \cos \omega t_1 - E_m \cos \omega t_2 - E(\omega t_2 - \omega t_1)] = 0 \quad (5\text{-}25)$$

Since t_1 lies in the first quadrant, and $\sin \omega t_1 = E/E_m$,

$$\cos \omega t_1 = +\sqrt{1 - \left(\frac{E}{E_m} \right)^2} \qquad (5\text{-}26)$$

For t_2 in the second quadrant,

$$\cos \omega t_2 = -\sqrt{1 - \left(\frac{E}{E_m} \right)^2} \qquad (5\text{-}27)$$

Substituting Eqs. (5-22) and (5-27) into Eq. (5-25) and rearranging gives,

$$\frac{R_1}{R_2} = \frac{1}{\pi} \left[\sqrt{\left(\frac{E_m}{E} \right)^2 - 1} - \left(\frac{\pi}{2} - \text{arc sin } \frac{E}{E_m} \right) \right] \qquad (5\text{-}28)$$

A given clipping level will fix the ratio of E/E_m, and the relative values of R_1 and R_2 may be determined. For given resistances R_1 and R_2, however, finding the resulting E/E_m ratio would be more difficult, and the results of Eq. (5-28) are best expressed graphically, where corresponding ratios are easily found. The curve of Fig. 5-38 is determined by substituting values for E/E_m into Eq. (5-28)

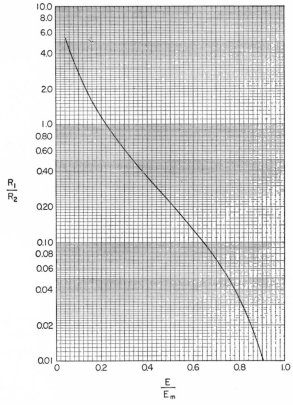

Fig. 5-38.   Plot of R_1/R_2 as a function of E/E_m.   (See Eq. 5-28.)

and solving for values of R_1/R_2. Rearrangement of the circuit as shown in Fig. 5-39 will not alter the bias relationships just derived, since the series circuit through which the capacitor charging current flows remains unchanged. The only difference is that the output of the circuit now presents the portions of the wave form removed by the circuit of Fig. 5-31.

If a sinusoidal input signal, with a period very much less than the time constant R_2C is applied to the input of the circuit shown in Fig. 5-36, the peaks will be clipped, as shown in Fig. 5-40. The

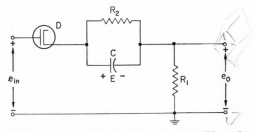

Fig. 5-39. Rearrangement of the circuit of Fig. 5-31.

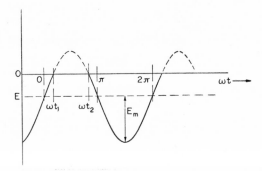

Fig. 5-40. Sine-wave input signal to the circuit of Fig. 5-36.

clipping level E and the peak voltage E_m are related by the circuit parameters R_1 and R_2. The net charge gained by the capacitor is

$$\frac{1}{\omega} \int_0^{\omega t_1} \left(\frac{E_m \sin \omega t - E}{R_2} \right) d(\omega t)$$

$$+ \frac{1}{\omega} \int_{\omega t_1}^{\omega t_2} \left(\frac{E_m \sin \omega t - E}{R_1 R_2} \right) (R_1 + R_2)\, d(\omega t)$$

$$+ \frac{1}{\omega} \int_{\omega t_2}^{2\pi} \left(\frac{E_m \sin \omega t - E}{R_2} \right) d(\omega t) = 0 \qquad (5\text{-}29)$$

Integration of Eq. (5-29) will give

$$- \frac{2\pi E}{R_2} - \frac{E_m \cos \omega t_2}{R_1} + \frac{E_m \cos \omega t_1}{R_1} - \frac{E}{R_1} (\omega t_2 - \omega t_1) = 0 \quad (5\text{-}30)$$

Due to the symmetry of the driving signal, $\cos \omega t_2 = - \cos \omega t_1$ and $\omega t_2 = \pi - \omega t_1$. Conduction begins when the signal voltage is equal to the bias value, or $\omega t_1 = \arc \sin E/E_m$.   Then

$$\cos \omega t_1 = \sqrt{1 - \left(\frac{E}{E_m}\right)^2} \qquad (5\text{-}31)$$

Substitution of these values into Eq. (5-30), with rearrangement, gives

$$\frac{R_1}{R_2} = \frac{1}{\pi}\left[\sqrt{\left(\frac{E_m}{E}\right)^2 - 1} - \left(\frac{\pi}{2} - \arc \sin \frac{E}{E_m}\right)\right] \qquad (5\text{-}32)$$

Fig. 5-41. Photo-graph of the output voltage of Fig. 5-31 for different magni-tudes of sine-wave input voltage.

This equation is identical with Eq. (5-28), plotted in Fig. 5-38.

A photograph of the output voltage for a circuit similar to that of Fig. 5-36 under conditions of a sine wave input signal is shown in Fig. 5-41.

The circuit of Fig. 5-36 may be formed in the grid circuit of a triode, and thus the bias obtained is of the *grid-leak type*.   This is shown in Fig. 5-42. If R_1 becomes sufficiently small, the clipping level goes to the extreme peak of the wave, and a clamping circuit

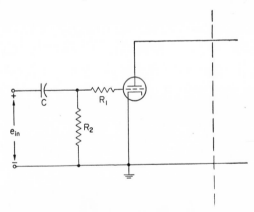

Fig. 5-42.   Triode clipping-clamping circuit.

results.   The circuits of Figs. 5-36 and 5-42 can be considered cases of imperfect clamping.

Similar poor clamping, or clamping with clipping, results when the internal resistance of the circuit supplying the signal to be

clamped is not negligible.   The equivalent circuit is shown in Fig.
5-43a.

A sinusoidal input voltage will be assumed, and the conducting
resistance of the diode will be neglected.   During the period of diode
conduction,

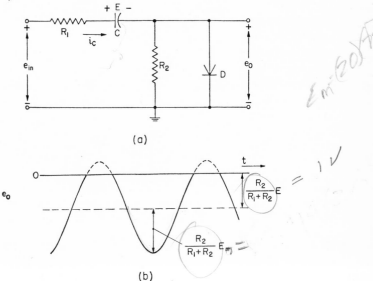

(a)

(b)

Fig. 5-43.   (a) Clamping circuit driven by source with appreciable resistance.
(b) Output voltage of (a).

$$i_C = \frac{E_m \sin \omega t - E}{R_1} \tag{5-33}$$

During the period of nonconduction,

$$i_C = \frac{E_m \sin \omega t - E}{R_1 + R_2} \tag{5-34}$$

The charge equation is

$$\frac{1}{\omega} \int_0^{\omega t_1} \left(\frac{E_m \sin \omega t - E}{R_1 + R_2} \right) d(\omega t)$$

$$+ \frac{1}{\omega} \int_{\omega t_1}^{\omega t_2} \left(\frac{E_m \sin \omega t - E}{R_1} \right) d(\omega t)$$

$$+ \frac{1}{\omega} \int_{\omega t_2}^{2\pi} \left(\frac{E_m \sin \omega t - E}{R_1 + R_2} \right) d(\omega t) = 0 \tag{5-35}$$

After integration and rearrangement, the results are

$$-\frac{2\pi E}{R_2} - \frac{E_m}{R_1}\cos\omega t_2 + \frac{E_m}{R_1}\cos\omega t_1 - \frac{E}{R_1}(\omega t_2 - \omega t_1) = 0 \quad (5\text{-}36)$$

This equation is identical to Eq. (5-30), so that the end results are the same, and the bias relationship is given by Fig. 5-38. During nonconduction of the diode, however, the net voltage in the loop is applied to both R_1 and R_2, and the output is only $R_2/(R_1 + R_2)$ of the total voltage. For the sinusoidal input, the output voltage is shown in Fig. 5-43.

If the conducting resistance of the diode in the circuits discussed in this section is not negligible as compared with the values of R_1 and R_2, similar techniques could be applied to the circuits to get a relationship between the parameters. This result would necessarily be more involved due to the added variables.

5-8 Clipping Circuits as Simple Square Wave Generators

Among the varied applications of clipping circuits is the use of these elements as simple means of providing square wave voltages.

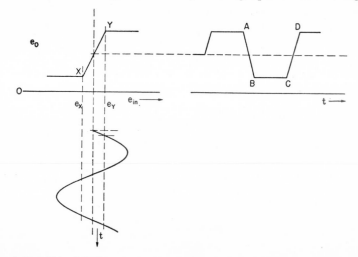

Fig. 5-44. Use of broken-line characteristic to form square waves from sine waves.

Square waves are of value in providing rapid checks of amplifier performance, as driving voltages for other wave form circuits, or as intermediate steps in providing timing pulses, as previously described. Means other than clipping circuits may provide improved squaring, but the result obtained from clipping sine waves is quite good, considering the simplicity of the circuits.

Consider a circuit element having the broken-line characteristic of Fig. 5-44. If to this element is applied a sinusoidal voltage with an amplitude larger than the signal range between the points where the slope changes, the resulting output wave shape will be approximately trapezoidal. The more rapid the change between the points A and B and between C and D, as compared with the time intervals from B to C or D to A, the more closely does the output wave approach the ideal square shape. This requires that the input voltage range x to y be small as compared to the amplitude of the input sinusoid. If this range is small, and capacitance effects are neglected, an approximate value for the rise time may be calculated.

5-9 Use of Clipping Circuits in Television Receivers

In a television receiver, the synchronizing pulses must be removed from the remainder of the signal in order to prevent the other signal changes from interfering with proper synchronization. Since the synchronizing pulses are placed at one extreme of the over-all modulation signal, they may be separated by the use of a clipping circuit. Since the clipping stage follows video detection, the polarity of the signal at the clipping stage will help to determine the type of clipping circuit used, in that the given polarity may eliminate the use of certain circuits. In general, circuits using signal bias are preferable, since such circuits tend to clip approximately the same portion of the wave form even though the input amplitude changes.

If the input signal gives the synchronizing pulses as the positive extreme of the wave form, a number of circuits may be used. One is the signal-biased triode clipper. Low plate voltages are sometimes used to reduce the cutoff potential. Typical wave forms are shown in Fig. 5-45.

Another circuit used with positive signals is that of Fig. 5-34. The capacitor charges during the duration of the synchronizing signal, and discharges during the remainder of the sweep cycle. The charging current gives an output pulse across R_1. If the wave form of Fig. 5-35 is used as an approximation to the over-all video wave form, an approximate ratio of R_2 to R_1 may be found for separation of the synchronizing pulses. The values could then be adjusted as necessary in the actual circuit for proper operation.

Some of the single diode clipper configurations of Sec. 5-3 might also be used. A practical form of the circuit shown in Fig. 5-15b

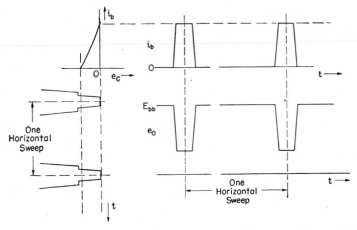

Fig. 5-45. Wave forms showing removal of synchronizing pulses from television video signal.

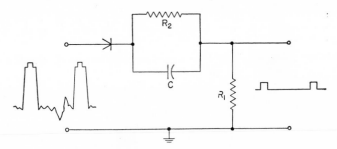

Fig. 5-46. Modified circuit of Fig. 5-15(b) used to remove synchronizing pulses from television video signal.

is resketched in Fig. 5-46. The combination of R_2 and C replaces the bias voltage E_0. The techniques of Sec. 5-8 may be applied to this circuit to find ratios of R_1 to R_2 for specified clipping levels. Reversal of the polarity of the diode, as shown in Fig. 5-47 will give separation if the synchronizing signals are the negative extremes of the over-all wave form.

Numerous other circuits have been used as synchronizing signal separators. The circuits shown here are given only as typical

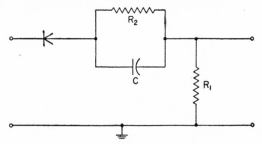

Fig. 5-47. Synchronizing signal separator for negative-going synchronizing pulses.

examples of their class. A number of other circuits may be found in the references given at the end of the chapter.

REFERENCES

1. Adler, Robert, "The 6BN6 Gated Beam Tube," *Proceedings of the National Electronic Conference*, 1949.
2. Brainerd, J. G.; Reich, H. J.; Koehler, G.; and Woodruff, L. F., *Ultra-High Frequency Techniques*. New York: D. Van Nostrand Company, Inc., 1942.
3. Brittain, Virgil, M., "Simple Deviation Limiter," *Electronics*, April, 1950, Vol. 23, p. 156.
4. Chance, Britton, "Some Precision Circuit Techniques Used in Wave-form Generation and Time Measurement," *Rev. Sci. Instruments*, October, 1946, Vol. 17, p. 396.
5. Chance, Britton; Hughes, Vernon; MacNichol, Edward F., Jr.; Sayre, David and Williams, Frederick C., *Waveforms*. New York: McGraw-Hill Book Co., Inc., 1949.
6. Chen, Tung Chang, "Diode Coincidence and Mixing Circuits in Digital Computers," *Proc. IRE*, May, 1950, Vol. 38, p. 511.
7. Cruft Laboratory Electronics Training Staff, *Electronic Circuits and Tubes*. New York: McGraw-Hill Book Co., Inc., 1947.
8. Emery, W. L., *Ultra-High Frequency Radio Engineering*. New York: The Macmillan Company, 1944.
9. Engineering Research Associates, Inc., *High-Speed Computing Devices*. New York: McGraw-Hill Book Co., Inc., 1950.

10. Finch, T. R., "An Impulse Generator—Electronic Switch for Visual Testing of Wide Band Networks," *Proc. IRE*, June, 1950, Vol. 38, p. 657.

11. Goldmuntz, L. A. and Krauss, H. L., "The Cathode-Coupled Clipper Circuit," *Proc. IRE*, September, 1948, Vol. 36, p. 1172.

12. Grob, Bernard, *Basic Television—Principles and Servicing.* New York: McGraw-Hill Book Co., Inc., 1949.

13. Harder, E. L., et al., "Magnetic Amplifier Studies on the Analog Computer," *Proceedings of the National Electronic Conference*, 1949.

14. Heiser, W., "Synch Separator Circuit Analysis," *Electronics*, July, 1950, Vol. 23, p. 108.

15. Howland, B.: Schroeder, C. A.; and Shipman, J. D., Jr., "Electronics for Cosmic-Ray Experiments," *Rev. Sci. Instruments*, August, 1947, Vol. 18, p. 551.

16. Kiver, Milton S., "Modern Television Receivers," *Radio News*, August, 1949, Vol. 42, p. 41; September, 1949, Vol. 42, p. 62; October, 1949, Vol. 42, p. 59.

17. Kretzmer, Ernest R., "Measuring Phase at Audio and Ultrasonic Frequencies," *Electronics*, October, 1949, Vol. 22, p. 114.

18. Leslie, C. B., "Megacycle Stepping Counter," *Proc. IRE*, August, 1948, Vol. 36, p. 1030.

19. Martin, Thomas L., Jr., *Ultra High Frequency Engineering.* New York: Prentice-Hall, Inc., 1950.

20. Mather, Norman W., "Clipping and Clamping," *Electronics*, July, 1947, Vol. 20, p. 111.

21. May, J. C., "Variable Length Pulse Generator," *Electronics*, January, 1950, Vol. 23, p. 109.

22. Moses, Robert C., "Germanium Diode Impulse Noise Limiter," *Sylvania Technologist*, October, 1950.

23. Moskowitz, Sidney and Racker, Joseph, "Pulse Shaping Circuits," *Radio News—Electronic Engr. Supplement*, March, 1948, Vol. 39, p. 14.

24. Page, C. H., "Digital Computer Switching Circuits," *Electronics*, September, 1948, Vol. 21, p. 110.

25. Reich, H. J., *Theory and Applications of Electron Tubes.* New York: McGraw-Hill Book Co., Inc., 1944.

26. Roe, John H., "New Television Field Pickup Equipment Using the Image Orthicon," *Proc. IRE*, December, 1947, Vol. 35, p. 1532.

27. Schultz, M. A., "Linear Amplifiers," *Proc. IRE*, May, 1950, Vol. 38, p. 475.

28. Schulz, E. H. and Anderson, L. T., *Experiments in Electronics and Communication Engineering.* New York: Harper and Brothers, 1943.

29. Skalnik, J. G., "Pulse Controlled Thyratron," *Electronics*, December, 1949, Vol. 22, p. 120.

30. Williams, F. C., "Introduction to Circuit Techniques for Radiolocation," *Proc. IEE*, Radiolocation Conv., No. 1, 1946, Vol. 93, p. 289.

31. Winkler, Marion, "Instantaneous Deviation Control," *Electronics*, September, 1949, Vol. 22, p. 97.

PROBLEMS

5-1 The wave form shown is applied to the circuit of Fig. 5-11 where $E_0 = 10$ volts and $R = 500,000$ ohms. Assuming the diode to have an ideal characteristic, sketch and label the output voltage.

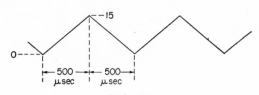

Prob. 5-1.

5-2 Repeat problem 1 for the circuit of Fig. 5-13.

5-3 In the circuit of Fig. 5-23 let $R_g = 1$ megohm, $R = 100,000$ ohms, $R_L = 25,000$ ohms, and $E_{bb} = 300$ volts. The tube is a 6J5. Assume the conducting grid-cathode resistance to be 1000 ohms when the grid is positive with respect to the cathode. Sketch and label the plate voltage for a 100-volt rms, 1000-cycle input sine wave.

5-4 In the circuit of Fig. 5-29 let $R = 500,000$ ohms, $R_k = 40,000$ ohms, and $E_{bb} = 300$ volts. The tube is a 6J5. Sketch and label the output voltage for a 150-volt rms, 1000-cycle sine wave.

5-5 A 10-volt rms, 1000-cycle sine wave is applied to the circuit of Fig. 5-36 where $C = 0.1$ microfarad, $R_1 = 75,000$ ohms, and $R_2 = 100,000$ ohms. Sketch and label the output voltage. Consider the diode to be ideal.

5-6 Repeat problem 5 for the circuit of Fig. 5-31.

5-7 Repeat problem 5 for the circuit of Fig. 5-34.

5-8 If the polarity of the battery is reversed in the circuit of Fig. 5-19, sketch and label the input-voltage, output-voltage characteristic.

5-9 If a cathode resistance is added to the circuit of Fig. 5-24, what will be the effect on the input-voltage, output-voltage characteristic and the wave form of Fig. 5-25?

5-10 Sketch and label the input-voltage, output-voltage characteristic for the circuit shown, assuming the diodes to be ideal.

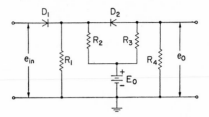

Prob. 5-10.

5-11 Sketch and label the input-voltage, output-voltage characteristic for the circuit shown, assuming that the diodes have infinite back resistance and a front resistance of $\bar{r}_p$. If the $\bar{r}_p$ of both diodes increases in the same manner, what will be the effect on the characteristic?

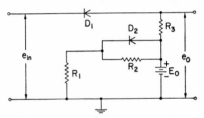

Prob. 5-11.

CHAPTER SIX

CIRCUITS FOR THE ELECTRIC DEFLECTION
OF CATHODE-RAY TUBES

Since the purpose of a cathode-ray tube is to provide information visually, it is necessary that the beam be deflected across the screen in a manner prescribed by the nature of the information. General cathode-ray oscillography, radar, television, and many industrial applications all require that the spot movement in some direction be a linear function of time. Because of this widespread use of time bases, the major part of this chapter will be concerned with circuits for development of the voltages necessary for such deflection.

The voltages delivered to the plates of electrostatic cathode-ray tubes are usually supplied by amplifiers. However, the subject of amplifiers is thoroughly covered in the existing literature, and no special study will be devoted to it here.

A few of the less conventional cathode-ray displays are also briefly discussed.

6-1 Linear Time Bases

The deflection of the spot for one set of deflection plates in a cathode-ray tube may be expressed:

$$D = k_1 \frac{e_d}{E_a} \tag{6-1}$$

where D is the deflection of the spot, e_d is the potential difference between the plates, E_a is the accelerating potential, and k_1 is a factor depending upon the size, shape, and spacing of the plates.

If the accelerating potential is held constant, then the deflection depends only on the deflecting voltage, or

$$D = k_2 e_d \tag{6-2}$$

In displaying a wave shape on a cathode-ray tube screen, it is usually desirable to have the amplitude shown as a function of time plotted to a linear scale.   The spot must move across the screen at a constant velocity so that equal increments of deflection represent equal increments of elapsed time.   The displacement of the spot may then be expressed

$$D = k_3 t \tag{6-3}$$

where k_3 is the spot velocity.   Combining Eq. (6-2) and Eq. (6-3) gives

$$k_2 e_d = k_3 t$$

or

$$e_d = \frac{k_3}{k_2} t \tag{6-4}$$

Consequently, a linear time base requires a voltage which increases linearly with time.

A time-base voltage which causes the spot to sweep across the screen is called a sweep voltage, and circuits generating such voltages are referred to as sweep circuits.

6-2 Linear Time Base Derived from Charging a Capacitor with a Constant Current

Consider a linear capacitor into which a constant current $i = k$ flows.   Assuming the capacitor to have an initial potential $e_C(0)$, the capacitor voltage will be

$$e_C = \frac{1}{C} \int_0^t i \, dt + e_C(0) = \frac{kt}{C} + e_C(0)$$

$$= k't + e_C(0) \tag{6-5}$$

The capacitor voltage will rise linearly with respect to time.   Thus if a capacitor is charged from a constant-current generator, the exact requirement for a sweep voltage is met.   While an ideal constant-current generator is difficult to obtain practically, there are numerous methods of obtaining acceptable approximations to such sources.   Two of the most easily obtained wave forms will next be considered with respect to sweep applications.

6-3 Use of an Exponential Sweep Voltage

When a capacitor is charged from a constant-voltage source

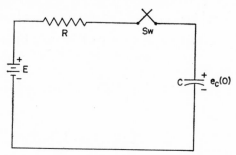

Fig. 6-1.   Capacitor charging circuit using a constant-voltage source and a linear resistor.

through a linear series resistor, as shown in Fig. 6-1, the capacitor voltage may be expressed

$$e_c = [E - e_c(0)](1 - e^{-t/RC}) + e_c(0) \qquad (6\text{-}6)$$

where $e_c = e_c(0)$ at $t = 0$.   Since only the time-varying part of the expression is of interest, Eq. (6-6) may be rewritten

$$\Delta e_c = E'(1 - e^{-t/RC}) \qquad (6\text{-}7)$$

where E' is the net voltage $E - e_c(0)$, tending initially to cause the capacitor to charge.   The term E' will be called the *effective* charging voltage.   Expanding Eq. (6-7) into a power series gives

$$\Delta e_c = E'\left[1 - \left(1 - \frac{t}{RC} + \frac{t^2}{2R^2C^2} + \cdots\right)\right] \qquad (6\text{-}8)$$

If t/RC is sufficiently small, all terms having exponents greater than unity may be eliminated.   Then

$$\Delta e_c \approx \frac{E't}{RC} \qquad (6\text{-}9)$$

Thus if the time constant of the circuit is much longer than the duration of the sweep, the charging current is essentially constant and equal to the k/C coefficient in Eq. (6-5), and the charging voltage of the capacitor is a linear function of time.

It might also be noted that if the voltage change is to be of reasonable magnitude (20 to 50 volts), the effective charging supply voltage E' must be quite large.

6-4 Deviation from Linearity of an Exponential Wave Form

While an exponential wave form may be used to approximate a linear rise, there is always some deviation from linearity, even for small values of t/RC.

Assume that in Fig. 6-2, the value D corresponds to the desired

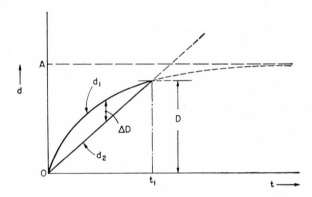

Fig. 6-2.   Determination of the nonlinearity of an exponential wave form.

maximum deflection.   The exponential function d_1 represents the actual sweep, while the desired linear function is d_2.

Since d_1 is always greater than d_2, the spot is always ahead of the proper position except at the two end points.   This deviation from linearity, $d_1 - d_2$, will be termed ΔD.   A measure of the quality of an exponential sweep may be obtained by the ratio of the maximum deviation from linearity, ΔD_{max}, to the total deflection D.

Let t_1 be the total time required for the deflection D.   From Fig. 6-2,

$$d_2 = \frac{D}{t_1} t \tag{6-10}$$

and $$d_1 = A(1 - e^{-t/RC}) \tag{6-11}$$

where A is the value d_1 would approach if the exponential rise were allowed to continue indefinitely. Since $d_1 = D$ at $t = t_1$,

$$A = \frac{D}{1 - e^{-t_1/RC}} \tag{6-12}$$

$$\Delta D = d_1 - d_2 = \frac{D}{1 - e^{-t_1/RC}} (1 - e^{-t/RC}) - \frac{D}{t_1} t \tag{6-13}$$

To find the time at which ΔD is a maximum,

$$\frac{\partial(\Delta D)}{\partial t} = 0 \tag{6-14}$$

or

$$e^{-t/RC} = \frac{RC}{t_1} (1 - e^{-t_1/RC}) \tag{6-15}$$

The maximum value of ΔD occurs when

$$t = -RC \ln \frac{RC(1 - e^{-t_1/RC})}{t_1} \tag{6-16}$$

Substituting this value into Eq. (6-13) and rearranging gives

$$\frac{\Delta D_{max}}{D} = \frac{1}{1 - e^{-t_1/RC}} - \frac{RC}{t_1} - \frac{RC}{t_1} \ln \left(\frac{t_1/RC}{1 - e^{-t_1/RC}} \right) \tag{6-17}$$

The quantity t_1/RC is the number of time constants used for the entire sweep, while $\Delta D_{max}/D$ is the ratio of the maximum deviation from linearity to the total deflection. Multiplication by 100 gives the maximum percentage deviation from linearity.

The information provided by this equation is most easily shown by the graph of Fig. 6-3, obtained from substitution of particular values of t_1/RC into Eq. (6-17). The curve again shows that the smaller the value of t_1/RC used, the better is the approach to linearity.

It is possible to give the maximum deviation from linearity in terms of the ratio of the maximum output voltage to the effective charging voltage. Let this ratio be called S. Then from Fig. 6-2,

$$S = \frac{D}{A} = 1 - e^{-t_1/RC} \tag{6-18}$$

or

$$\frac{t_1}{RC} = -\ln (1 - S) \tag{6-19}$$

Substituting into Eq. (6-17) gives

$$\frac{\Delta D_{max}}{D} = \frac{1}{S} + \frac{1}{\ln{(1 - S)}} \left[1 + \ln{\left(\frac{1}{S} \ln{\frac{1}{1 - S}} \right)} \right] \quad (6\text{-}20)$$

Again, this is not a simple function, and its information is best expressed graphically. The curve shows that S must be small if

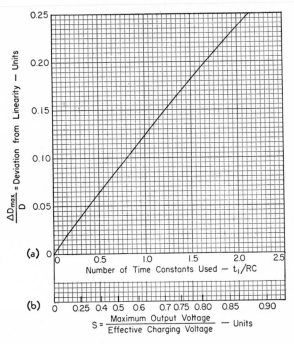

Fig. 6-3. Deviation from linearity versus (a) the number of time constants used; (b) ratio of maximum output voltage to effective charging voltage.

the linearity is to be good, and that the effective charging potential must be high for reasonable output magnitudes.

6-5 Use of a Sine Wave as a Sweep Voltage

Consider the circuit shown in Fig. 6-4. The switch Sw has been closed for a long time. If it is assumed that the coil has negligible resistance, the capacitor C will have no initial charge. Then, with the switch opened at $t = 0$, the circuit becomes similar to that of

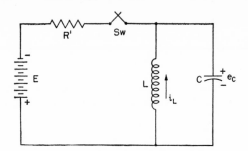

Fig. 6-4.   Circuit to obtain sine-wave sweep voltage.

Fig. 2-20, with $R_1 = 0$ and $R_2 = \infty$, and Eq. (2-43) may be written

$$e_C = i_L(0) \sqrt{\frac{L}{C}} \sin \frac{t}{\sqrt{LC}} \tag{6-21}$$

Since $i_L(0) = E/R'$,

$$e_C = \frac{E}{R'} \sqrt{\frac{L}{C}} \sin \frac{t}{\sqrt{LC}} = A \sin \omega t \tag{6-22}$$

where $A = (E/R') \sqrt{L/C}$ and $\omega = 1/\sqrt{LC}$. Expanding Eq. (6-22) into a power series gives

$$e_C = A \left[\omega t - \frac{(\omega t)^3}{3!} + \frac{(\omega t)^5}{5!} + \cdots \right] \tag{6-23}$$

If ωt is sufficiently small, all terms with powers greater than unity become negligible, and

$$e_C = A\omega t = \frac{Et}{R'C} \tag{6-24}$$

This implies that if t is sufficiently small, the current in the coil continues to flow at the initial rate E/R', and this is the constant current k of Eq. (6-5). Thus the capacitor voltage will be suitable for use as a time base.

6-6 Deviation from Linearity of a Sinusoidal Wave Form

As was true with the exponential wave form, even if the time t is made quite small, the sine wave always has some deviation from exact linearity. In Fig. 6-5, let the sine wave be expressed $d_1 =$

$A \sin \omega t$ and let the total deflection at time t_1 be termed D.   Then the linear sweep for the same deflection and time would be $d_2 = (D/t_1)t$.   Also, $D = A \sin \omega t_1$ and $d_1 = (D/\sin \omega t_1) \sin \omega t$.   Again letting the difference between the two functions be ΔD,

$$\Delta D = \frac{D}{\sin \omega t_1} \sin \omega t - \frac{D}{t_1} t \tag{6-25}$$

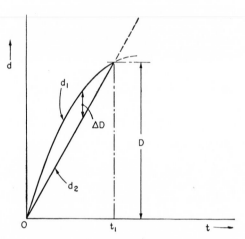

Fig. 6-5.   Determination of the nonlinearity of a sine wave.

Maximizing, $$\frac{\partial(\Delta D)}{\partial t} = 0 \tag{6-26}$$

or $$\cos \omega t = \frac{\sin \omega t_1}{\omega t_1} \tag{6-27}$$

Maximum deviation occurs at

$$t = \frac{1}{\omega} \text{ arc cos} \left(\frac{\sin \omega t_1}{\omega t_1} \right) \tag{6-28}$$

and at this point,

$$\sin \omega t = \sqrt{1 - \cos^2 \omega t} = \sqrt{1 - \frac{\sin^2 \omega t_1}{(\omega t_1)^2}} \tag{6-29}$$

Substitution of these values into Eq. (6-25) and subsequent rearrangement gives

$$\frac{(\Delta D)_{max}}{D} = \frac{1}{\omega t_1} \left[\sqrt{\frac{(\omega t_1)^2}{\sin^2 \omega t_1} - 1} - \text{arc cos} \left(\frac{\sin \omega t_1}{\omega t_1} \right) \right] \tag{6-30}$$

This expression has been plotted, on a percentage basis, in Fig. (6-6).

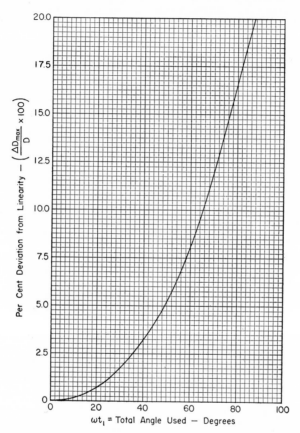

Fig. 6-6.   Deviation from linearity versus total angle for a sine-wave sweep system.

It would, of course, be possible to obtain an expression for the maximum percentage deviation from linearity in terms of the ratio of the total deflection voltage to the amplitude of the sinusoid.

6-7 General Requirements for a Repeated Sweep Voltage Generator

In general, it is desirable to have the voltage wave form under observation appear repetitively on a cathode-ray oscilloscope so that

changes may be noted.   The case in which the beam sweeps across
the screen but a single time will be considered to be a variation of
the general case.

If all the wave form is to be shown correctly, the beam should
sweep across the screen linearly with time, return instantaneously to
the starting position, and then repeat the operation.   Although an
instantaneous retrace is impossible to achieve practically, under
some conditions the retrace time can be minimized until it is almost
negligible.

A complete sweep generator, using a capacitor as the storage
element across which the output voltage appears, might be represented by the configuration shown in Fig. 6-7.

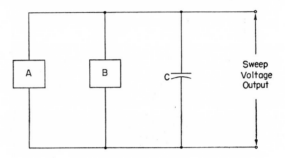

Fig. 6-7.   Generalized electrostatic sweep system.

The element A is the charging source.   There are numerous
types that this might assume, including rather complex networks of
which the capacitor C is ordinarily considered a part, such as a
blocking oscillator, multivibrator, or other forms of relaxation oscillators.   The charging source should supply a constant current to
the capacitor.

The element B is the discharge device.   It should have no effect
on the circuit during the charging interval, and therefore its resistance should ideally be infinite during that time.   At the conclusion
of the charging interval, this resistance should change rapidly to a
very low value in order that the discharge time be as small as
possible.

The action of A and B in initiating the charge or discharge may
be interdependent, with either effectively self-starting the entire
cycle, in which case the sweep is continuous and "free-running."

However, A and B might be so constructed as to be influenced by some continuous external signal such that the frequency of the sweep is some submultiple of the external signal frequency. In this case, the sweep is continuous and *synchronized*. However, to have this designation, the sweep must revert to free-running operation when the external synchronizing signal is removed.

If A and B are so designed as to execute but one sweep cycle when an external pulse is supplied, it is called a *slave sweep*, or the oscilloscope in which it is used is sometimes called a *synchroscope*.

6-8 Free-Running Sweep Circuits

The operation of a free-running sweep circuit may be considered a function of the two limits of the potential difference across the discharge element, since this is also the output voltage. For example, assume that discharge will start when the potential across the discharge element reaches the value e_i and will cease when the potential drops to e_e. The charging element will become operative as soon as e_e is reached, and the capacitor will charge toward e_i, repeating the cycle.

If the charging element supplies a constant current I_C to the capacitor, and the discharge element is designed to discharge the capacitor in a time interval which is negligible as compared with the charging interval, the sketch of Fig. 6-8a will apply.

Then
$$I_C \, \Delta t = \Delta Q = C(e_i - e_e)$$

or
$$\Delta t = \frac{C(e_i - e_e)}{I_C} \qquad (6\text{-}31)$$

The repetition frequency of the circuit will be

$$f = \frac{1}{\Delta t} = \frac{I_C}{C(e_i - e_e)} \qquad (6\text{-}32)$$

If the charging circuit is equivalent to a linear resistor R in series with a constant voltage source E', and the discharge time is neglected, the conditions are as shown in Fig. 6-8b. Then

$$E' - e_i = (E' - e_e)(e^{-\Delta t/RC}) \qquad (6\text{-}33)$$

or
$$\Delta t = RC \ln \frac{E' - e_e}{E' - e_i} \qquad (6\text{-}34)$$

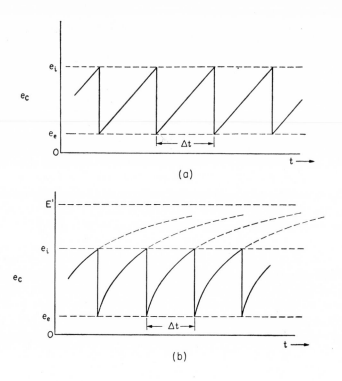

(a)

(b)

Fig. 6-8.   Wave forms for the system of Fig. 6-7 for (a) constant-current charging source; (b) linear resistive charging source.

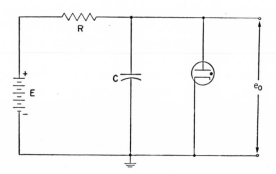

Fig. 6-9.   Gas-diode sweep circuit.

The frequency of the sweep is

$$f = \frac{1}{RC \ln (E' - e_e)/(E' - e_i)} \tag{6-35}$$

One of the simpler types of free-running sweep circuits is the circuit shown in Fig. 6-9. As shown in Chapter 1, the gas-filled diode operates between definite potential values represented by e_e and e_i of Fig. 6-8b.

The value of R must be chosen sufficiently high so that the charging current at e_e, $(E - e_e)/R$, is less than the current necessary to maintain firing. Since a gas diode will permit passage of a very minute current without firing, the value of R must not be chosen so high that the charging current approaches this value, or the capacitor will never charge to the firing potential.

Although the resistance and inductance of the leads, and the deionization time and other properties of the tube, make the discharge period finite, it may be minimized by proper design so that Eq. (6-35) will give the approximate sweep frequency.

6-9 Synchronized Continuous Sweep Circuits

Since small random changes occur in circuit parameters due to uncontrollable factors (for example, variation in the ambient temperature), it is highly improbable that a free-running sweep circuit would, for long periods, maintain exactly the same frequency as that of the observed signal, even if it were initially adjusted to that exact value. It is thus usually desirable to force synchronization of the sweep with the signal to be viewed, and thus in effect, correct any slight variations as they occur, cycle for cycle. This is done by injecting into some part of the sweep generator a fraction of the observed signal. If synchronization is to be effected, the variations of these injected signals must somehow be reflected back to the discharge element. It may usually be considered that the synchronizing voltage modifies the firing potential of the discharge element, and effectively makes its value some function of the instantaneous synchronizing signal voltage. While this is not, in general, a linear process, it will be so assumed here for ease of illustration. For the same reason, a sinusoidal input will be used. The firing potential will then appear as in Fig. 6-10. It will be assumed that the storage element across which the output appears is again a capacitor.

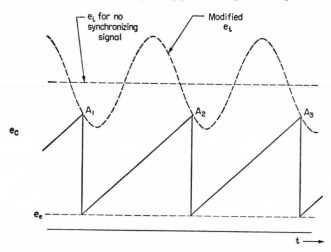

Fig. 6-10. Synchronization effected by the modification of the firing potential of the discharge element.

The capacitor will charge until its potential reaches that of point A_1, whereupon the discharge element becomes operative. The capacitor then discharges to the extinction potential e_e, the discharge ceases, and the charge cycle begins again. If the circuit is so adjusted that after a time interval equal to n (an integral number) periods of the input wave form, the intersection A_2 occurs at the same point in the $(n + 1)$ cycle as the point A_1 in the first cycle, the sweep will be synchronized, and a steady trace of n cycles of the input signal will appear on the screen. If the circuit adjustment does not give A_2 at the same point in the $(n + 1)$ cycle as A_1 of the first cycle, the next trace on the screen will not appear the same as the last. It is possible that synchronization might occur at some other point in the cycle, or then again, the signal may never give synchronization, in which case the signal wave form seems to move across the screen. Stability, along with other synchronization problems, will be considered in more detail in the next section.

An approach to the synchronization of a gas diode sweep circuit is shown in Fig. 6-11. The circuit element represented as A effectively biases the diode with an amplified version of the input signal. The effective gain will be determined by the magnitudes of the required bias voltage and input signal.

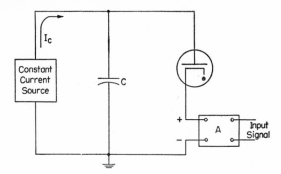

Fig. 6-11.   Synchronization of the gas-diode sweep circuit.

This circuit is of little practical value for several reasons.   Since the synchronizing signal is in series with the diode, the output of A is effectively added to the extinction potential as well as to the ignition potential.   If the discharge time is considered instantaneous, the capacitor will discharge to a value equal to the sum of the instantaneous signal from A and the extinction potential.   If this sum is negative (the output of A has the negative polarity of that shown, and is greater in magnitude than the extinction potential), and if the output resistance of A is small, current flow in the discharge loop will first discharge the capacitor from its original polarity and then charge it in the opposite direction.   While it might be reasoned that sufficient output resistance of the element A would prevent such recharging action, it should be noted that such resistance would also greatly disturb the original discharge and overly extend the retrace time of the sweep.

The magnitude of the output signal will remain constant regardless of the point at which synchronization occurs, as shown by the curves labeled A, B, and C in Fig. 6-12.   These figures illustrate the action of the circuit for the case in which the synchronizing signal amplitude is less than the extinction potential (a) and for the case in which it is greater (b).

If the charging rate and synchronizing signal amplitude are proper for a particular synchronized condition, a change from these values and subsequent return may cause synchronization to occur at a

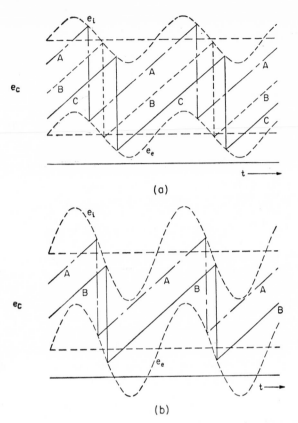

(a)

(b)

Fig. 6-12. Wave forms for the circuit of Fig. 6-11; sine-wave-synchronization. Synchronizing signal amplitude less (a) and greater (b) than the extinction potential.

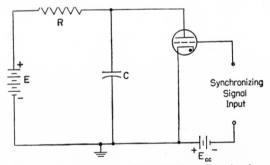

Fig. 6-13. Synchronized gas-triode sweep circuit.

new point in the cycle rather than at the original synchronized point. The synchronizing signal amplitude and the charging rate of the circuit of Fig. 6-11 are rather critical, and stability is not good.

One of the more popular synchronized circuits of a relatively simple nature uses a thyratron as shown in Fig. 6-13. The grid voltage of the thyratron is the sum of the constant bias and the synchronizing signal. The firing characteristic of the tube might be represented as in Fig. 6-14. The firing potential varies with the

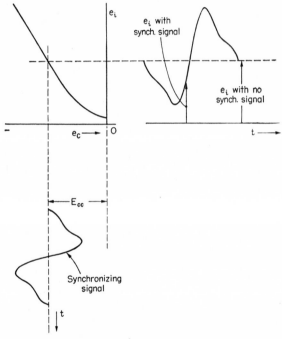

Fig. 6-14. Effect of synchronizing signal on the firing potential of the gas triode.

instantaneous signal in an approximately linear fashion, if the proper bias is chosen. However, in the thyratron, once the tube fires, the grid loses control, and the extinction potential is little affected by the synchronizing signal. Synchronization therefore occurs much as shown in Fig. 6-15. Since $e_i - e_e$ is the same for only two points in each cycle of the synchronizing signal, instead of for every point as in the diode circuit, this arrangement using the thyratron gives much better stability.   The circuit is discussed in further detail in Sec. 6-10.

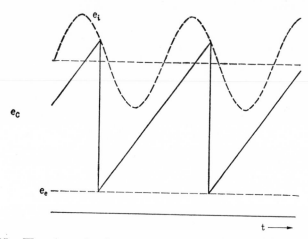

Fig. 6-15.   Wave forms for the gas-triode sweep circuit; sine-wave synchronization.

6-10 Stability and Oversynchronization

Since signals of many varied wave shapes come under oscilloscopic observation, a general study of synchronization would be quite difficult.   Only a few specific points would be considered here, and only two types of synchronizing wave shapes will be discussed. The first will consist of a series of narrow pulses with steep wave fronts, and the other will be sinusoidal.

Probably the most important consideration involves the charging rate of the capacitor.   Assume that n cycles of some signal are to be displayed on the screen (this will hereafter be termed *multiple synchronization at n cycles*), and that the synchronizing signal will consist of sharp pulses of the same frequency as the signal to be observed.   For these conditions, the capacitor voltage must not reach e_i, the unsynchronized firing potential, until the nth pulse arrives.   For positive action, the capacitor voltage should still be considerably less than this value just before the arrival of the nth pulse, which should then be sufficiently greater than this difference to insure discharge.   This implies that for such cases, the free-running, or "natural" frequency of the sweep f_n, should be less than

$1/n$ times the frequency of the observed signal f_s.   Improper conditions are shown in Fig. 6-16a, while proper adjustment is shown in Fig. 6-16b.

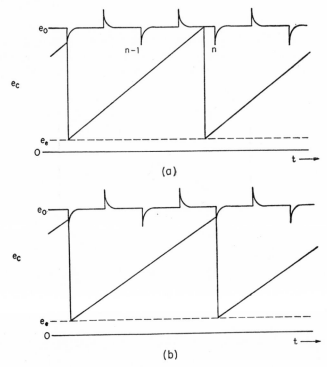

Fig. 6-16.   (a) Improper conditions for pulse synchronization of the gas-triode sweep circuit.   (b) Proper conditions for pulse synchronization of the gas-triode sweep circuit.

The firing potential of the tube under synchronized conditions may be expressed

$$e_i' = e_i - A_s(t) \tag{6-36}$$

where $A_s(t)$ is the negative of the component of the firing potential due to the synchronizing signal.

Assuming a linear charging action, the capacitor voltage will be $e_C = kt + e_e$.   The difference between the actual firing potential and the capacitor voltage is then

$$\Delta e = e_i - [kt + e_e + A_s(t)] \tag{6-37}$$

This equation states that the component due to the synchronizing signal may be added to the capacitor voltage, and the intersection of this curve with the constant value of e_i will determine the firing point.   In some sweep circuits which do not use thyratrons, the actual potential which determines the discharge remains constant, while the synchronizing voltage is added to the capacitor voltage. This sum actually controls the firing.   Applying this change to the wave forms of Fig. 6-16b gives the results shown in Fig. 6-17.

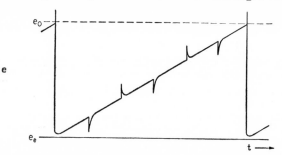

Fig. 6-17.   Wave forms showing operation equivalent to that of Fig. 6-16.

Synchronization tends to occur at a point on the curve where the slope is high.   Consider the conditions illustrated in Fig. 6-18.   If the charging rate had changed slightly so that the combined curve is

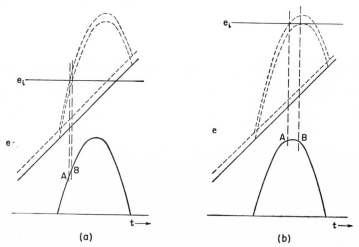

Fig. 6-18.   (a) Stable synchronization.   (b) Unstable synchronization.

somewhat higher than it would otherwise have been, the change in synchronizing angle is small, as in Fig. 6-18a, while if temporary equilibrium had been established in the region of the curve shown in Fig. 6-18b, a much greater change would have resulted. Synchronization as shown in Fig. 6-18b tends to be unstable, and the equilibrium point will shift until a more stable point on the curve is reached, as in Fig. 6-18a, unless the circuit conditions are quite unsuitable, in which case no stable point may exist.

In multiple synchronization at n cycles, it is possible that an increase of the synchronizing signal amplitude (usually in an attempt to secure greater stability) may result in premature discharge due to the $n - 1$ cycle intersecting the discharge line. The condition where the amplitude is just sufficient to give this difficulty is shown in Fig. 6-19, which gives only the expanded view of the

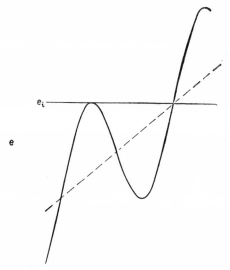

Fig. 6-19.   Example of excessive synchronizing signal amplitude.

operation at the end of the sweep.   Assume that the discharge is instantaneous, and that synchronism has been established at n cycles.   The capacitor voltage is, with a constant charging current, $e_C = kt + e_e$, while the synchronizing component is $B \sin (2\pi f_s t + \psi)$ where t is measured from the start of the capacitor charge.   The total value to be compared with e_i is then

$$e_s = kt + e_e + B \sin (2\pi f_s t + \psi) \tag{6-38}$$

This equation shows that if stable operation occurs, the angle ψ is determined by the value of k and B for a given signal with a frequency f_s. Finding the maximum point on this wave,

$$\frac{\partial e_s}{\partial t} = k + 2\pi B f_s \cos (2\pi f_s t_m + \psi) = 0$$

or $\qquad\qquad 2\pi f_s t_m + \psi = \text{arc cos } \dfrac{-k}{2\pi B f_s} \tag{6-39}$

The arc cos term is multiple-valued, however, and the proper value must be obtained. From the sketch, it can be seen that the maximum occurs in the second quadrant, and thus

$$2\pi f_s t_m + \psi = (n - 1)(2\pi) + \text{arc cos } \frac{-k}{2\pi B f_s} \tag{6-40}$$

or $\qquad t_m = \dfrac{1}{2\pi f_s} \left[2\pi(n - 1) + \text{arc cos } \left(\dfrac{-k}{2\pi B f_s} \right) - \psi \right] \tag{6-41}$

where the principal value of the arc cos term is always taken. Also, since $\sin x = \sqrt{1 - \cos^2 x}$, at this point,

$$\sin (2\pi f_s t_m) = \sqrt{1 - \left(\frac{k}{2\pi B f_s} \right)^2} \tag{6-42}$$

Substituting into Eq. (6-38) gives the voltage at the maximum point,

$$(e_s)_{\text{max}} = \frac{k}{2\pi f_s} \left[2\pi(n - 1) + \text{arc cos } \left(\frac{-k}{2\pi B f_s} \right) - \psi \right]$$
$$+ B \sqrt{1 - \left(\frac{k}{2\pi B f_s} \right)^2} + e_e \tag{6-43}$$

For the maximum allowable value of B, this value will be equal to e_i. Furthermore, if there were no synchronizing signal, $e_i = kt_f + e_e$, where t_f is the time required for the capacitor to charge to e_i. Since $1/t_f = f_f$, the free-running frequency,

$$e_i - e_e = \frac{k}{f_f}$$

or $\qquad\qquad k = f_f(e_i - e_e) \tag{6-44}$

Substitution of this value into Eq. (6-43) gives, at the maximum allowable value of B,

$$e_i = \frac{f_f(e_i - e_e)}{2\pi f_s} \left\{ 2\pi(n - 1) + \text{arc cos} \left[\frac{-f_f(e_i - e_c)}{2\pi B f_s} \right] - \psi \right\}$$
$$+ B \sqrt{1 - \left[\frac{f_f(e_i - e_e)}{2\pi B f_s} \right]^2} + e_e \quad (6\text{-}45)$$

Since synchronization has been assumed to occur at n cycles,

$$e_i = kt_n + e_e + B \sin (2\pi f_s t_n + \psi) \quad (6\text{-}46)$$

where t_n is the time required for n cycles.   The time required for one

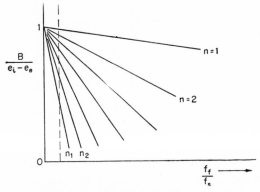

Fig. 6-20.   Curves showing $B/(e_i - e_e)$ versus f_f/f_s for different values of n (see Eq. 6-50).

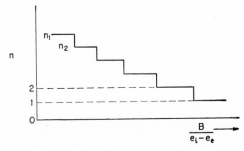

Fig. 6-21.   Effect of synchronizing signal amplitude on n. [n versus $B/(e_i - e_e)$.]

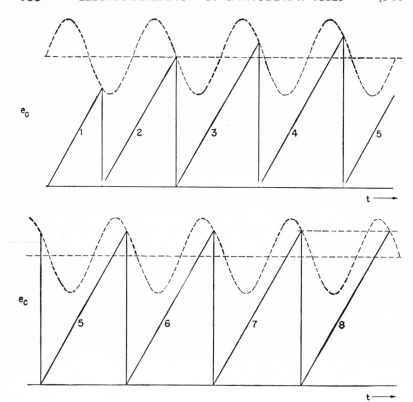

Fig. 6-22.   Transient occurring when synchronized sweep generator is first started.   Operation eventually becomes periodic.

cycle is t_n/n.   Since this is equal to $1/f_s$,

$$t_n = \frac{n}{f_s} \tag{6-47}$$

or $$e_i = \frac{kn}{f_s} + e_e + B \sin \psi \tag{6-48}$$

Solving this equation,

$$\psi = \text{arc sin } \frac{1}{B} \left(e_i - e_c - \frac{kn}{f_s} \right)$$

$$= \text{arc sin } \left(\frac{e_i - e_e}{B} \right) \left(1 - \frac{nf_f}{f_s} \right) \tag{6-49}$$

where the principal value of the arc sine term is taken. Substitution of this value of ψ into Eq. (6-45), and division by $e_i - e_e$, gives

$$\frac{f_f}{2\pi f_s} \left\{ 2\pi(n-1) + \text{arc cos} \left[\frac{-f_f(e_i - e_e)}{2\pi B f_s} \right] \right.$$
$$\left. - \text{arc sin} \left(\frac{e_i - e_e}{B} \right) \left(1 - \frac{n f_f}{f_s} \right) \right\} + \frac{B}{e_i - e_e}$$
$$\sqrt{1 - \left[\frac{f_f(e_i - e_e)}{2\pi B f_s} \right]^2} = 1 \quad (6\text{-}50)$$

This involved transcendental equation indicates that the ratio of the maximum allowable amplitude of the synchronizing signal component of the firing voltage to the unsynchronized value is a function of the ratio of the free-running sweep frequency to the frequency of the synchronizing signal and the number of cycles at which synchronization occurs. The information conveyed by this expression would best be expressed graphically with the ratio $B/(e_i - e_e)$ plotted against f_f/f_s with n as a parameter. The values of the ratio $B/e_i - e_e$ could be found by arbitrarily choosing values of f_f/f_s and n, substituting these values into Eq. (6-50), and solving the resulting equation by trial and error. The ensuing set of curves would resemble the sketch of Fig. 6-20.

If a particular signal is applied to the oscilloscope, and the sweep is set at a free-running frequency much lower than the signal frequency, a gradual increase in the synchronizing signal would have the result of gradually increasing the value of B in the previous equations. Then, on the curves of Fig. 6-20, this is equivalent to a gradual increase of the value $B/(e_i - e_e)$ following the particular f_f/f_s line corresponding to the circuit values. This path will first intersect the curve for a particular value of n, n_1; then it will intersect the curve for the next lower value of n, n_2, until finally the maximum allowable value, $n = 1$, is reached. The trace on the screen will first show the particular number of cycles, n_1, and then as the synchronizing signal is increased, one cycle less will be shown (n_2 cycles on the screen), and continuing increase in the synchronizing signal will gradually decrease by one the number of cycles shown on the screen until single synchronization is reached. As the value of $B/(e_i - e_e)$ intersects the curve for $n = 1$, the synchronizing signal becomes too large for even one cycle, and an undistorted trace is impossible to obtain. The number of cycles shown on the screen varies with the synchronizing signal in a manner similar to that expressed by Fig. 6-21. The same technique could be applied to other wave forms for which analytical expressions are available.

The manner in which a sweep, under suitable operating conditions, gradually synchronizes at the proper phase angle is illustrated in Fig. 6-22. The trace slips by on the screen as intersection first occurs at one point in the cycle and then another, and then becomes stable as intersection repeatedly occurs at the same point in each cycle.

6-11 Limitations of Thyratron Sweep Circuits

In addition to its ease of synchronization, the thyratron sweep circuit of Fig. 6-13 permits adjustment of the output magnitude, since the average firing potential is a function of the fixed bias. However, with the resistive charging system shown, the linearity is a function of the ratio of the output voltage to the effective charging supply, and this factor may limit the output magnitude.

If R is chosen sufficiently high as compared with the average resistance of the discharge circuit, the discharge time may be made small as compared with the charging time. However, there are other practical limitations on the size of the charging resistance. If the resistance is made very large in an attempt to reduce the charging rate and lower the sweep frequency, the charging current may become comparable with that which flows through the tube without firing (See Sec. 6-8). The capacitor will never charge sufficiently to cause the tube to fire, and the circuit will become inoperative.

A lower limit of resistance magnitude exists, however, because the value must not be made so small that the current flow from the source during discharge gives insufficient voltage drop across the resistor to bring the net voltage across the tube to a value below the extinction potential. In this case, the tube will draw current continuously, and the output voltage will remain constant.

For fixed capacitor and bias values, these resistance factors effectively limit the range of frequencies over which the circuit may operate. It may be reasoned then, that an optimum charging resistance value may be used, forcing the capacitance value to be the determining element in the charging circuit time constant, and permitting an almost unlimited frequency range.   This is true for low frequencies, so long as the leakage of the capacitor is negligible.

In addition to the resistance factor, the maximum attainable frequency may be limited by the capacitances of the tube, or by the deionization time.   The latter effect tends to make the discharge time longer in comparison with the charging time, so that as the frequency is increased, the discharge time may become an appreciable percentage of the period.   A resistor is also usually inserted in series with the thyratron to prevent damage by limiting the plate current when discharge begins.   This also causes an increase in the time required for discharge.

The previous section discussed the effect of oversynchronization in causing early firing.   With thyratrons, another similar effect may be obtained even before the synchronizing signal is sufficiently

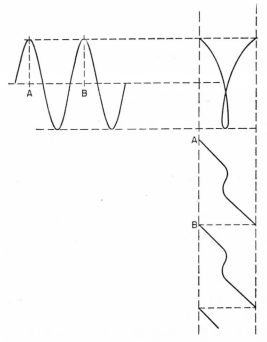

Fig. 6-23.   Oversynchronization giving the effect of time running backward.

large to cause firing. Before firing occurs there is a small flow of plate current, the magnitude of which depends upon both the plate and grid voltages. When the net grid voltage closely approaches but does not quite reach the firing potential for the instantaneous plate voltage, this current will increase. If the charging current is of the same order of magnitude as this value, the rate of charge of the capacitor will change, with a resultant sweep distortion. If the current through the tube is greater than the charging current, the capacitor will begin to discharge. It is possible, therefore, to have the trace on the screen reverse direction, as illustrated in Fig. 6-23, giving the impression of time running backwards.

6-12 Modification of the Thyratron Sweep Circuit

A typical thyratron sweep circuit is shown in Fig. 6-24. The sweep frequency is primarily varied by changes in the charging

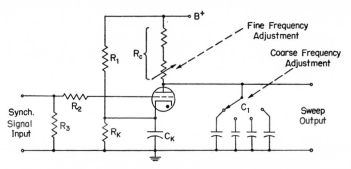

Fig. 6-24. Gas-triode sweep generator with provision for coarse and fine frequency adjustment.

circuit, as indicated by the two frequency adjustments shown. Voltage divider action between R_1 and R_k provides grid bias, and R_k also tends to limit the discharge current. The cathode capacitor C_k stabilizes the bias voltage, but must not be made so large as to nullify the action of R_k in limiting the current when discharge begins. If C_k is large, or if bias is obtained by other methods, a resistor may be included directly in series with the plate. However, if the current is limited by either a cathode or a plate resistor, the discharge time is increased. With higher sweep frequencies, this may cause the discharge period to become an appreciable part of the entire sweep cycle, and limiting resistors may be placed directly in series with the large values of capacitance used for low sweep frequencies. The smaller capacitors are then left with no series resistors, on the assumption that the energy stored therein will not be sufficiently great to damage the tube.

The resistor R_2 prevents appreciable current flow in the grid circuit when the tube fires.   The synchronizing signal is applied across R_3.

To obtain a greater output voltage with good linearity, a nonlinear resistor may be used to replace the linear charging resistor R_c.   This subject is discussed in greater detail in Sec. 6-15.

An inductor is sometimes used in the thyratron plate circuit instead of a current-limiting resistor.   A typical circuit, with its equivalent for the instant just after the tube fires, is shown in Fig. 6-25.   The battery e_e represents the extinction potential of the tube.

The inductor not only limits the peak plate current by making

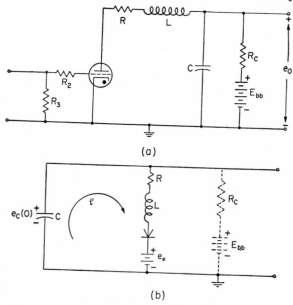

Fig. 6-25.   (a) Gas-triode sweep generator with inductor as current limiting device.   (b) Equivalent circuit for (a).

the discharge wave shape sinusoidal rather than exponential, but also gives greater sweep magnitude. These effects are obtained by making the parameters of the circuit such that it becomes oscillatory during the retrace time. Most of the energy in the capacitor before discharge is transferred to the inductor and then back to the capacitor in the opposite polarity.

If the charging resistor R_C is of such a low value as to cause appreciable damping, the advantages of using the inductor are nullified. It will be assumed, then, that R_c is large and that for an approximate solution the charging branch can be omitted completely.[1] The resistance of the inductor is indicated as R.

The integrodifferential equation of the circuit during the discharge interval is then

$$-e_i + \frac{1}{C} \int_0^t i \, dt + iR + L \frac{di}{dt} + e_e = 0 \qquad (6\text{-}51)$$

Differentiating with respect to t gives

$$\frac{i}{C} + R \frac{di}{dt} + L \frac{d^2i}{dt^2} = 0 \qquad (6\text{-}52)$$

or in D operator form,

$$\left(D^2 + \frac{R}{L} D + \frac{1}{LC} \right) i = 0 \qquad (6\text{-}53)$$

The solution of this equation is

$$i = \frac{e_i - e_e}{\omega L} e^{-Rt/2L} \sin \omega t \qquad (6\text{-}54)$$

where $\omega = \sqrt{1/LC - (R/2L)^2}$.

[1] If the charging branch is retained, a rigorous solution of the resulting two-loop network gives the following expression for the capacitor voltage.

$$e_C = \frac{E_{bb}R_k + e_e R_C}{R + R_C} + \frac{e^{-(L+R_C C R/2 L C R_C)t}}{R_L + R_C} \left\{ [R(e_i - E_{bb}) + R_C(e_i - e_e)] \cos \omega t \right.$$

$$- \frac{1}{2\omega L} \left[e_i(R + R_C) \left(\frac{L}{R_C C} - R_L \right) - \frac{E_{bb}L(R + 2R_C)}{R_C C} - E_{bb}R_L{}^2 - e_e R_C \right.$$

$$\left. \left. \left(\frac{L}{R_C C} + R \right) \right] \sin \omega t \right\}$$

where $\omega = \sqrt{(R + R_C)/(LR_C C) - (L + R_C R C)^2/(2LR_C C)^2}$

If R_C is allowed to increase without limit, this equation reduces to Eq. (6-53).

The current can never flow backward through the tube, that is, i cannot be negative, and the above expression is valid only during the first half cycle, or from $\omega t = 0$ to $\omega t = \pi$. The capacitor voltage at any time t is

$$e_C = e_i - \frac{1}{C} \int_0^t i \, dt \tag{6-55}$$

Substituting for i and carrying out the integration,

$$e_C = e_i - \frac{(e_i - e_e)}{\omega} \left[e^{-Rt/2L} \left(-\frac{R}{2L} \sin \omega t - \omega \cos \omega t \right) + \omega \right] \tag{6-56}$$

At the end of the discharge interval, or at $\omega t = \pi$

$$e_C \Big|_{\omega t = \pi} = e_i - (e_i - e_e)(1 + e^{-\pi R/2\omega L}) \tag{6-57}$$

If $\omega L/R$ (the Q of the coil at the natural frequency) is sufficiently high, $\pi R/2\omega L$ will be small and $e^{-\pi R/2\omega L}$ may be only slightly less than unity. Then

$$e_C \Big|_{\omega t = \pi} = e_i - 2(e_i - e_e) \tag{6-58}$$

The wave shape of the voltage during discharge is shown in Fig. 6-26. The change in the capacitor voltage during discharge is

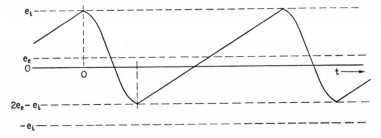

Fig. 6-26.   Wave form for the circuit of Fig. 6-25.

$2(e_i - e_e)$. This is twice the value which would have been obtained if the inductor had been omitted. If the natural frequency is made high enough so that the half-cycle discharge time is negligible as compared with the charging time, the sweep frequency will be approximately halved, while the amplitude will be nearly doubled.

6-13 Vacuum Tube Sweep Circuits

While a thyratron may serve satisfactorily as a discharge device, its loss of grid control after firing renders it rather unsuitable in cases where a tube is to be used as a switch, closed only for small time intervals.

If a thyratron is used to discharge a capacitor, a time delay will occur before the capacitor can begin to recharge, since both discharge and deionization require finite time. Because a vacuum tube has no deionization time, and because the grid can exercise absolute control at all times, it can be used as the control element in a completely synchronized sweep circuit. Thus it can be actuated without delay (except for that due to the shunt capacitance) upon application of intermittent pulses. In addition, removal of the deionization period permits satisfactory sweep operation at higher frequencies than may be secured with thyratrons.

A typical vacuum tube sweep circuit is shown in Fig. 6-27. The

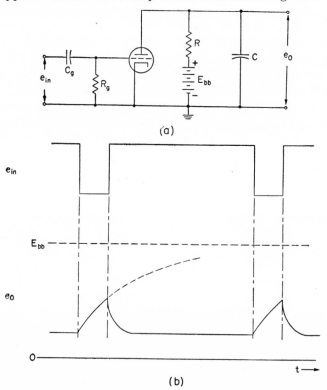

(a)

(b)

Fig. 6-27.   (a) Vacuum-triode sweep circuit.   (b) Wave forms for the circuit of (a).

parameters R_g and C_g are chosen to form a good coupling circuit, and the square wave input signal is therefore clamped with the positive peaks at zero voltage. Since the input wave is at the higher value over most of the period, the condition of zero grid voltage will be considered the normal circuit condition. The duration of this grid condition will be assumed sufficiently long for all transient effects to have disappeared. (For the solution of a system in which this static condition has not been assumed, the equations of Sec. 7-6 may be consulted.) The voltage across the tube is then constant at a value determined from the plate characteristics, by the intersection of the zero grid curve and the load line for R_L.

The amplitude of the input signal is great enough to drive the tube below cutoff. When this occurs, the capacitor C immediately begins to charge from the quiescent voltage toward the final value E_{bb}. For good linearity, only a small percentage of the exponential change should occur before the grid voltage returns to zero. When this occurs, the added charge on the capacitor drains off through the tube, and the circuit remains in the normal state of minimum output voltage until the next pulse again drives the grid below cutoff.

The circuit of Fig. 6-27 may be operated as a sweep generator in a manner just opposite to that previously discussed. Assume that the input signal to the tube consists of rectangular pulses of rather short positive duration, clamped at zero grid volts as shown in Fig. 6-28. The tube is normally cut off and the capacitor is charged to the supply voltage. The positive pulse drives the tube into

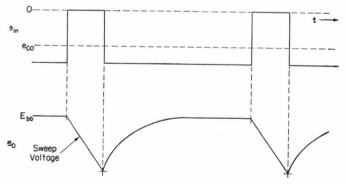

Fig. 6-28.   Wave forms for the circuit of Fig. 6-27(a); sweep occurring when the tube is conducting.

conduction, and the capacitor begins to discharge. Before the circuit comes to a quiescent condition, the grid voltage again returns to a value below cutoff, and the capacitor recharges through the load resistance. The discharge wave shape is used as the sweep. The charging resistor is usually chosen so that it is considerably larger than the static resistance of the tube at the zero grid voltage operating point, for two reasons. This not only limits the tube current, but by reducing the quiescent voltage, increases the range through which the capacitor voltage would change if the circuit remained at zero grid voltage. Sufficient time should elapse between pulses, then, to permit the capacitor to recharge; however, the problem can still be solved if this is not so.

If the discharge voltage of the capacitor is used as the sweep, changing characteristics of the tube may affect the sweep by a greater amount than would occur in the original form of operation. In addition, the static resistance of the tube increases as the capacitor discharges, and the sweep wave shape deviates more from linearity than would be the case for a fixed time constant.

The equivalent of the parallel circuit containing the charging source and the tube will necessarily be represented by a nonlinear volt-ampere characteristic. This curve may be used as explained in Sec. 2-2 to obtain the sweep output.

The circuit of Fig. 6-29 shows a modification of the vacuum tube sweep circuit previously discussed. A pentode has been substituted for the triode, and an inductor has been added in series with the plate supply. Although under certain conditions the addition of the inductor might be considered a means of linearity correction, the operation of the circuit is fundamentally different from that of the circuits of Figs. 6-26 and 6-27. The circuit parameters may be chosen so that a large value of resistance is not necessary to limit the tube current, and R might then represent the resistance of the inductor. Since an extremely large value of inductance is used, the series RLC circuit formed when the tube is cut off may be oscillatory. The magnitude of the voltage developed across the capacitor will be dependent upon the initial coil current; therefore a pentode is used in order to obtain high current sensitivity and a quiescent or starting current which is relatively independent of the supply voltage.

The input signal, with positive peaks clamped at zero, is a square

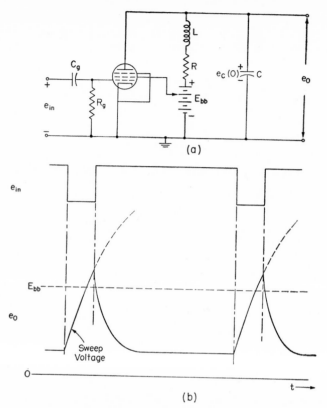

Fig. 6-29. (a) *RLC* sweep circuit. (b) Wave forms for the circuit of (a).

wave of sufficient magnitude to drive the tube to cutoff, and to hold it in that condition for the duration of the sweep. If there is sufficient time between sweeps for the tube current to reach a quiescent value of I_0, the following equations can be written when the tube is suddenly driven to cutoff. The circuit is shown in Fig. 6-30.

$$E_{bb} = iR + L \frac{di}{dt} + \frac{1}{C} \int_0^t i \, dt + e_c(0) \qquad (6\text{-}59)$$

This equation might be written

$$E_{bb} = R \frac{dq}{dt} + L \frac{d^2q}{dt^2} + \frac{q}{C} \qquad (6\text{-}60)$$

and $$q(0) = Ce_c(0) = C(E_{bb} - I_0R)$$

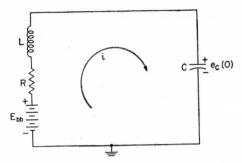

Fig. 6-30.   Circuit equivalent to that of Fig. 6-29(a) when the triode is cut off.

In D operator form this equation is

$$\left(D^2 + \frac{R}{L} D + \frac{1}{LC}\right) q = \frac{E_{bb}}{L} \tag{6-61}$$

The solution of the equation is

$$q = e^{-Rt/2L}(A \cos \omega t + B \sin \omega t) + CE_{bb} \tag{6-62}$$

Since $q = q(0) = C(E_{bb} - I_0 R)$ at $t = 0$,

$$A = -RCI_0 \tag{6-63}$$

Using the condition $\left.\dfrac{dq}{dt}\right|_{t=0} = I_0$ gives

$$B = \frac{I_0}{\omega}\left(1 - \frac{R^2 C}{2L}\right) \tag{6-64}$$

Then

$$q = I_0 e^{-Rt/2L}\left[-RC \cos \omega t + \frac{1}{\omega}\left(1 - \frac{R^2 C}{2L}\right) \sin \omega t\right] + CE_{bb} \tag{6-65}$$

or

$$e_C = \frac{q}{c} = I_0 e^{-Rt/2L}\left\{-R \cos \omega t + \frac{1}{\omega C}\left(1 - \frac{R^2 C}{2L}\right) \sin \omega t\right\} + E_{bb} \tag{6-66}$$

If $R/2L$ is small, then for a small part of a cycle, $e^{-Rt/2L} \approx 1$. The change in voltage across the capacitor is then

$$\Delta e_C \approx I_0(1 - \cos \omega t) + \frac{I_0}{\omega C}\left(1 - \frac{R^2 C}{2L}\right) \sin \omega t \tag{6-67}$$

Since the damping has been assumed to be small, $\omega = 1/\sqrt{LC}$. The value of L has been chosen large, giving a small value of ω. Thus for a small value of time, $\cos \omega t \approx 1$ and

$$\Delta e_C \approx \frac{I_0}{\omega C} \sin \omega t \tag{6-68}$$

Fig. 6-6 shows that if the deviation from linearity is to be small, only a few degrees of the first half cycle should be used. Then $\sin \omega t \approx \omega t$, and

$$\Delta e_C \approx \frac{I_0}{C} t \tag{6-69}$$

This equation states that for a large value of L and a small value of R, the current through the conductor will continue at the original rate, the charge transferred to the capacitor will be $I_0 \Delta t$, and the capacitor voltage change is this charge divided by C. Since the capacitor voltage increases during the sweep, the input pulse amplitude must be greater than the cutoff voltage for the value of the maximum capacitor voltage (the sum of the quiescent tube voltage and the sweep amplitude).

6-14 Linearity Improvement of Sweep Wave Forms

The output wave form of a particular sweep circuit making use of an exponential charging wave form may not be of sufficient linearity for some applications. For example, close linearity tolerance is necessary in the case where the range of a radar target is determined by a scale factor applied to the sweep of the beam across a cathode-ray tube. Some means of improving the linearity must therefore be used in these cases. Figure 6-3 shows that if the time constant of a circuit generating an exponential wave form is made much larger than the sweep period, the deviation from linearity is quite small. Thus one means of improving the linearity is to increase the time constant of the generator circuit. This means that a smaller portion of the over-all exponential curve is used, and therefore, if the charging supply remains unchanged, the sweep amplitude will be reduced. Consequently, to improve the linearity of a given sweep across the screen, both the circuit time constant and the charging supply voltage must be increased. A number of other methods of linearity correction are available, and some of these will be considered in detail in the following sections.

6-15 Sweep Linearity Improvement by the Use of Nonlinear Elements

It was shown in Sec. 6-2 that a linear sweep voltage is obtained when a capacitor is charged from a constant-current source.   If in the series circuit of Fig. 6-31, the resistance decreases as the voltage across the capacitor increases, the current will tend to remain constant.   The resistance-voltage and the current-voltage characteristics required for linearity are shown in Fig. 6-32.

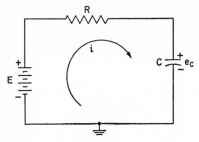

Fig. 6-31.   Series RC circuit used to demonstrate the use of a nonlinear charging resistance.

Among the more familiar devices which have current-voltage characteristics approaching that shown in Fig. 6-32 are saturated diodes and pentodes.   Since at low voltages the currents in these two elements decrease, the capacitor will not be allowed to charge to the supply voltage.   The current in a saturated diode changes considerably for small changes in filament heating power, and the capacitor charging rate would therefore change with variations in filament supply voltage.   The characteristics of a diode designed particularly for emission saturation were shown in Fig. 5-5.   Changes in the filament supply voltage of the pentode, however, are much less critical, and the use of negative feedback may even further stabilize the plate current.   For these reasons, pentodes are the common choice for constant-current charging devices.

A thyratron sweep circuit using a pentode as a constant-current charging device is shown in Fig. 6-33.   The curves for a pentode, similar to those of Fig. 6-34, show that over a range of plate voltage between points A and B, the current is approximately constant for a fixed bias value.   When the plate voltage is less than the value at A, the current begins to decrease.   In the circuit of Fig. 6-33, however, the cathode resistor R_k provides some compensation.   A reduction in current reduces the bias, permitting more current to flow, so that at equilibrium the current tends to remain more con-

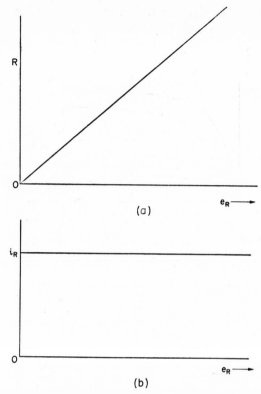

(a)

(b)

Fig. 6-32.   Characteristic needed to produce a linear current in the circuit of Fig. 6-31: (a) R versus e_R; (b) i_R versus e_R.

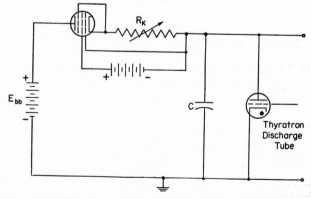

Fig. 6-33.   Pentode charging circuit.

stant than would be the case with constant bias voltage.   In Fig.
6-35, the curve for a 6CB6 pentode with fixed bias is contrasted

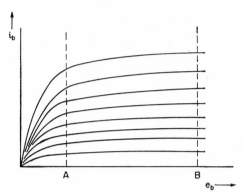

Fig. 6-34.   Volt-ampere characteristics for a pentode.

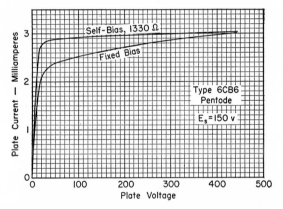

Fig. 6-35.   Effect of self-bias in the circuit of Fig. 6-33.

with that for self-bias obtained for a cathode resistance of 1330
ohms.   The circuit of Fig. 6-33 has several disadvantages.   If the
output voltage is to be of considerable magnitude, the cathode
potential of the pentode will be considerably above ground, and to
avoid exceeding the allowable rating of the voltage between cathode
and heater, it may be necessary to use a separate filament transformer.   Difficulty may also be encountered in obtaining the proper
screen-cathode voltage.   The latter difficulty will be remedied, of
course, by keeping the pentode at ground and the thyratron above

ground, but in this case, neither the output circuit nor the synchronizing input circuit will have one side at ground potential. In addition, the problem of cathode-heater potential is merely transferred to the thyratron. If the linearity requirements of the sweep are not overly great but a high output voltage is needed, it might possibly be simpler and less expensive to use a resistance-capacitance circuit of increased time constant, as discussed in Sec. 6-14, followed by a conventional amplifier stage.

A circuit which is sometimes used to improve the linearity of an intermittent sweep is shown in Fig. 6-36. The disadvantages of

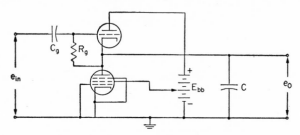

Fig. 6-36.   Pentode discharge circuit.

having one cathode far above ground potential are again present here.

The input signal consists of a negative rectangular pulse with a duration equal to the sweep period. This signal will be clamped so that the positive peaks give zero grid voltage on the triode. If the time between negative pulses is sufficiently long, the capacitor will charge to a value determined by the static plate resistances. The tubes conduct in series, and since the pentode has a greater plate resistance than the triode, most of the voltage will appear across the pentode.

The voltage across the capacitor C cannot instantaneously change, therefore the cathode potential of the triode cannot suddenly change. When the input signal drops at the beginning of a sweep pulse, the drop must appear instantaneously across R_g, driving the triode to cutoff. Capacitor C will then discharge linearly through the pentode.

If the input driving source has a low internal resistance compared with R_g, the decrease in voltage across the parallel pentode and capacitor combination will manifest itself as an increase in the grid voltage of the triode, and the magnitude of the input signal must be greater than the sum of the sweep magnitude and the magnitude of the cutoff voltage for the triode at its maximum plate voltage. The wave forms of the voltages across the various circuit elements are shown in Fig. 6-37.   At the end of the sweep period, the capacitor C recharges through the triode.

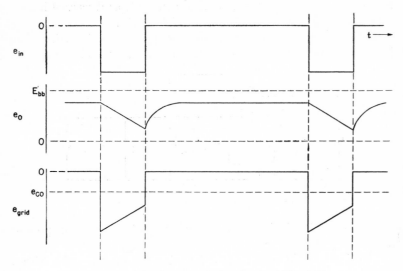

Fig. 6-37.   Wave forms for the circuit of Fig. 6-36.

Another means of linearity improvement utilizes an amplifier stage with a nonlinear dynamic characteristic.   An exponential sweep wave form generated by a conventional RC combination is applied to the grid of the amplifier.   If the curvature of the characteristic is opposite to that of the input wave form and the proper bias value is chosen, correction may be possible.   Figure 6-38 shows that if linearity is to be achieved, the dynamic characteristic must be exponential in form, and the signal must be adjusted so that the effective zero and asymptotic voltages agree.   This may also be shown mathematically.   If the input wave form is

$$e_{in} = k(1 - e^{-\alpha t}) \tag{6-70}$$

and the dynamic characteristic has the form

$$e_C = k'(1 - e^{-\alpha' i}) \tag{6-71}$$

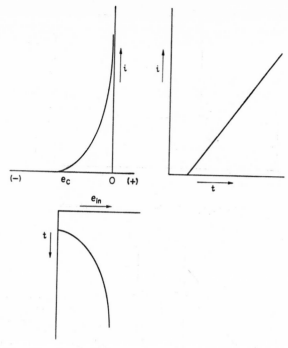

Fig. 6-38.   Use of a nonlinear amplifier to linearize the sweep voltage.

then $$k(1 - e^{-\alpha t}) = k'(1 - e^{-\alpha' i}) \tag{6-72}$$

As mentioned above, k must equal k', in which case

$$\alpha t = \alpha' i$$

or $$i = \frac{\alpha}{\alpha'} t \tag{6-73}$$

No vacuum tube has a characteristic which exactly fits the requirements described, but the characteristics of some tubes approach the proper curve over some portions of the characteristic, and considerable improvement may be obtained.   For instance, with the circuit of Fig. 6-39 the current wave form shown in Fig. 6-40 is obtained. The output current obtained from a linear amplifier with the same maximum and minimum values is also plotted to show the linearity correction.

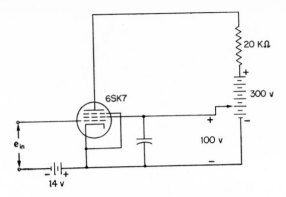

Fig. 6-39.   Nonlinear amplifier circuit.

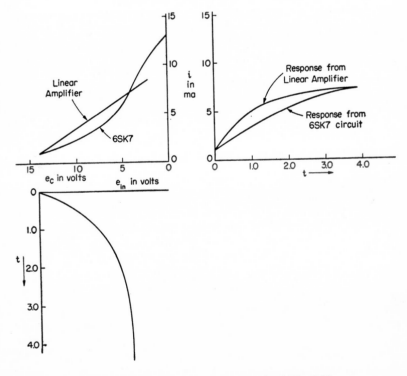

Fig. 6-40.   Wave forms for the circuit of Fig 6-39.

6-16 Linearity Correction by Use of Feedback Amplifiers

An interesting method of linearity correction involves the use of an amplifier with the RC combination in the feedback loop. Two generalized connections are shown in Fig. 6-41. The symbol A

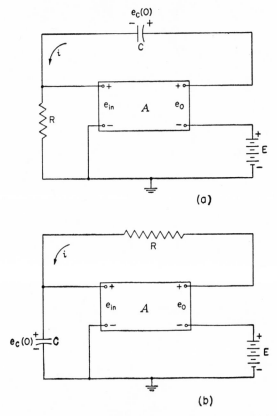

Fig. 6-41. Use of feedback to improve linearity: (a) capacitive feedback; (b) resistive feedback.

denotes the gain of the amplifier, that is, A is the ratio of the change in output voltage to the change in input voltage. Since the amplifier will be assumed to contain no energy storage elements, an instantaneous change in input signal will cause an instantaneous change in the output voltage. It will be assumed that the voltage E is the potential difference which causes the initial flow of current in the resistor at the instant the operation begins.

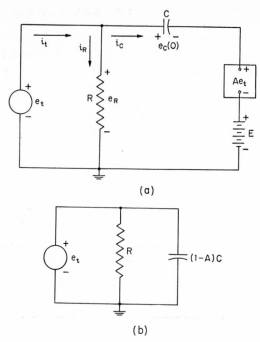

(a)

(b)

Fig. 6-42.   (a) Test generator applied to the circuit of Fig. 6-41(a) to determine equivalent circuit.   (b) Equivalent circuit found by the process of (a).

For the circuit of Fig. 6-41a at any time t after operation begins,

$$E + e_0 - \frac{1}{C} \int_0^t i\, dt - e_C(0) - iR = 0 \qquad (6\text{-}74)$$

$$e_0 = Ae_{\text{in}} = AiR \qquad (6\text{-}75)$$

Substituting,

$$E + AiR - \frac{1}{C} \int_0^t i\, dt - e_C(0) - iR = 0 \qquad (6\text{-}76)$$

The solution of this equation is,

$$i = \frac{E - e_C(0)}{R(1 - A)}\, e^{-t/(1-A)(RC)} \qquad (6\text{-}77)$$

giving an output voltage,

$$e_0 = \frac{A[E - e_C(0)]}{(1-A)}\, e^{-t/(1-A)(RC)} \qquad (6\text{-}78)$$

Since A may be a positive or a negative real number, Eq. (6-78) may take several different forms.   For example, if $A < 0$

$$|e_0| = \frac{|A|}{1 + |A|} \{E - e_C(0)\} \, e^{-t(1+|A|)(RC)} \tag{6-79}$$

The time constant of the circuit has been effectively increased by a factor $(1 + |A|)$.

If $0 < A < 1$, the time constant of the circuit has been decreased.

If the value of A approaches unity, the capacitor will charge to the final value of E volts in zero time.

For a value of A greater than unity, the current will increase exponentially, giving a regenerative system.

The only useful possibility, as far as linearity correction is concerned, is the case where A is less than zero.   This implies inversion, and thus only one tube need be used in the amplifier.   Such a system will be further investigated after the possibilities of the circuit of Fig. 6-41b have been examined.

At any time t, after operation begins in the circuit of Fig. 6-41b,

$$E + e_0 - iR - e_C(0) - \frac{1}{C} \int_0^t i \, dt = 0 \tag{6-80}$$

Since only the changing part of the input voltage to the amplifier will be amplified,

$$e_{\text{in}} = \frac{1}{C} \int_0^t i \, dt \tag{6-81}$$

Then $\qquad E + \dfrac{A}{C} \displaystyle\int_0^t i \, dt - iR - e_C(0) - \dfrac{1}{C} \int_0^t i \, dt = 0 \tag{6-82}$

This equation yields the solution

$$i = \frac{E - e_C(0)}{R} \, e^{-(1-A)t/RC} \tag{6-83}$$

Also, $\qquad e_0 = \dfrac{A}{1 - A} [E - e_C(0)][1 - e^{-(1-A)t(RC)}] \tag{6-84}$

Again four different forms of operation are possible.

If $A < 0$, the time constant of the circuit is decreased, while if $0 < A < 1$ the time constant of the circuit is increased.   When $A = 1$, the initial equation reduces to $E - iR - e_C(0) = 0$.   If

$A > 1$, the current increases exponentially, and the circuit is regenerative.

The useful possibilities here are the second and third, that is, when $0 < A \leq 1$. When $A = 1$ the ideal constant current charging system is obtained.

A test generator can be inserted across the amplifier input terminals in the circuit of Fig. 6-41a to determine the equivalent circuit as shown in Fig. 6-42a. The following equations can be written.

$$e_t = e_c + Ae_t + E \tag{6-85}$$

$$i_t = \frac{e_R}{R} + C\frac{de_C}{dt} = \frac{e_t}{R} - C\frac{d}{dt}(E + Ae_t - e_t)$$

$$= \frac{e_t}{R} + C(1 - A)\frac{de_t}{dt} \tag{6-86}$$

This equation fits the equivalent circuit of Fig. 6-42b. The action of the amplifier circuit with the connection from output to input effectively adds to the amplifier input terminals a value of capacitance equal to $(1 - A)$ times the input capacitance C.

J. M. Miller was the first to show that in a conventional triode amplifier, the presence of the grid-plate capacitance modifies the circuit so that the effective capacitance between grid and cathode becomes $C_{gk} + (1 - A)C_{gp}$.[2] Since the circuit of Fig. 6-41a reflects the $(1 - A)C$ term back into the grid circuit much like the Miller effect with interelectrode capacitance, circuits using this connection for linearity correction are usually called Miller sweep circuits.

A practical Miller sweep circuit is shown in Fig. 6-43. During the period in which the sweep is inoperative, the suppressor grid is sufficiently negative to prevent any plate current. The arrival of a pulse bringing the suppressor to, or within a few volts of, the cathode potential will permit plate current to flow. Since feedback is present, the magnitude of this current depends upon the over-all circuit, and may be found by the method which will be indicated. The plate current reduces the plate potential, and since the plate is coupled to the grid, the grid potential instantaneously drops. If the plate potential would remain the same, the drop in the grid

[2] See reference 47 at end of chapter.

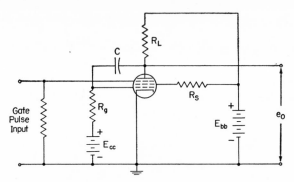

Fig. 6-43.   Miller sweep circuit.

circuit would decrease exponentially, or the grid signal would be an exponential rise.   This rise is effectively amplified by the tube, however, and the plate voltage tends to drop exponentially.   Coupling to the grid thus prevents the grid potential from rising as rapidly as it otherwise would, and this over-all effect of increasing the rise time may be considered an increase in the time constant of the charging circuit.

The bias E_{cc} is usually made positive as shown.   If the tube has been at cutoff long enough for the circuit to reach steady-state conditions, and if R_g is very much greater than the grid-cathode conducting resistance, the grid potential will be close to zero.   The capacitor will be charged to approximately E_{bb}.   At the instant the tube is returned to conduction, the circuit may be redrawn as shown in Fig. 6-44.   With respect to the plate circuit, the open-circuit voltage is $E_{bb} + R_L E_{cc}/(R_L + R_g)$, while the equivalent resistance is $R_L R_g/(R_L + R_g)$.   If the primed quantities indicate conditions at $t = 0$, then

$$e_b' = E_{bb} + \frac{R_L E_{cc}}{R_L + R_g} - \frac{i_b' R_L R_g}{R_L + R_g} \tag{6-87}$$

Summing currents at the grid will give

$$e_c' = \frac{R_L}{R_L + R_g} (E_{cc} - i_b' R_g) \tag{6-88}$$

These equations may be plotted on the tube characteristics.   Since i_b' must be the same in both Eq. (6-87) and Eq. (6-88), the intersection of the two curves gives the value of i_b', the plate current just after operation begins.

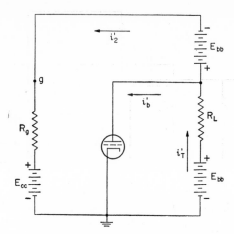

Fig. 6-44.   Circuit equivalent to that of Fig. 6-43 at the instant the tube has
returned to conduction.

The dynamic equivalent of the circuit, assuming linear operation, is shown in Fig. 6-45a.   A further reduction by Thevenin's theorem gives the circuit of Fig. 6-45b.

From Fig. 6-45b,

$$\mu e_g \frac{R_L}{r_p + R_L} + i_2 \left(\frac{r_p R_L}{r_p + R_L} + R_g \right) + \frac{1}{C} \int_0^t i_2 \, dt = 0 \quad (6\text{-}89)$$

Since $e_g = i_2 R_g$, this may be rearranged to give

$$\left(\frac{r_p R_L}{r_p + R_L} + R_g + \frac{\mu R_L R_g}{r_p + R_L} \right) i_2 + \frac{1}{C} \int_0^t i_2 \, dt = 0 \quad (6\text{-}90)$$

or

$$\frac{di_2}{dt} + \frac{i_2}{R'C} = 0 \quad (6\text{-}91)$$

where

$$R' = \frac{r_p R_L}{r_p + R_L} + R_g + \frac{\mu R_L R_g}{r_p + R_L} \quad (6\text{-}92)$$

The solution of Eq. (6-91) gives

$$i_2 = k e^{-t/R'C} \quad (6\text{-}93)$$

where k is the value of i_2 at $t = 0$.   This was previously shown to be obtainable from the value of i_b' found graphically.

The wave forms of the various circuit voltages are shown in Fig. 6-46.

The solution of the generalized circuit of Fig. 6-41a assumed zero

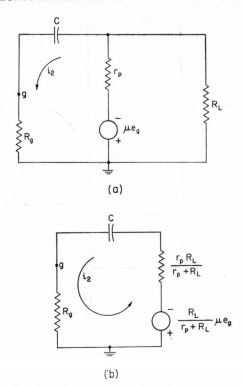

Fig. 6-45.   (a) Dynamic equivalent for the circuit of Fig. 6-44.   (b) Further
reduction by Thevenin's theorem.

resistance in the amplifier output circuit and also showed how the
time constant was effectively increased by a factor $(1 - A)$.   The
time constant in the circuit actually used was found to be

$$\tau = \left[\frac{r_p R_L}{r_p + R_L} + R_g\left(1 + \frac{\mu R_L}{r_p + R_L}\right)\right] C \qquad (6\text{-}94)$$

The term $\mu R_L/(r_p + R_L)$ will be recognized as the negative of the
gain of the amplifier stage, while the first term is the output resistance of the amplifier.   This shows that the results obtained are in
agreement with those expected from the generalized study.

Linear operation of the amplifier stage was assumed in the foregoing analysis.   The amount of feedback present tends to reduce the
effects of curvature of the dynamic characteristic, and unless the

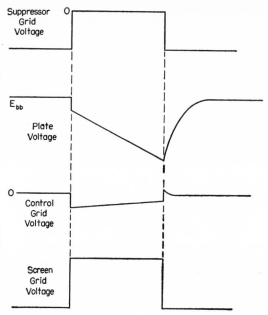

Fig. 6-46.   Wave forms for the circuit of Fig. 6-43.

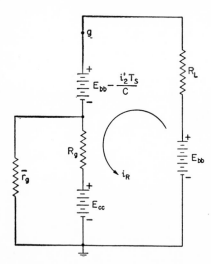

Fig. 6-47. Circuit equivalent to that of Fig. 6-44 at the instant the tube is cut off.

tube is operated over a considerable range, linear operation is approached.

The maximum charge which could be transferred during a sweep period of T_s duration would be $i_0 T_s$, but since the current decreases exponentially, the total transferred charged will always be less than this value. At the end of the sweep period, when the suppressor is again driven sufficiently negative to cut off the plate current, the circuit becomes that shown in Fig. 6-47. However, since the grid-cathode conducting resistance is much less than R_g or R_L, the grid may with small error be considered to be at ground potential. The recharging current is then

$$i_R \approx \left[E_{bb} - \left(E_{bb} - \frac{i_2' T_s}{C} \right) \right] \frac{1}{R_L} e^{-t/R_L C} = \frac{i_2' T_s}{R_L C} e^{-t/R_L C} \quad (6\text{-}95)$$

While an infinite time duration would be theoretically required to complete the charging of the capacitor, approximately four time constants will be sufficient. The circuit will work satisfactorily with much less time between sweeps, although the initial conditions will not be the same as those previously assumed.

It was previously shown that if the gain of the amplifier in the circuit of Fig. 6-41b was unity, the current flowing through the resistor would be constant. In this case, the voltage drop across the resistor is constant since the change in capacitor voltage is added to the charging voltage at each point. Because of this feedback action, the term *bootstrap* is applied to circuits using this principle. A practical bootstrap sweep circuit is shown in Fig. 6-48.

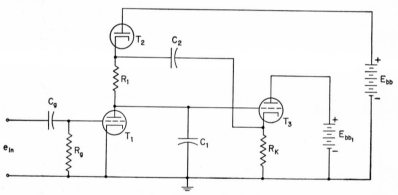

Fig. 6-48.   Bootstrap sweep circuit.

The gain of the cathode follower which is used as the feedback amplifier can never be exactly unity, but proper design can permit a close approach to this value, and the time constant of the circuit can be considerably increased. Since the cathode of the cathode follower cannot be returned directly to the junction of R_1 and the diode without destroying the d-c potentials necessary for the correct class A operation of the cathode follower, a battery or a coupling capacitor must be used. A coupling capacitor is more convenient and is made quite large, so that there will be very little change in its voltage during the time of the sweep. A square wave with an amplitude sufficient to drive the grid of T_1 to cutoff will be the input signal, and will be clamped with the positive peaks at zero if the time constant $R_g C_g$ is made quite large.

If the period between sweeps is sufficiently long, the circuit will be in a steady-state condition with the grid of T_1 at zero, and the capacitor C_1 at its minimum voltage. The plate supply voltage will be effectively connected to C_2 and R_1 if the static conducting resistance of the diode T_2 is small. At the start of the sweep period, the grid voltage of T_1 drops below cutoff, and T_1 is effectively removed from the circuit. Since the voltages across C_1 and C_2 cannot change instantaneously, the operating point of the cathode follower does not instantaneously change. The potential difference across R_1 also instantaneously remains at the value existing just before T_1 was cut off, and therefore the same current must continue to flow through that element. The only component through which this current may now flow after leaving R_1 is C_1, and this capacitor begins to charge. With the gain of the cathode follower near unity, the increase in voltage across C_1 gives approximately the same increase across R_k. This reflected increase in potential, transferred through C_2, cuts off the diode, and C_2 then acts as the charging source. If C_2 is very much larger than C_1, it can supply the necessary current to charge C_1 without seriously changing its own potential. Since the increase in voltage across C_1 is effectively added to the charging source, the current through R_1 will be essentially constant, and the sweep voltage across C_1 will be nearly linear.

A quantitative analysis of the circuit will next be made. If the resistance of the diode is neglected, R_1 and T_1 are in series across the supply voltage. The initial voltage across C_1, which will be termed e_1, is equal to the quiescent voltage across T_1. This can be determined from the plate characteristics for T_1 at the intersection of a load line for R_1 and the zero grid voltage curve. The steady-state voltage across the cathode resistor R_k may be found by the use of the plate characteristics of T_3; the voltage across C_2 is then the difference between the supply voltage and this voltage across R_k.

The dynamic circuit is shown in Fig. 6-49. Using the notation

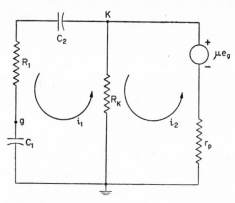

Fig. 6-49.   Dynamic circuit for the system of Fig. 6-48.

shown there, the following equations may be written:

$$(i_1 - i_2)R_k + \frac{1}{C_2} \int_0^t i_1 \, dt + i_1 R_1 + \frac{1}{C_1} \int_0^t i_1 \, dt = 0 \quad (6\text{-}96)$$

$$\mu e_g = (i_2 - i_1)R_k + i_2 r_p \quad (6\text{-}97)$$

$$e_g = (i_1 - i_2)R_k + \frac{1}{C_1} \int_0^t i_1 \, dt \quad (6\text{-}98)$$

Substituting Eq. (6-98) into Eq. (6-97) and solving for i_2 gives

$$i_2 = \frac{1}{r_p + (1 + \mu)R_k} \left[\frac{\mu}{C_1} \int_0^t i_1 \, dt + R_k(1 + \mu)i_1 \right] \quad (6\text{-}99)$$

Subsequent substitution for i_2 in Eq. (6-95) leads to

$$\left[\frac{R_k r_p}{r_p + (1 + \mu)R_k} + R_1 \right] i_1$$
$$+ \left[\frac{1}{C_2} + \frac{1}{C_1} \left(\frac{r_p + R_k}{r_p + (1 + \mu)R_k} \right) \right] \int_0^t i_1 \, dt = 0 \quad (6\text{-}100)$$

Let R'' represent the coefficient of i_1 and $1/C''$ represent the coefficient of the integral term. Differentiating with respect to t gives

$$R'' \frac{di_1}{dt} + \frac{i_1}{C''} = 0 \quad (6\text{-}101)$$

which has the solution

$$i_1 = k e^{-t/R''C''} \quad (6\text{-}102)$$

where k is the value of i_1 at $t = 0$. This was found earlier to be $(E_{bb} - e_1)/R_1$. Thus,

$$i_1 = \frac{E_{bb} - e_1}{R_1} e^{-t/R''C''} \qquad (6\text{-}103)$$

If the cathode follower stage is assumed to be operating class A at all times, the gain may be found as

$$A = \frac{\mu R_k}{r_p + (1 + \mu)R_k} \qquad (6\text{-}104)$$

with an output resistance of

$$R_0 = \frac{r_p A}{\mu} \qquad (6\text{-}105)$$

Substitution gives

$$R'' = \frac{r_p A}{\mu} + R_1 \qquad (6\text{-}106)$$

and

$$\frac{1}{C''} = \frac{1}{C_2} + \frac{1}{C_1}(1 - A) \qquad (6\text{-}107)$$

Therefore

$$i_1 = \frac{E_{bb} - e_1}{R_1} e^{-\alpha t} \qquad (6\text{-}108)$$

where

$$\alpha = \frac{1}{C_1\left(R_1 + \dfrac{r_p A}{\mu}\right)} \left(\frac{C_1}{C_2} + 1 - A\right) \qquad (6\text{-}109)$$

The usual value of R_1 ranges from 50,000 to 500,000 ohms. If a tube with a value of μ as low as 10 and a plate resistance as high as 20,000 ohms is used, the value of $r_p A/\mu$ will be approximately 2000 ohms for $A = 1$. Higher values of μ and lower values of r_p may be used, and since A is usually less than unity, the resulting values will be less than 2000 ohms, and thus may usually be neglected as compared with R_1.

Then

$$i_1 = \frac{E_{bb} - e_1}{R_1} e^{-\frac{t}{R_1 C_1}\left(\frac{C_1}{C_2} + 1 - A\right)} \qquad (6\text{-}110)$$

The analysis of the generalized circuit of Fig. 6-41b showed that the time constant was decreased by a factor $(1 - A)$. The actual circuit provided an additional term C_1/C_2 that further lessened the time constant. Since $|1 - A| < 1$, the feedback tends to increase the time constant, but this feedback effect is reduced by the C_1/C_2 term. This term should therefore be made as small as practicable, probably less than one-twentieth. Aside from this, the physical circuit does give results as anticipated from the generalized analysis.

If there were no feedback present in the circuit the charging current would be

$$i = \frac{E_{bb} - e_1}{R_1} e^{-t/R_1 C} \tag{6-111}$$

It may be noted that the currents in both cases, with or without feedback, are the same at $t = 0$, but with feedback the current is not so rapidly reduced. The initial slopes of the output voltage in both cases will be the same, but with feedback, the capacitor voltage will not deviate from linearity so rapidly. Typical voltage and current waveforms are sketched in Fig. 6-50 for comparison.

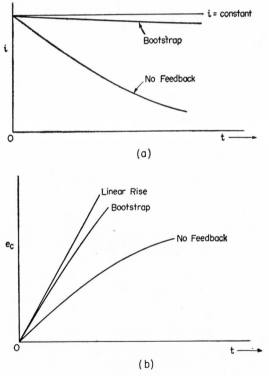

Fig. 6-50. Wave forms for the bootstrap circuit with and without feedback: (a) i versus t; (b) e_C versus t.

A photograph showing a typical sweep voltage, with and without feedback, is shown in Fig. 6-51.

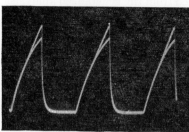

Fig. 6-51. Photograph of bootstrap sweep voltage with and without feedback.

In Fig. 6-3, the percentage deviation from linearity of a simple exponential sweep was plotted as a function of t_1/R_1C, where t_1 was the total sweep period. These results may be used here for comparison of the deviation obtained from a particular RC circuit with and without the bootstrap connection.

Let the particular circuit have a cathode-follower gain of 0.8, and let $C_1/C_2 = 1/20$. Then, for a given value of sweep time, the value of the exponent for the bootstrap circuit is 1/4 of that obtained for the regular circuit. The deviations are plotted in Fig. 6-52 for various values of t_1 in terms of R_1C_1, the time constant of the original charging circuit.

It can be seen that even for the conservative values used, a con-

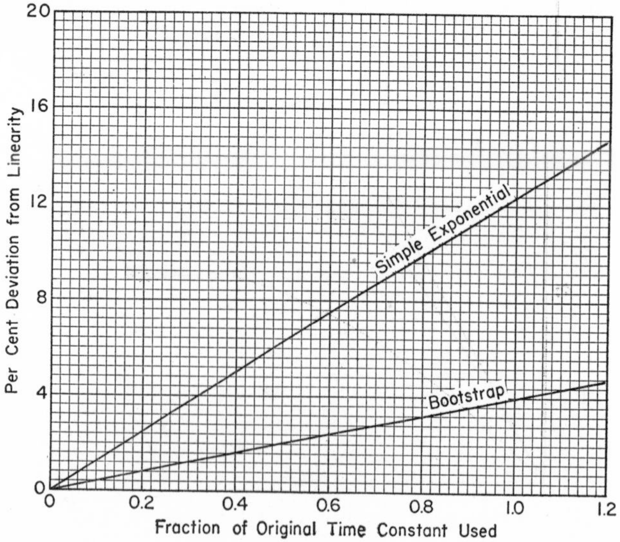

Fig. 6-52. Deviation from linearity for the bootstrap and simple exponential sweep circuits.

siderable correction in linearity results. The gain A can rather easily be increased to 0.95 or more, and the value of C_2 may be increased to limits largely determined by the economics involved or by the time available for retrace.

At the end of the sweep, and before another sweep is started, C_2 should be charged to the maximum obtainable voltage. The time required for total recovery may be longer than the period between sweeps. When this occurs, the circuit reaches a state of equilibrium in which the charge lost by C_2 during a sweep is just equal to that gained between sweeps. When the time between sweeps is not sufficiently long, the initial resistor current, the charging rate, and therefore the initial slope of the sweep change as the repetition rate changes. The diode used in the circuit of Fig. 6-48 makes the recharging time constant of the circuit containing C_2 lower than would be the case if a resistor were used instead. The recovery time can be further reduced by lowering the value of R_k, but this also reduces the gain of the cathode follower.

When the tube T_1 is returned to conduction, the capacitor C_1 will discharge through the plate circuit of this tube. Thus the grid potential of T_3 will drop. At the same time, C_2 will recharge through the cathode resistor R_k. This combination may or may not drive the tube T_3 to cutoff, but in either case, at some time during the recovery period, both the recharging current of C_2 and the plate current of T_3 will flow through R_k. Thus the current through C_2 will be affected as if the series resistance of the circuit were changing.

There are numerous variations of both the Miller and bootstrap circuits, and techniques similar to those already discussed may be used in their solutions.

6-17 Linearity Correction by Use of an Additional Transient

It was shown in Sec. 3-5 that if a voltage $e_{in} = E_m e^{-\alpha t}$ is applied to the series combination of a resistor R and a capacitor C, where

$\alpha = 1/RC$; then

$$i = \frac{1}{R} [E_m - e_C(0) + \alpha t E_m] e^{-\alpha t} \qquad (6\text{-}112)$$

The voltage across the capacitor at $t = 0$ is $e_C(0)$. For this particular case, an additional term has been introduced much like the case of critical damping in a RLC circuit, where the characteristic equation has a double root. This result can be used to improve the linearity of an exponential sweep voltage.

The circuit of Fig. 6-53a shows a capacitor tapped across the load

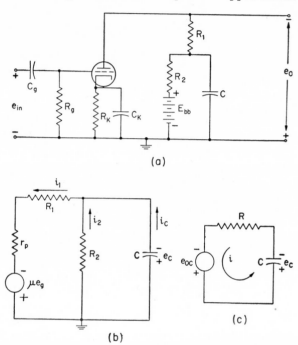

(a)

(b)   (c)

Fig. 6-53.   (a) Circuit to correct linearity by the use of an additional transient. (b) Dynamic equivalent of (a).   (c) Reduction of (b).

resistor of an amplifier stage in the same manner as low frequency compensation is achieved in audio frequency amplifiers. If an exponential sweep voltage is considered from a frequency component viewpoint, it might be reasoned that the sweep voltage is nonlinear because the circuit from which it is obtained has a poor low-frequency response. Since the capacitor improves the low-frequency response, its use will improve the sweep linearity.

If the tube is assumed to be operating Class A, the equivalent circuit of Fig. 6-53b may be used, and this can be further reduced to that of Fig. 6-53c where

$$R = \frac{R_2(R_1 + r_p)}{R_2 + R_1 + r_p} \qquad (6\text{-}113)$$

$$e_{oc} = \frac{\mu R_2 e_g}{R_2 + R_1 + r_p} \qquad (6\text{-}114)$$

The input signal is to be $e_{in} = E_m(1 - e^{-\alpha t})$ and the circuit components shall be chosen such that $1/\alpha = RC$. Then, for the circuit of Fig. 6-53c,

$$e_{oc} = \frac{\mu R_2 E_m}{R_2 + R_1 + r_p} (1 - e^{-\alpha t}) = iR + \frac{1}{C} \int_0^t i \, dt \qquad (6\text{-}115)$$

For convenience let the quantity A' be defined as

$$A' = \frac{\mu R_2}{R_2 + R_1 + r_p} \qquad (6\text{-}116)$$

Differentiating Eq. (6-115) and rewriting in D operator form,

$$\left(RD + \frac{1}{C}\right) i = \alpha A' E_m e^{-\alpha t}$$

or

$$(D + \alpha)i = \frac{\alpha A' E_m e^{-\alpha t}}{R} \qquad (6\text{-}117)$$

This equation has the solution

$$i = \frac{\alpha A' E_m t}{R} e^{-\alpha t} \qquad (6\text{-}118)$$

The capacitor voltage is

$$e_C = \frac{1}{C} \int_0^t i \, dt = A' E_m [1 - (1 + \alpha t)e^{-\alpha t}] \qquad (6\text{-}119)$$

Since in Fig. 6-53b, R_2 is in parallel with C, this must also be the voltage across R_2, and

$$i_2 = \frac{A' E_m}{R_2} [1 - (1 + \alpha t)e^{-\alpha t}] \qquad (6\text{-}120)$$

The current i_1 is the sum of i_2 and the capacitor current, and is therefore

$$i_1 = \frac{A' E_m}{R_2} [1 - (1 + \alpha t)e^{-\alpha t}] + \frac{A' E_m \alpha t}{R} e^{-\alpha t} \qquad (6\text{-}121)$$

The output voltage is

$$e_0 = e_C + i_1 R_1$$

$$= \frac{R_1 A' E_m}{R_2}[1 - (1 + \alpha t)e^{-\alpha t}] + \frac{R_1 A' E_m \alpha t}{R} e^{-\alpha t}$$

$$+ A' E_m[1 - (1 + \alpha t)e^{-\alpha t}] \quad (6\text{-}122)$$

This may be arranged to give

$$e_0 = \frac{\mu E_m(R_1 + R_2)}{R_2 + R_1 + r_p}\left[1 - e^{-\alpha t} - \frac{r_p R_2 \alpha e^{-\alpha t}}{(R_1 + r_p)(R_1 + R_2)}\right] \quad (6\text{-}123)$$

The first two terms give the output which would be obtained if no capacitor were used in the amplifier. The third term represents a correction introduced by the transient response of the added RC circuit. If $r_p = 0$, there will be no correction, for the tube would then feed directly to the output terminals an amplified version of the input signal.

If the combination of R_1 and R_2 constitutes a potentiometer in the physical circuit, the sum of R_1 and R_2 is constant, as is the sum of R_1, R_2, and r_p. The output voltage may then be written

$$e_0 = B' E_m[1 - (1 + \alpha x t)e^{-\alpha t}] \quad (6\text{-}124)$$

where

$$B' = \frac{\mu(R_1 + R_2)}{R_2 + R_1 + r_p} \quad (6\text{-}125)$$

and

$$x = \frac{r_p R_2}{(R_1 + r_p)(R_1 + R_2)} \quad (6\text{-}126)$$

The variable x is dependent upon the position of the potentiometer tap.

If an attempt is made to apply to this circuit, the procedure used in finding the percentage deviation from linearity of the exponential sweep, the expressions become unwieldy because of the $\alpha t e^{-\alpha t}$ term.

In Fig. 6-54 the expression $[1 - (1 + \alpha x t)e^{-\alpha t}]$ is plotted as a function of αt with x as a parameter.

When $x = 0$, there is no correction, but merely the amplification of the input exponential. Comparison of the curves of Fig. 6-54 shows that the value of x to be chosen depends upon the number of time constants used for the original wave form. If the maximum

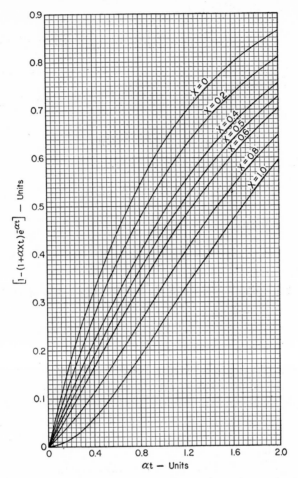

Fig. 6-54.   Plot of $[1 - (1 + \alpha x t)]e^{-\alpha t}$ versus αt for various values of x (see Eq. 6-124).

value of αt is 2, a straightedge placed through zero and the other end points will show that minimum deviation occurs for an x of approximately 0.8.   If the input wave form uses but one time constant, a value of x of approximately 0.6 gives the best results.   If αt is 0.5 or less, a value of x of approximately 0.5 may be used.   If the expression $[1 - (1 + \alpha x t)e^{-\alpha t}]$ is expanded into a power series, there results

$$[1 - (1 + \alpha x t)e^{-\alpha t}] = \alpha t(1 - x)$$

$$+ \alpha^2 t^2 \left(x - \frac{1}{2} \right) + \alpha^3 t^3 \left(\frac{1}{6} - \frac{x}{2} \right) + \cdots \quad (6\text{-}127)$$

When $x = 0.5$, the square term disappears, while the cube term will be small for values of αt less than 0.5.

It was earlier stated that the value of x is determined by the potentiometer tap position. Let

$$R_2 = y(R_1 + R_2) \qquad (6\text{-}128)$$

Then since

$$x = \frac{r_p R_2}{(R_1 + r_p)(R_1 + R_2)} \qquad (6\text{-}129)$$

the value of y must be

$$y = \frac{x(r_p + R_1 + R_2)}{r_p + x(R_1 + R_2)} \qquad (6\text{-}130)$$

If the total resistance $R_1 + R_2$ is known, the value of R_2 is determined for a specific value of x. Since

$$\frac{1}{\alpha C} = \frac{R_2(r_p + R_1)}{R_2 + R_1 + r_p} \qquad (6\text{-}131)$$

from the requirements set earlier, it follows that if a particular tube and a particular value of C are selected, the value of $R_1 + R_2$ is fixed from the above expression. A solution for this value in terms of r_p, y, α, and C then involves a quadratic equation. If a value for $R_1 + R_2$ is chosen instead, the necessary magnitude of C may be readily found.

It should be noted that a resistance-inductance combination might be similarly used for linearity correction, but the usual disadvantages incident to the use of an inductor make the resistance-capacitance combination more practical.

6-18 Circular Sweep Presentations

If the trace on a cathode-ray tube screen is made to travel around the circumference of a circle at a uniform rate, a time base approximately three times as long as that obtained by a linear motion along a diameter may be secured for a given size of tube. Time marker signals can then appear as radial "pips," rapid changes in the circle radius for small durations of time. A sketch is shown in Fig. 6-55.

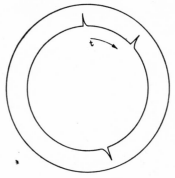

If two sinusoids differing in time phase by 90 degrees are plotted against each other, as shown in Fig. 6-56, the resulting pattern is a circle. Since the radius of the circle is equal to the amplitudes of the sinusoids, any change in the magnitudes of the sinusoids will result in a change in radius. Thus markers are obtained by sudden increases of short duration in the amplitudes of the sinusoids.

Fig. 6-55.   Radial deflection on circular sweep.

The components of the deflection may be written

$$D_v = R \sin \omega t \qquad (6\text{-}132)$$

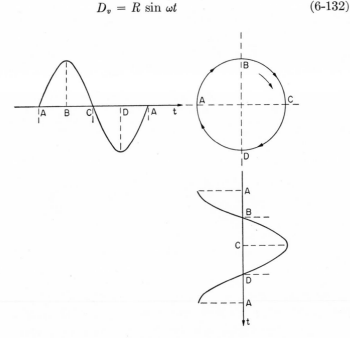

Fig. 6-56.   Sine waves used to produce circular sweep.

$$D_h = R \sin\left(\omega t - \frac{\pi}{2}\right) \qquad (6\text{-}133)$$

Since the deflection in an electrostatic cathode-ray tube equals the product of the signal voltage and the deflection sensitivity,

$$D_v = e_v S_v \qquad (6\text{-}134)$$

$$D_h = e_h S_h \qquad (6\text{-}135)$$

where the e's are the respective signals, and the S's are the corresponding sensitivities. One set of plates is nearer the screen; therefore the sensitivities are usually not quite equal. The required signals are then

$$e_v = \frac{R}{S_v} \sin \omega t \qquad (6\text{-}136)$$

$$e_h = \frac{R}{S_h} \sin\left(\omega t - \frac{\pi}{2}\right) \qquad (6\text{-}137)$$

where the value of R must have sudden changes to obtain the marker pips.

One method of securing the necessary signals is by the use of amplifiers with variable gain. If the amplifiers for the vertical and horizontal systems are made identical, the input signals to each must be adjusted according to the deflection sensitivities, and must have the necessary phase relationship.

A pentode may be used as an amplifier with variable gain by control of the screen grid potential. The anode current in a pentode is a function of both the screen grid potential and the control grid potential. If the screen grid is held at a fixed value, an increase of control voltage will increase the tube current. The screen grid would have a similar effect for a fixed control grid potential. Thus it may be considered that each grid has an amplification factor.

If a steady signal is imposed on the control grid, and there is a variation of the screen potential, the output voltage will change in amplitude according to the change in screen potential. The screen voltage thus *modulates* the signal applied to the control grid.

A typical circuit arrangement for a circular time presentation is shown in Fig. 6-57. The signals e_v and e_h are adjusted according to

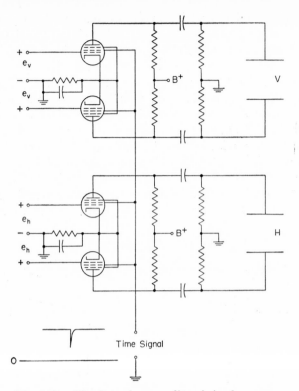

Fig. 6-57.   Circuit to change radius of circular sweep.

Eqs. (6-136) and (6-137).   The required phase difference may be obtained from any of the numerous phase-shifting methods.

If the screen voltage is suddenly changed, the output voltage will instantly change, and use of a screen signal as shown will give an inwardly directed marker.

6-19 The PPI and Spiral Type Presentations

The term *PPI*, Plan Position Indicator, pertains to a radar presentation that gives a screen picture resembling a relief map of the area surrounding the radar transmitter.   A sweep is directed outwardly from the screen center to the tube edge, but this radial sweep is constantly rotated over the tube face in synchronism with the rotation of the radar antenna.   The operation of the pulse circuits in the radar also triggers the sweep on the screen, so that its outward movement begins either at the same instant as the outgoing radar pulse, or has a definite time relationship. When an echo from a target is received, an intensifying signal is applied to the beam, and a brighter spot appears on the screen. The radial distance of such a spot is made directly proportional to the time between pulse and echo, and this is proportional to the actual distance from transmitter to target. All targets are shown as bright spots on a relatively darker background. A radar on a ship near a coast line can thus present on the screen a bright pattern of the coast line, or of other reflecting objects within range.

If distance is to be measured accurately along a radial line, the sweep must be linear from the center of the screen to the edge.

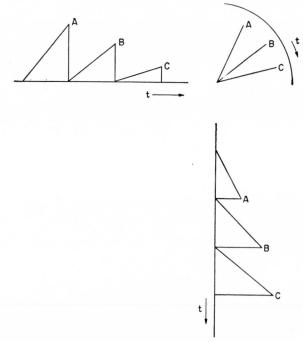

Fig. 6-58.   Relationships necessary for linear radial sweeps.

Figure 6-58 shows the necessary relationship between deflection voltages on the two axes for linear sweeps at three different angles on the screen. If the trace is to be uniform with respect to distance regardless of the angle on the screen, the time for all sawtooth waves is the same.   The slope must vary, however, if the angle is to change. If the locus of the points A, B, C, etc. on the screen is a circle, the locus of the peak voltage applied to each set of plates must be sinusoidal.   The voltages for the two sets of plates, then, are sinusoidally modulated sawtooth patterns, with a quadrature phase relationship between the modulation for each set of plates.   This is shown in Fig. 6-59.

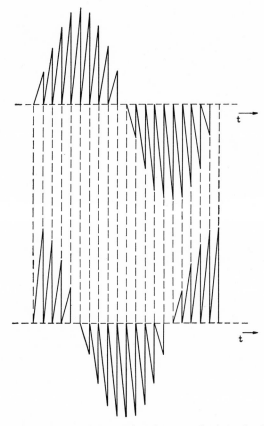

Fig. 6-59.   Modulation of sawtooth voltage to obtain a circular sweep.

One method of obtaining these voltages is by applying the saw-tooth sweep to a sine-cosine potentiometer.   This is a continuously wound potentiometer with a taper that gives the desired sinusoidal resistance.   One might be represented as shown in Fig. 6-60.   The voltage to be divided is applied between the points A and B, and the output voltage is taken from the slider D to point C.

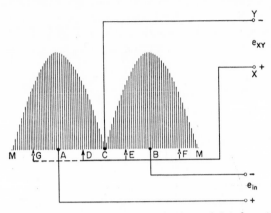

Fig. 6-60.   Use of potentiometer to obtain modulated sawtooth.

With a d-c voltage applied, movement of the slider from C to A to M to B and back to C would give the sinusoid shown in Fig. 6-61.   If e_{in} is a function of time rather than a d-c quantity, the division remains the same as that shown in Fig. 6-61, and $e_{xy} = e_{in} \sin \theta/2$.

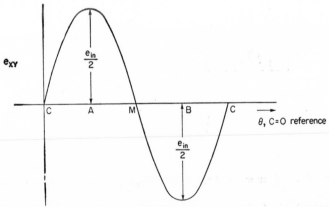

Fig. 6-61.   Output voltage of the circuit of Fig. 6-60 as a function of slider position.

The required 90-degree phase shift could be accomplished by placing two such devices, displaced 90 mechanical degrees from each other, on the same shaft.   Another method would have the two devices in the same mechanical position, but the input voltage to one potentiometer would be applied from M to C instead of from A to B, and the slide return would be changed from point C to point A.   The other potentiometer would be left unchanged.

To secure the sinusoidal sawtooth modulation of Fig. 6-59, it is necessary only to supply the constant amplitude sawtooth voltage to the potentiometer and to rotate the mechanical shaft.

It is emphasized that this is only one method of obtaining a PPI indication, and the system is susceptible to difficulties with wear, brushes, and other mechanical details.   Pentodes can be used to obtain the required modulation, but careful circuit adjustment is necessary in such cases to obtain reasonable linearity.

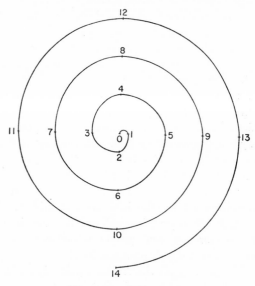

Fig. 6-62.   Spiral sweep.

In the PPI presentation, the sawtooth frequency is large as compared with the frequency of the sinusoid.   If the procedure is reversed, that is, the sawtooth frequency is made small as compared to the sinusoidal frequency, a spiral sweep results.   The PPI and spiral are fundamentally the same, and similar circuit techniques may be used to obtain a spiral sweep as are used in the PPI. The spiral can also be considered another means of obtaining a much greater time base for a given size tube. A spiral in which the distance from the center increases linearly with time is shown in Fig. 6-62.

6-20 Other Special Cathode-Ray Tube Presentations

In addition to the cathode-ray systems already discussed, a number of varied presentations have been devised for use in specialized applications. A few of these will be mentioned here.

By choice of proper horizontal and vertical frequencies, a plane may be shown on the screen in the same oblique representation commonly used in engineering drawing.[3] Addition of proper vertical voltage values will permit planes such as $y = A \sin t$ to be shown. It is also possible to combine such a representation with intensity modulation, so that the screen of a radar will present an oblique bas-relief of the scanned area, or so that a mechanical transducer will give a reproduction of a mechanically scanned item, as for example, a steel shaft.

The use of half-silvered mirrors will permit images from several screens or other sources to be optically superimposed. An extension of this technique will allow a third dimension of depth to be added to the picture by a stereoscopic system. In the case of television, for example, two cameras can be fed from the same deflection and synchronizing systems, and the signals from each then supplied to separate screens. These images are plane polarized at right angles, and then superimposed by the half-silvered mirror. The use of polarized spectacles then permits each eye to view the output from only one of the cameras, and proper adjustment of the camera angles will give correct depth presentation.[4]

Methods of presenting all the Arabic numerals on a cathode-ray screen have been devised.[5] Such techniques, of course, suggest that circuits may be used to give outputs which will reproduce on a screen almost any type of data represented by lines alone.

---

[3] See reference 62 at end of chapter.
[4] See reference 4 at end of chapter.
[5] See reference 24 at end of chapter.

REFERENCES

1. Abbenhouse, R. P., "General Purpose Oscilloscope," *Electronics*, August, 1949, Vol. 22, p. 106.
2. Attree, V. H., "A Slow Sweep Time-Base," *J. Sci. Instruments*, August, 1949, Vol. 26, p. 257.
3. Batcher, Ralph R., "Circular and Polar Sweeps," *Electronic Industries*, September, 1944, Vol. 3, p. 80.
4. Berkley, C., "Three-Dimensional Representation on Cathode Ray Tubes," *Proc. IRE*, December, 1948, Vol. 36, p. 1530.
5. Black, D. H., "A New Hard Valve Relaxation Oscillator," *Elec. Commun.* July, 1939, Vol. 18, p. 50.
6. Bocking, Geoffrey, "Tracing Valve Characteristics Using the Cathode-Ray Oscillograph," *Wireless Engr.*, December, 1942, Vol. 19, p. 556.
7. Bussard, E. J. H. and Michel, T. J., "A Wide-Band High-Frequency Sweep," *Electronics*, May, 1942, Vol. 15, p. 58.
8. Brainerd, J. G.; Reich, H. J.; Koehler, G.; and Woodruff, L. F., *Ultra-High Frequency Techniques*. New York: D. Van Nostrand Company, Inc., 1942.
9. Clarke, Arthur C., "Linearity Circuits," *Wireless Engr.*, June, 1944, Vol. 21, p. 256.
10. Chance, Britton, "Some Precision Circuit Techniques Used in Waveform Generation and Time Measurement," *Rev. Sci. Instruments*, October, 1946, Vol. 17, p. 396.
11. Chance, Britton, "Time Demodulation," *Proc. IRE*, October, 1947, Vol. 35, p. 1045.
12. Chance, Britton; Hughes, Vernon; MacNichol, Edward F., Jr.; Sayre, David; and Williams, Frederick C., *Waveforms*. New York: McGraw-Hill Book Co., Inc., 1949.
13. Cocking, W. T., "Linear Sawtooth Oscillators," *Wireless World*, May, 1939, Vol. 16, p. 425.
14. Cruft Laboratory Electronics Training Staff, *Electronic Circuits and Tubes*. New York: McGraw-Hill Book Co., Inc., 1947.
15. Day, J. R., "Serrasoid F-M Modulator," *Electronics*, October, 1948, Vol. 21, p. 73.
16. den Hartog, H. and Muller, F. A., "Oscilloscope Time-Base Circuit," *Wireless Engr.*, October, 1947, Vol. 24, p. 287.
17. Dye, D. W., "Improved Cathode Ray Tube Method for the Harmonic Comparison of Frequencies," *Proc. Phys. Soc.*, February, 1925, Vol. 37, p. 158.
18. East, T. W. R. and Standing, A. F., "A Circular Time-Base Frequency Comparator," *J. Sci. Instruments*, July, 1949, Vol. 26, p. 236.

19. Electronics Staff, "A Signal-Synchronized Sweep Circuit for Cathode-Ray Oscillography," *Electronics*, May, 1935, Vol. 8, p. 158.

20. Elmore, William C. and Sands, Matthew, *Electronics-Experimental Techniques*. New York: McGraw-Hill Book Co., Inc., 1949.

21. Emery, W. L., *Ultra-High Frequency Radio Engineering*. New York: The Macmillan Company, 1944.

22. Emrich, R. J., "Spiral Chronograph for Measurement of Single Millisecond Time Intervals with Microsecond Accuracy," *Rev. Sci. Instruments*, March, 1947, Vol. 18, p. 150.

23. Fleming-Williams, B. C., "A Single-Valve Time Base Circuit," *Wireless Engr.*, April, 1940, Vol. 17, p. 161.

24. Fuller, H. W., "Numeroscope for Cathode-Ray Printing," *Electronics*, February, 1948, Vol, 21, p. 98.

25. Gibbs, D. F. and Rushton, W. A. H., "A Linear Time Base of Wide Range," *J. Sci. Instruments*, November, 1946, Vol. 23, p. 27.

26. Gilson, W. E., "CRO Delayed Single Sweep," *Electronics*, March, 1942, Vol. 15, p. 57.

27. Goehegan, William A., "A Flexible Sweep Circuit and Deflection Amplifier for C-R Oscillographs," *Electronics*, December, 1941, Vol. 14, p. 38.

28. Goldsmith, T. T., and Richards, L. A., "A High Frequency Sweep Circuit," *Proc. IRE*, June, 1935, Vol. 23, p. 653.

29. Haller Cecil E., "A Linear Timing Axis for Cathode-Ray Oscillographs," *Rev. Sci. Instruments*, July, 1933, Vol. 4, p. 385.

30. Haworth, L. J., "A Discontinuous Oscillographic Sweep Circuit," *Rev. Sci. Instruments*, October, 1941, Vol. 12, p. 478.

31. Herrenden Harker, G. F., "The Mechanism of Synchronization in the Linear Time Base," *Phil. Mag.*, August, 1938, Vol. 26, p. 193.

32. Hershberger, W. D., "Circuit for Generating Circular Traces of Different Frequencies on an Oscillograph," *Proc. IRE*, April, 1944, Vol. 32, p. 205.

33. Keen, A. W., "Linear Saw Tooth Generators," *Wireless Engr.*, July, 1948, Vol. 25, p. 710.

34. Keen, A. W., "Television Time Base Linearization," *Electronic Eng.*, June, 1949, Vol. 21, p. 195.

35. Kelley, G. G., "A High Speed Synchroscope," *Rev. Sci. Instruments*, January, 1950, Vol. 21, p. 71.

36. Knight, S. A., "Cathode-Ray Oscilloscope," *Wireless World*, December, 1948, Vol. 54, p. 432.

37. Kock, Winston E., "A Stabilized Sweep Circuit Oscillator," *Electronics*, April, 1939, Vol. 12, p. 20.

38. Langbergh, E. L., "Analysis of Linear Sweep Generator," *Electronics*, November, 1946, Vol. 19, p. 194.

39. Laws, C. A., "A Precision-Ranging Equipment Using A Crystal Oscillator As A Timing Standard," *Proc. IRE*, Radiolocation Conv., No. 1, 1946, Vol. 93.

40. Leeds, Laurance M., "A Cathode-Ray Time Axis for High Frequency," *Proc. IRE*, June, 1936, Vol. 24, p. 872.

41. Lewis, I. A. D., "The Miller Circuit as a Low Speed Precision Integrator," *Electronic Eng.*, April, 1950, Vol. 22, p. 141.

42. Ludman, Walter W., "Time Base Calibration," *Electronics*, September, 1945, Vol. 18, p. 117.

43. MacGregor-Morris, J. T. and Henley, J. A., *Cathode Ray Oscillography*. London: Chapman and Hall, Ltd., 1936.

44. MacLean, W. R., "The Synchronization of Oscilloscope Sweep Circuits," *Communications*, March, 1943, Vol. 23, p. 23.

45. Martin, Thomas L., Jr., *Ultra High Frequency Engineering*. New York: Prentice-Hall, Inc., 1950.

46. Meier, W. L. and Richards, P. A., "Power Supply and Linear Time Base for Cathode Ray Oscillographs," *Electronics*, April, 1934, Vol. 7, p. 110.

47. Miller, J. M. "Dependence of the Input Impedance of a Three-Electrode Vacuum Tube Upon the Load in the Plate Circuit," *Nat. Bur. Standards Sci. Paper 351*.

48. M.I.T. Radar School Staff, *Principles of Radar*. New York: McGraw-Hill Book Co., Inc., 1946.

49. Morgan, J. C., "Circuits Producing Sharp Electrical Impulses Free From Curvature and Their Use in Oscillographic Work," *Rev. Sci. Instruments*, June, 1938, Vol. 9, p. 183.

50. Nagy, P. and Goddard, M. J., "The Signal Converter," *Wireless Engr.*, June, 1943, Vol. 20, p. 273.

51. Owen, Robert P., "Linear Sweep Circuits," *Electronics*, December, 1946, Vol. 19, p. 136.

52. Pollard Ernest C. and Sturtevant, Julian M., *Microwaves and Radar Electronics*. New York: John Wiley and Sons, Inc., 1948.

53. Potter, J. L., "Sweep Circuits," *Proc. IRE*, June, 1938, Vol. 26, p. 713.

54. Puckle, O. S., *Time Bases*. New York: John Wiley and Sons, Inc., 1943.

55. Rawcliffe, G. H. "Shock-Impulsed Spiral Time Base," *Wireless Engr.*, July, 1949, Vol. 26, p. 242.

56. Reich, H. J., *Theory and Applications of Electron Tubes*. New York: McGraw-Hill Book Co., Inc., 1944.

57. Reyner, J. H., *Cathode-Ray Oscillographs*. London: Sir Isaac Pitman and Sons, 1940.

58. Reyner, J. H., "Direct Coupled Oscilloscope," *Electronics*, July, 1948, Vol. 21, p. 102.

59. Rider, John F. and Uslan, Semour D., *Encyclopedia on Cathode-Ray Oscilloscopes and Their Uses.* New York: John F. Rider Publisher, Inc. 1950. (An extensive bibliography on all phases of cathode-ray tube work appears at the end of this volume.)

60. Samuel, A. L., "A Method of Obtaining a Linear Time Axis for a Cathode Ray Oscillograph," *Rev. Sci. Instruments,* September, 1931, Vol. 2, p. 532.

61. Sayre, David, "Linear Sweep Generation," *Electronics,* July, 1950, Vol. 23, p. 171.

62. Schmitt, O. H., "Cathode Ray Presentation of Three Dimensional Data," *J. Applied Phys.,* September, 1947, Vol. 18, p. 819.

63. Seeley, Samuel, *Electron-Tube Circuits.* New York: McGraw-Hill Book Co., Inc., 1950.

64. Soller, J. Theodore; Starr, M. A.; and Valley, George E., Jr., *Cathode Ray Tube Displays.* New York: McGraw-Hill Book Co., Inc., 1948.

65. Sundt, E. V. and Fett, G. H., "A Timing Method for Cathode Ray Oscillographs," *Rev. Sci. Instruments,* November, 1934, Vol. 5, p. 402.

66. Sulzer, P. G., "A Wide-Range Saw-Tooth Generator," *Rev. Sci. Instruments,* January, 1949, Vol. 20, p. 78.

67. Talbot, Samuel A., "A Multiple Sweep System for Cathode-Ray Oscillography," *Rev. Sci. Instruments,* September, 1940, Vol. 11, p. 289.

68. Taylor, Albert J., "A Single-Stroke Oscilloscope Sweep," *Radio News-Electronic Engr. Supplement,* September, 1940.

69. Vaughan, J. F. O., "General Purpose Oscilloscope," *Wireless World,* May, 1948, Vol. 54, p. 160.

70. von Ardenne, Manfred, "A New Polar Co-ordinate Cathode-Ray Oscillograph with Extremely Linear Time Scale," *Wireless Engr.,* January, 1937, Vol. 14, p. 5.

71. von Ardenne, Manfred, "Distortion of Saw-Tooth Waveforms," *Electronics,* November, 1937, Vol. 10, p. 37.

72. Watson-Watt, R. A.; Herd, J. F.; and Barnbridge-Bell, L. H., *The Cathode Ray Oscillograph in Radio Research.* London: His Majesty's Stationery Office, 1933.

73. Watts, R. J., "Method of Linearizing the Voltage Rise of A Relaxation Oscillator," *Rev. Sci. Instruments,* January, 1949, Vol. 20, p. 81.

74. Williams, F. C. and Beattie, R. K., "A Multi-Channel Oscillograph Amplifier," *Wireless Engr.,* March, 1939, Vol. 16, p. 126.

75. Williams, F. C. and Fairweather, Alan, "Inductance Linearized Time Base," *Wireless Engr.,* Part I, June, 1941, Vol. 18, p. 224; Part II, July, 1941, Vol. 18, p. 271.

76. Williams, F. C., "Introduction to Circuit Techniques for Radiolocation," *Proc. IEE,* Radiolocation Conv., No. 1, 1946, Vol. 93, p. 289.

77. Williams, F. C.; Howell, W. D.; and Briggs, B. H., "Plan-Position Indicator Circuits," *Proc. IEE*, Radiolocation Conv., No. 7, 1946, Vol. 9, p. 1219.
78. Williams, F. C. and Moody, N. F., "Ranging Circuits, Linear Time Base Generators and Associated Circuits," *Proc. IEE*, Radiolocation Conv., No. 1, 1946, Vol. 93, p. 320.
79. Williams, F. C. and Wolfenden, J. P., "Time Sweep of a Cathode-Ray Oscillograph," *Wireless Engr.*, June, 1937, Vol. 14, p. 315.

PROBLEMS

6-1 A sweep circuit uses a pentode to charge a capacitor at a constant rate. A thyratron with an extinction potential of 15 volts and a firing potential of 125 volts is used as the discharge element. If the pentode current is 10 milliamperes, find the capacitor required for a sweep frequency of 2000 cycles per second, assuming negligible discharge time.

6-2 Sketch and label the output voltage for the accompanying circuit

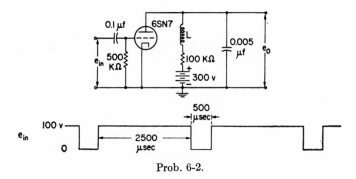

Prob. 6-2.

if (a) $L = 0$; (b) $L = 25$ henrys; (c) $L = 100$ henrys; (d) $L = 500$ henrys.

6-3 (a) Repeat problem 6-2(a) if the 2500-microsecond period in the input signal is reduced to 500 microseconds.   The original 500-microsecond period is left unchanged.   (b) Repeat 6-3(a) using the data of problem 6-2(d).

6-4 (a) In the phase inverter shown, what must be the value of R in

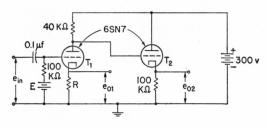

Prob. 6-4.

order to obtain output voltages of equal magnitude and opposite phase? (b) What should be the magnitude and polarity of the source E?

6-5 (a) Derive the equation shown in the footnote of Sec. 6-12.   (b) Show that this equation reduces to Eq. (6-56) if the charging path is neglected.

6-6 In the circuit shown T_1 is a 6J5 tube, and T_2 is a 6CB6.   Sketch

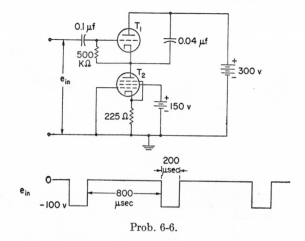

Prob. 6-6.

and label the steady-state plate voltage of the pentode, showing the relationship to the input signal.

6-7 (a) If $R_k = 2000$ ohms in the accompanying circuit, sketch and label the steady-state plate voltage of T_2.   (b) Plot a curve of frequency versus

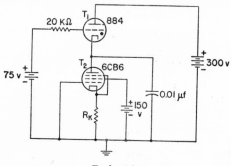

Prob. 6-7.

R_k for values of R_k ranging from 500 ohms to 5000 ohms.   (c) How could the circuit be synchronized?

6-8 In the circuit shown the sweep is started by opening the switch Sw. Assuming the dynamic behavior of the tube is linear, find an expression for

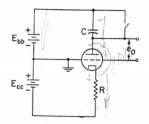

Prob. 6-8.

the output voltage.   Show how the initial voltages and currents may be obtained from the tube characteristics.

6-9 Using the circuit of Fig. 6-48 and the given input signal, sketch and label the steady-state cathode voltage of T_2.   The diode may be con-

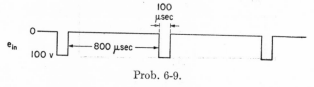

Prob. 6-9.

sidered to have negligible resistance.   A 6SN7 tube is used for T_1 and T_3. The rest of the parameters are $R_1 = 50,000$ ohms, $C_1 = 0.01$ microfarad,

$C_2 = 0.02$ microfarad, $R_k = 10,000$ ohms, $R_g = 500,000$ ohms, $C = 0.2$ microfarad, $E_{bb} = 300$ volts, and $E_{bb1} = 250$ volts.

6-10 For the circuit of Fig. 6-48 calculate in general terms the initial charging current of C_1 if the sweep time is Δt_1 and the time between sweeps is Δt_2. Assume the diode to have a constant static conducting resistance r_d, and the cathode follower to operate linearly.

6-11 (a) Explain the operation of the given sweep circuit. (b) If $R_k =$

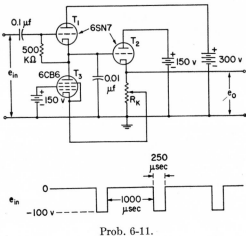

Prob. 6-11.

50,000 ohms and the tap is in the middle, sketch and label the steady-state output voltage for the input signal as shown.

6-12 (a) Explain the operation of the given sweep circuit. (b) Using

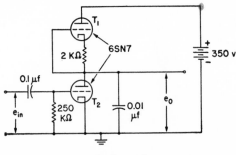

Prob. 6-12.

the input signal of problem 6-11, sketch and label the output voltage.

6-13 (a) Explain the operation of the given sweep circuit, noting any differences with respect to the circuit of Fig. 6-48. (b) Derive an expression

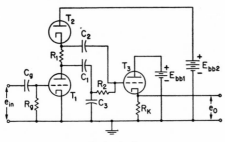

Prob. 6-13.

for the cathode voltage of T_3 for an input signal similar to that of problem 6-11.

6-14 Derive an expression for the plate voltage of T_1, using an input

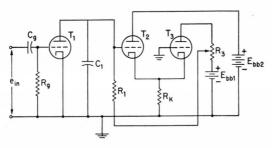

Prob. 6-14.

signal similar to that of problem 6-11.

6-15 The input signal of (a) is used to form a sweep voltage similar to (b). The wave form of (c) is used to blank out the cathode-ray tube between sweeps. It is desired to be able to select any 200-microsecond period during the sweep and present this short period over the same portion of the cathode ray tube that the original long sweep occupied. Such a sweep wave form might appear as (d) with the corresponding intensifying wave form of (e). In order that it be readily apparent which 200 microseconds of the long sweep is being presented, a sharp marker pulse could be added to the intensifying wave form. Devise a circuit to fit the above specifications which will supply all necessary sweep and intensifying wave forms. Only two controls need be in evidence: (1) a switch to select either

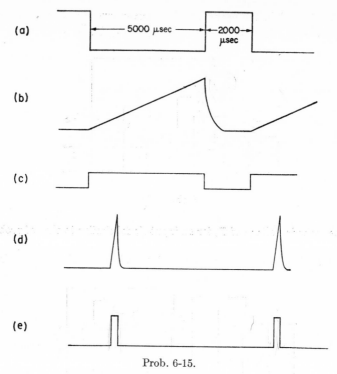

Prob. 6-15.

the long or the expanded sweep, (2) a control to select the position of the 200-microsecond sweep.

CHAPTER SEVEN

CIRCUITS FOR THE MAGNETIC DEFLECTION

OF CATHODE-RAY TUBES

It can be shown that under certain conditions, the spot deflection in a magnetic type cathode-ray tube is linear. That is, for a given tube, and for low values of magnetic flux density, the deflection is directly proportional to the flux density. The flux density in turn is a function of the current in the deflection coils. If these deflection coils are of the air-cored variety, or have iron cores operating in the linear range, the flux density will be proportional to the current. Thus the spot deflection can be made directly proportional to the current, and the system obtained is analogous to the electric deflection system where the spot deflection is directly proportional to the voltage between the deflection plates.

In the preceding chapter the general problem was to manufacture the necessary voltage wave forms to achieve a given spot deflection. The problem discussed in the present chapter, however, is the analogous case, that of devising current wave forms which will cause the desired deflection in a magnetic system. Several different circuits and methods for doing this will be discussed, with particular emphasis on one wave shape, the linear current sweep.

7-1 Deflection Coils

As discussed in the introduction, the purpose of the deflection coil is to develop a magnetic field, and thus a spot deflection, which is proportional to the current in the coil. The direction of this magnetic field must be at right angles to the direction of the electron stream in the tube. To move the spot from its undeflected position at the center of the screen to any other given point, it is necessary that the magnetic field be able to take any direction in the plane at right angles to the electron stream. As in the case for electric deflection, this can be done by making up the total magnetic field of two components, usually one horizontal and the other vertical. If the magnitude and direction of the horizontal and vertical components of the magnetic field are controlled, any desired total value may be obtained.

One form that the deflection coils may take is shown in Fig. 7-1.

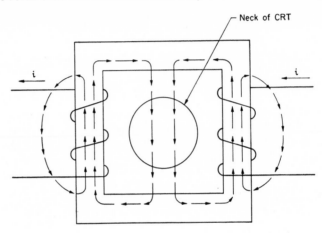

Fig. 7-1.   Deflection coil to provide horizontal deflection.

Only the coils which cause deflection in the horizontal direction are shown. The coils for vertical deflection would be wound about the upper and lower supports. These supports may be either iron or some nonmagnetic material. In the latter case, the system is the equivalent of two air-cored solenoids with the neck of the tube between them. For currents in the direction shown, the fluxes from each coil are additive in the neck of the tube, that is, the magnetic circuits of the two coils are in parallel. As far as the electric circuit is concerned, the two coils may be connected either in series or in parallel, with the series connection preferred. If the coils are connected in parallel, small differences in the low coil resistances may cause an unequal division of current.

The system of Fig. 7-1 is quite inefficient from one point of view, in that only a small fraction of the total flux through a coil passes through the neck of the tube.

Iron-cored coils are commonly used, but several restrictions must be imposed. The material comprising the coil should be of a low retentivity, or a spot deflection will be observed when there is no coil current. The material should be operated well down on the saturation curve in order that excessive distortion can be avoided. The core material should necessarily have low losses. This condition is improved by laminating the core to reduce eddy currents.

Another method of arranging the deflection coils is shown in Fig. 7-2. In this case nearly all the flux that passes through a coil also

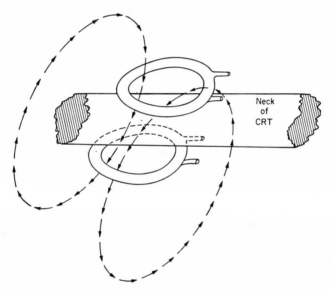

Fig. 7-2.   Alternative method of arranging deflection coils.

passes through the other coil and the neck of the tube. The magnetic circuits are thus in series, although the electric circuits may be either in series or in parallel as before. The reluctance of the circuit as shown in Fig. 7-2 is usually much higher than that of Fig. 7-1; therefore the number of ampere turns must also be higher in order to achieve the same deflection.

The use of deflection coils for magnetic tubes gives one possibility which cannot be practically achieved in electric deflection systems. That is, the whole deflection coil system may be rotated, allowing a corresponding movement of the total magnetic field and the trace on the screen.   In order to rotate the deflection coils it is best that

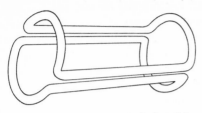

they have circular symmetry. The system of Fig. 7-2 can be formed into this shape as shown by Fig. 7-3.

Quite often it is advantageous to use a push-pull deflecting system.   In this case it is necessary to wind two coils on each leg of the core as shown in

Fig. 7-3.   Deflection coils designed for rotation.

Fig. 7-4.   If the currents in the two windings are of the same magnitude, there will be no net flux through the neck of the tube, and

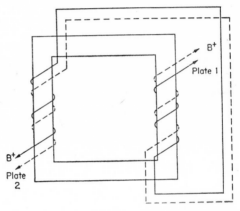

Fig. 7-4.   Connections for push-pull deflection.

the spot will be at its normal position at the center of the tube.   To move the spot, the current in one coil is increased and the current in the other is decreased.

Another factor that must be considered in the construction of deflection coils is the possibility of coupling between the coils for horizontal and vertical deflection.   This coupling will be minimized if each coil is placed symmetrically upon the core.   Every coil will then be linked by flux from each of the adjacent coils, but these fluxes will be equal in magnitude and of opposite polarity.

In an attempt to reduce the flux around the coils which does not contribute to the deflection, shields are sometimes added.   Addition of a shield also helps to prevent interaction of the fields from the deflection coils with magnetic fields of other sources.   A shield may also cause the effective value of the coil inductance to be lowered and the total losses to be increased.

The equivalent circuit of the deflection coil can, in general, be drawn as shown in the circuit of Fig. 7-5.   The inductance, the

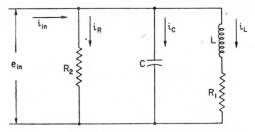

Fig. 7-5.   Equivalent circuit for deflection coil.

series resistance, and the distributed capacitance of the coil are indicated as L, R_1, and C, respectively.   The resistance R_2 is included to take care of the losses due to the iron core, if any, and the damping resistance which must usually be added.   If the coil is shielded, the inductance L can be considered to be the primary of a transformer.   The secondary of the transformer is effectively loaded by the losses in the shield.

7-2 General Considerations in Developing a Current Sweep

The form of the coil current is determined by the required spot deflection.   It is then necessary to find the input current and voltage to the complete deflection coil, that is, to find the input current and voltage to the circuit of Fig. 7-5 when the coil current is known. This can be done for any given current wave form, but the shape most commonly needed is the linear current sweep.   The following calculations are performed on this basis.

For a coil current of the form $i_L = kt$, the applied voltage must be

$$e_{in} = L\frac{di}{dt} + Ri \tag{7-1}$$

$$= kL + kR_1 t \tag{7-2}$$

The source which provides this voltage must be able to supply the following current:

$$i_{in} = i_R + i_L + i_C \tag{7-3}$$

Since $i_L = kt$,

$$i_R = \frac{e_{\text{in}}}{R_2} = \frac{kL}{R_2} + \frac{kR_1}{R_2}t \tag{7-4}$$

In finding the capacitor current, a small resistance is temporarily placed in series with C to simplify calculations. Assuming zero initial charge on the capacitor, the following equation can be written.

$$kL + kR_1t = R_x i_{c'} + \frac{1}{C} \int_0^t i_{c'} \, dt \tag{7-5}$$

where
$$i_C = \lim_{R_x \to 0} i_{c'} \tag{7-6}$$

Solving,

$$\left(D + \frac{1}{R_x C} \right) i_{c'} = \frac{kR_1}{R_x} \tag{7-7}$$

$$i_{c'} = A e^{-t/R_x C} + kR_1 C \tag{7-8}$$

From Eq. (7-5),

$$i_{c'}(0) = \frac{kL}{R_x} \tag{7-9}$$

Therefore
$$A = \frac{kL}{R_x} - kR_1 C \tag{7-10}$$

$$i_{c'} = \left(\frac{kL}{R_x} - kR_1 C \right) e^{-t/R_x C} + kR_1 C \tag{7-11}$$

$$i_C = \lim_{R_x \to 0} i_{c'} = kR_1 C + kL \lim_{R_x \to 0} \frac{1}{R_x} e^{-t/R_x C} \tag{7-12}$$

The second term in the above equation constitutes a current pulse which, in the limit as $R_x \to 0$ becomes infinite in magnitude but of zero duration. It is an impulse which delivers a finite and determinable amount of charge to the capacitor.

The total current will then be

$$i_{\text{in}} = \left(kR_1 C + \frac{kL}{R_2} \right) + \left(k + \frac{kR_1}{R_2} \right) t + kL \lim_{R_x \to 0} \frac{1}{R_x} e^{-t/R_x C} \tag{7-13}$$

The input current wave form is sketched in Fig. 7-6.

Since no physical source can supply the infinite current pulse indicated by Eq. (7-13), only an approximation to the linear sweep can be made. In the case of very slow sweeps or deflection coils with low values of distributed capacitance, the lack of the impulse term is not objectionable.

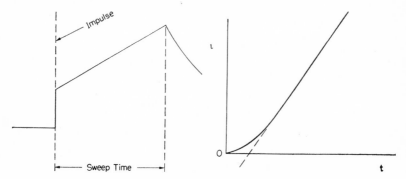

Fig. 7-6. Input current to deflection coil to obtain sawtooth magnetic field.

Fig. 7-7. Coil current if impulse term is not provided.

In general, if all current terms except the pulse term were provided, the current through the coil would not be linear. The exact form could be calculated, but the process would be rather cumbersome and will not be attempted here. The usual effect of ignoring the impulse term is to delay the start of the linear current in the inductor. The rigorous solution would show that the coil current could be oscillatory, critically damped, or overdamped; however, the parameters of the deflection coil are usually such that the system will be overdamped, giving a dip at the start of the sweep as shown in Fig. 7-7.

7-3 Exponential Current Through RL Circuit

The circuit shown in Fig. 7-8 is analogous to the resistive-capacitive charging system if the losses in the coil and the distributed capacitance of the coil are neglected. Instead of using the exponential increase in voltage across a capacitor in an RC circuit, the exponential current through an RL circuit is utilized. As before, only a small portion of the total exponential curve is used in order that the sweep current may be as linear as possible. All equations

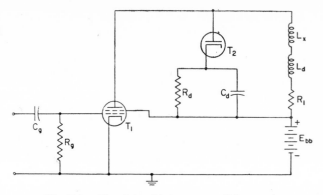

Fig. 7-8.   Circuit to obtain exponential current.

as derived in the preceding chapter with reference to the nonlinearity of an exponential sweep are applicable here.

Usually the inductance of the deflection coil will be too small to make the time constant sufficiently large.   A large series inductor L_x can then be added in series with the deflection coil to increase the time constant.   During the time that the current is increasing, the diode will not conduct, so T_2, R_d, and C_d need not be considered during the sweep.

The input signal will be a square wave with the positive peaks clamped at zero.   The amplitude must be great enough to place the negative peaks of the square wave below cutoff.   If tetrodes or power pentodes are used, the combination of a low plate voltage and zero grid voltage places operation below the knee of the plate characteristics.   The volt-ampere characteristic in this region is essentially linear, and has such a slope that the conducting resistance is very low, possibly in the neighborhood of 500 ohms.   At the instant that the grid voltage rises instantaneously from cutoff to zero, the plate voltage is also zero, since no current actually exists. The entire plate supply voltage appears as $L(di/dt)$ drop at this time.   The current then increases according to the expression

$$i_L = \frac{E_{bb}}{R}\,(1 - e^{-Rt/L}) \tag{7-14}$$

where R is the sum of the coil resistance and the effective tube resistance.   The initial rate of change of current is

$$\frac{di_L}{dt}\bigg|_{t=0} = \frac{E_{bb}}{R} \times \frac{R}{L} = \frac{E_{bb}}{L} \qquad (7\text{-}15)$$

For sweep lengths which are short with respect to the time constant, this slope will be nearly constant. For longer sweeps, exponential curvature becomes evident.

At the end of the sweep, T_1 is cut off by the applied square wave, leaving a large amount of energy stored in the inductors. If it is desired to start another sweep immediately, this energy must be dissipated as quickly as possible without allowing the plate voltage to rise to an excessive value. The induced voltage in L_d and L_x will now have a polarity which will cause the diode T_2 to conduct and place the R_dC_d circuit in parallel with the deflection coils. The capacitor is not necessary if there is a long time between sweeps, since the energy will be dissipated eventually in R_d with or without the capacitor. However, if the resistance is adjusted for a rapid discharge, a high plate voltage will result. The use of a capacitor allows a critically damped circuit, which is the best compromise between maximum induced voltage and minimum recovery time.

A typical set of wave forms for the circuit of Fig. 7-8 is shown in Fig. 7-9.

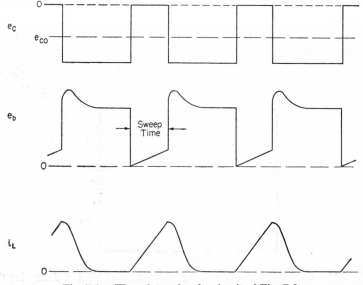

Fig. 7-9.   Wave forms for the circuit of Fig. 7-8.

7-4 Means of Linearizing the Exponential Current Sweep

When the tube T_1 of Fig. 7-8 is operating below the knee of the curves, the static plate resistance is very close to being linear, and the corresponding current is then approximately exponential in form. A different form for the tube resistance could perhaps produce a current which is more nearly linear.

Consider the circuit of Fig. 7-10 which is similar to that of Fig. 7-8.

From this figure,

$$i_L = \frac{E_{bb}}{R_L + \bar{r}_p}\left[1 - e^{-\frac{(R_L + \bar{r}_p)}{L}t}\right] \tag{7-16}$$

$$= E_{bb}\left[\frac{t}{L} - \frac{(R_L + \bar{r}_p)}{2!L^2}t^2 + \frac{(R_L + \bar{r}_p)^2}{3!L^3}t^3 + \cdots\right] \tag{7-17}$$

If the effective static resistance of the tube $\bar{r}_p$ were negative and equal in magnitude to R_L, the original slope E_{bb}/L would be maintained, making the current linear with time. The problem then becomes that of finding an input signal to the tube which will allow a linear current to flow. If this is done, the tube can be considered to be acting as a negative resistance. The circuit of Fig. 7-10 will be changed to that of Fig. 7-11. Starting at $t = 0$, a plate current of the form $i_L = i_b = kt$ will be assumed. The plate voltage is then fixed as

$$e_b = E_{bb} - kL - kR_Lt \tag{7-18}$$

In Fig. 7-12 the plate voltage and the plate current are plotted as

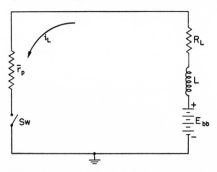

Fig. 7-10. Series RLC circuit used to demonstrate method of linearizing the current wave shape.

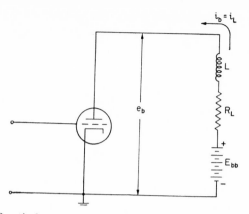

Fig. 7-11.   Practical means of obtaining the equivalent circuit of Fig. 7-10.

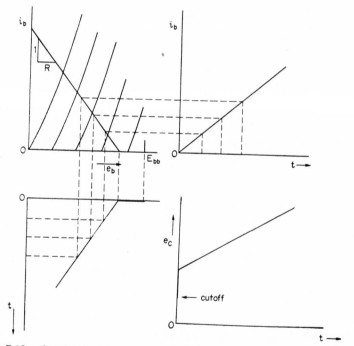

Fig. 7-12.   Graphical construction used to obtain the necessary grid voltage in the circuit of Fig. 7-11.

functions of time, adjacent to the plate characteristics of a triode. Practically, a pentode or tetrode with its higher current sensitivity would probably be used.

For every value of plate current there is a specified value for the plate voltage. Thus the tube must have a definite static resistance at every point. This resistance can be achieved by applying the correct voltage to the grid of the tube. By noting the grid voltage necessary to obtain several corresponding values of plate current and plate voltage, a plot of grid voltage versus time may be obtained. In the sketches of Fig. 7-12, the tube has been held below cutoff until the start of the sweep.

The projected line on the plate characteristics has a reciprocal slope equal to the negative of the external resistance, although the tube does not act like a negative resistance alone, but rather like the series combination of a negative resistance and a d-c source.

No mention has been made of the disposition of the energy which has been placed in the deflection coil during the sweep. This energy may be dissipated in a resistor as shown in Fig. 7-8, or it may be returned to the power source as demonstrated in Fig. 7-38.

7-5 Class A Amplifier as Current Sweep

As previously explained, the sweep current in Fig. 7-11 starts at zero and rises to some maximum value. By altering the input signal to this circuit, the starting current can be made some value other than zero, and class A operation is obtained. If this operation takes place in the linear region, equivalent dynamic circuits can be used.

The usual procedure in analyzing a class A amplifier is to take a given input voltage and calculate the resulting form and magnitude of the output voltage. For the circuits to be discussed, however, the only known quantity is the coil current. With this information the necessary input signal may be found. The next step would be to find a circuit which would provide the required driving voltage for the class A amplifier.

Consider the circuit of Fig. 7-13 and its dynamic equivalent in Fig. 7-14. The capacitance of the coil has been neglected, but a resistance has been placed in parallel with the coil. This resistance can be considered to be any damping resistance plus the equivalent resistance due to iron losses in the coil.

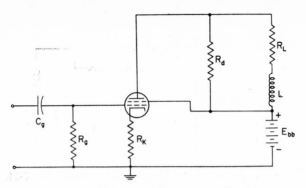

Fig. 7-13. Class A amplifier as current sweep.

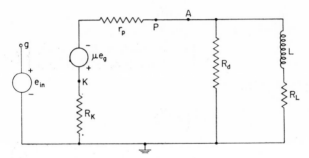

Fig. 7-14. Dynamic equivalent for the circuit of Fig. 7-11.

An equivalent for the circuit to the left of point A in Fig. 7-14 can be obtained by finding the open-circuit voltage and the resistance looking back into the system. The open-circuit voltage is

$$(e_A)_{oc} = \mu e_{in} \qquad (7\text{-}19)$$

The short-circuit current is

$$(i_A)_{sc} = \frac{\mu e_{in}}{r_p + R_k(1 + \mu)} \qquad (7\text{-}20)$$

Therefore the resistance looking back from point A is

$$R_A = r_p + R_k(1 + \mu) \qquad (7\text{-}21)$$

The fraction $R_d/[R_d + r_p + R_k(1 + \mu)]$ of μe_{in} is applied to the parallel combination of R_d and R_A, which in turn is in series with L

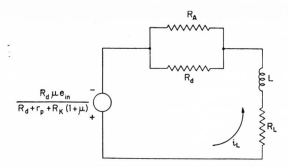

Fig. 7-15.   Simplified circuit equivalent to that of Fig. 7-14.

and R_L as shown in Fig. 7-15.   Thus

$$\frac{R_d}{R_d + r_p + R_k(1 + \mu)}\, \mu e_{\text{in}} = L\frac{di_L}{dt}$$
$$+ \left\{ R_L + \frac{R_d[r_p + R_k(1 + \mu)]}{R_d + r_p + R_k(1 + \mu)} \right\} i_L \quad (7\text{-}22)$$

Solving for e_{in} gives

$$e_{\text{in}} = \frac{R_d + r_p + R_k(1 + \mu)}{\mu R_d} \left(L\frac{di_L}{dt} \right.$$
$$\left. + \left\{ R_L + \frac{R_d[r_p + R_k(1 + \mu)]}{R_d + r_p + R_k(1 + \mu)} \right\} i_L \right) \quad (7\text{-}23)$$

If i_L is to be linear, that is, if $i_L = kt$,

$$e_{\text{in}} = \frac{kL}{\mu R_d}[R_d + r_p + R_k(1 + \mu)]$$
$$+ \frac{k}{\mu R_d}[R_k(1 + \mu)(R_L + R_d) + r_p(R_d + R_L) + R_dR_L]t \quad (7\text{-}24)$$

In some cases, the coil resistance might be small as compared to the output resistance of the system.   Then

$$e_{\text{in}} = \frac{kL}{\mu R_d}[R_d + r_p + R_k(1 + \mu)] + \frac{k}{\mu}[r_p + R_k(1 + \mu)]t \quad (7\text{-}25)$$

If R_k is by-passed with a sufficiently large capacitor, or if R_k is zero and the bias is obtained from another source,

$$e_{\text{in}} = \frac{kL}{\mu R_d}(R_d + r_p) + \frac{r_p k}{\mu} t \quad (7\text{-}26)$$

These simplifications have changed only the magnitude and not the general shape of the required input signal, and like the output voltage applied to the deflection coil, the input signal is always of the form

$$e_{in} = k_1 + k_2 t \qquad (7\text{-}27)$$

It is quite possible to put the deflection coil in the cathode circuit of a class A amplifier as shown in Fig. 7-16a. No damping resist-

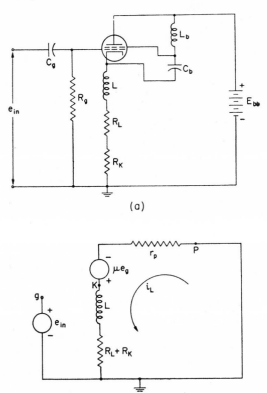

(a)

(b)

Fig. 7-16. (a) Cathode follower as current sweep. (b) Dynamic equivalent for the circuit of (a).

ance will usually be required, since the output resistance of the cathode circuit is much lower than the plate output resistance. The equivalent circuit is shown in Fig. 7-16b. The inductor L_b and the capacitor C_b allow the screen to be held at a high positive, but constant, potential with respect to the cathode.   From Fig. 7-16b,

$$\mu e_g = L \frac{di_L}{dt} + i_L(r_p + R_L + R_k) \tag{7-28}$$

But

$$e_g = e_{in} - \left[L \frac{di_L}{dt} + (R_L + R_k)i_L \right] \tag{7-29}$$

Then

$$e_{in} = \frac{1 + \mu}{\mu} \left[L \frac{di_L}{dt} + \left(R_L + R_k + \frac{r_p}{1 + \mu} \right) i_L \right] \tag{7-30}$$

If the current is to be linear during the sweep time, that is, $i_L = kt$

$$e_{in} = \frac{1 + \mu}{\mu} \left[kL + \left(R_L + R_k + \frac{r_p}{1 + \mu} \right) kt \right] \tag{7-31}$$

7-6 Formation of Trapezoidal Driving Voltage

In the preceding section two circuits which could produce a linear sweep current in a deflection coil were discussed.   However, each of these circuits must be driven by a trapezoidal signal of particular magnitude and shape.

Since the circuits to be driven consist of class A amplifiers operating in the negative grid region, the driving source does not have to supply any appreciable current.

A circuit to provide a trapezoidal voltage may be found by referring to Figs. 2-5 and 2-7.   In general form the circuit of Fig. 2-5 is reproduced in Fig. 7-17.

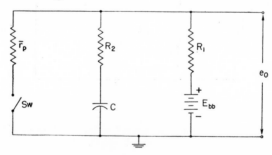

Fig. 7-17.   Circuit to produce trapezoidal voltage.

Assume that the switch is to open periodically for a period of time equal to Δt_1, and to close for a period Δt_2.   The steady-state output voltage can be sketched in general form as shown in Fig. 7-18.   If the switch were to stay open for a long time, the output voltage would rise to a value of E_{1m}, while if it were to stay closed indefinitely, the output would drop to E_{2m}.

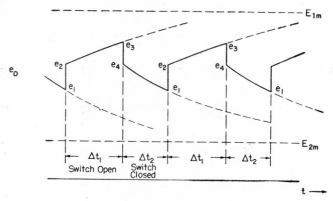

Fig. 7-18.   Wave forms for the circuit of Fig. 7-17.

To evaluate e_1, e_2, e_3, and e_4 the following equations may be written:

$$e_1 = e_4 + (E_{2m} - e_4)(1 - e^{-\Delta t_2/R_A C}) \tag{7-32}$$

$$e_3 = e_2 + (E_{1m} - e_2)(1 - e^{-\Delta t_1/R_B C}) \tag{7-33}$$

$$e_1 = \frac{\bar{r}_p}{\bar{r}_p + R_1 R_2/(R_1 + R_2)} \, e_2 \tag{7-34}$$

$$e_4 = \frac{\bar{r}_p}{\bar{r}_p + R_1 R_2/(R_1 + R_2)} \, e_3 \tag{7-35}$$

where

$$R_A = \frac{\bar{r}_p R_1}{\bar{r}_p + R_1} + R_2 \tag{7-36}$$

$$R_B = R_1 + R_2 \tag{7-37}$$

$$E_{1m} = E_{bb} \tag{7-38}$$

$$E_{2m} = \frac{\bar{r}_p}{R_1 + \bar{r}_p} \, E_{bb} \tag{7-39}$$

For greater accuracy, the magnitude of E_{2m} may be determined from the plate characteristics.

The solutions of the previous equations are rather unwieldy, but are of sufficient importance to record here. For simplicity in writing, let

$$a_1 = 1 - e^{-\Delta t_2/R_A C} \qquad (a)$$

$$a_2 = 1 - e^{-\Delta t_1/R_B C} \qquad (b) \qquad (7\text{-}40)$$

$$a_3 = \frac{\bar{r}_p}{\bar{r}_p + R_1 R_2/(R_1 + R_2)} \qquad (c)$$

Then

$$e_1 = \frac{a_1 E_{2m} - a_2 a_3 (a_1 - 1) E_{1m}}{[1 - (a_1 - 1)(a_2 - 1)]} \qquad (7\text{-}41)$$

$$e_2 = \frac{a_1 E_{2m} - a_2 a_3 (a_1 - 1) E_{1m}}{a_3 [1 - (a_1 - 1)(a_2 - 1)]} \qquad (7\text{-}42)$$

$$e_3 = \frac{a_2 a_3 E_{1m} - a_1 (a_2 - 1) E_{2m}}{a_3 [1 - (a_1 - 1)(a_2 - 1)]} \qquad (7\text{-}43)$$

$$e_4 = \frac{a_2 a_3 E_{1m} - a_1 (a_2 - 1) E_{2m}}{[1 - (a_1 - 1)(a_2 - 1)]} \qquad (7\text{-}44)$$

As specified by Eq. (7-27), the driving signal to the sawtooth current generator must be of the form

$$e_{\text{in}} = k_1 + k_2 t \qquad (7\text{-}45)$$

The term k_1 is the positive jump voltage, or in terms of Fig. 7-18,

$$\text{Jump} = k_1 = e_2 - e_1 \qquad (7\text{-}46)$$

$$= \frac{(1 - a_3)[a_1 E_{2m} - a_2 a_3 (a_1 - 1) E_{1m}]}{a_3 [1 - (a_1 - 1)(a_2 - 1)]} \qquad (7\text{-}47)$$

The sweep takes place during the Δt_1 time, and the driving signal should have a constant slope of k_2 volts per second during this time. The output voltage from the circuit of Fig. 7-17 has an exponential form during the sweep time, but if the sweep length is short as compared with the charging time constant, the resulting voltage is satisfactory. Expressed mathematically,

$$R_B C \gg \Delta t_1$$

or

$$(R_1 + R_2)C \gg \Delta t_1 \qquad (7\text{-}48)$$

If the condition of Eq. (7-48) is satisfied,

$$1 - e^{-\Delta t_1/R_B C} \approx \frac{\Delta t_1}{R_B C} \qquad (7\text{-}49)$$

Using Eqs. (7-49) and (7-33), the slope of the sweep can be written as

$$\text{Slope} = k_2 = \frac{E_{1m} - e_2}{R_B C} \tag{7-50}$$

$$= \frac{a_1(a_3 E_{1m} - E_{2m})}{a_3 R_B C[1 - (a_1 - 1)(a_2 - 1)]} \tag{7-51}$$

It has been shown that the circuit of Fig. 7-17 will supply a trapezoidal voltage. This circuit can be obtained practically by substituting a clamped triode in place of the resistor $\bar{r}_p$ and the switch, with the triode being driven by a square wave. In the preceding equations $\bar{r}_p$, the static resistance of the triode at zero grid voltage, has been assumed to be a constant.

Both Eqs. (7-47) and (7-51) must be satisfied if a linear current is to be obtained in the deflection coil. For example, if the trapezoidal generator is being used to drive the circuit of Fig. 7-13, as shown in Fig. 7-19, the following relationships must exist.

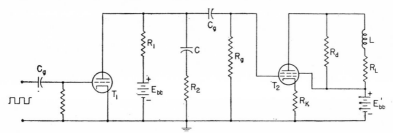

Fig. 7-19.   Complete sawtooth current generator

$$\frac{kL}{\mu R_d}[R_d + r_p + R_k(1 + \mu)] = \frac{(1 - a_3)[a_1 E_{2m} - a_2 a_3(a_1 - 1)E_{1m}]}{a_3[1 - (a_1 - 1)(a_2 - 1)]} \tag{7-52}$$

$$\frac{k}{\mu}[r_p + R_k(1 + \mu)] = \frac{a_1(a_3 E_{1m} - E_{2m})}{a_3 R_B C[1 - (a_1 - 1)(a_2 - 1)]} \tag{7-53}$$

Care must be taken to clearly differentiate between r_p and $\bar{r}_p$. The resistance r_p is the dynamic resistance of the sawtooth current amplifier, while $\bar{r}_p$ is the static conducting resistance of the tube in the trapezoidal generator.

In many cases, the time between successive current sweeps is long as compared to the discharge time constant, that is,

$$R_A C < \Delta t_2 \tag{7-54}$$

The expressions for the jump and sweep voltages become much simplified under these conditions and are given in Eqs. (7-55) and (7-56), respectively.

$$\text{Jump} = \frac{R_1 R_2 E_{bb}}{(R_1 + R_2)(R_1 + \bar{r}_p)} \tag{7-55}$$

$$\text{Slope} = \frac{R_1^2 E_{bb}}{C(R_1 + R_2)(R_1 + \bar{r}_p)} \tag{7-56}$$

A sketch of the wave forms for the circuit of Fig. 7-19 under the condition of Eq. (7-54) is shown in Fig. 7-20.

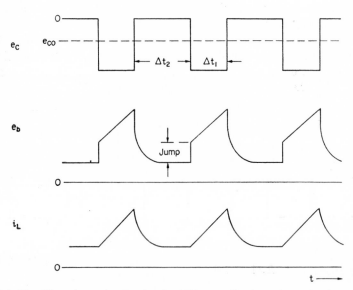

Fig. 7-20.   Wave forms for the circuit of Fig. 7-19 if a long time exists between successive sweeps.

7-7 Modification of Trapezoidal Generator and Current Sweep Generator

In some cases, particularly those of long sweep duration, the exponential rise in the output voltage of the circuit of Fig. 7-17 is not sufficiently linear.   It is quite possible to use a bootstrap system to improve the linearity as discussed in Sec. 6-16, if one important change is realized.   In the bootstrap systems already treated, the output voltage was added to the supply voltage in order to make the charging current a constant.   In the present system a voltage which is proportional to the output current, but not the output voltage, is brought back and added to the supply voltage.   This is necessary because the output voltage consists of a jump and a slope, while the output current is composed of the slope alone.   A circuit is shown in Fig. 7-21.

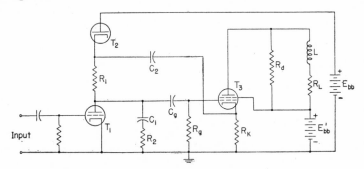

Fig. 7-21.   Use of bootstrap system to linearize current sweep.

This circuit is similar to that of Fig. 6-50 except for the source of the feedback voltage.   If the total resistance is taken as the sum of R_1 and R_2, Eq. (6-64) may be used directly to determine the form of the slope voltage.

There is a coupling circuit composed of R_g and C_g in the grid circuit of T_3.   Thus the steady-state voltage at point A has a zero average value.   Bias for T_3 is provided by R_k but could, if necessary, be partially supplied by a negative d-c source in series with R_g.   If the time between current sweeps is changed to a new value, the steady-state voltage will again be such that it has no average value.   However, the potential with respect to ground of any given point on the wave form at A will have changed, since the general shape of the wave form has been altered.   Thus if the sweep length is held constant and the sweep frequency is changed, the starting current in the coil will be changed, along with the starting point of the trace on the screen.   A centering system, consisting of a means of placing a d-c control current in the deflection coil, can be used to recenter the trace.   A more satisfactory method would be to clamp some point of the voltage wave form driving T_3 at a given level.   The negative peaks of the trapezoidal wave form can be clamped at a negative bias potential by replacing R_g with

the network shown in Fig. 7-22.   If the most negative portion of
the driving wave form is fixed in potential, regardless of the sweep

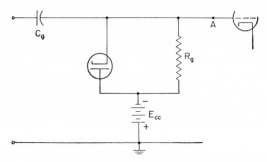

Fig. 7-22.   Use of clamping to hold the trapezoidal wave form at a fixed level
independent of duty cycle.

frequency, the starting current and the starting position of the
trace are also fixed.   Variation of E_{cc} gives a centering control.

7-8 Methods of Overcoming Distributed Capacitance of Deflection Coils

The past few sections have neglected the fact that the deflection
coil may have appreciable distributed capacitance.   For very slow
sweeps, the effect of this capacitance may not be noticeable, but
for faster systems the delay at the start of the sweep may be quite
pronounced.   As shown in Sec. 7-2, this delay can be eliminated by
supplying the pulse term and the constant term in the total current
expression.   The pulse term offers the most difficulty, since it is of
negligible width and infinite magnitude.   It can, however, be
approximated by a small finite pulse.   Consider the circuit of Fig.
7-23.   The circuit is driven by a square wave with the positive
peaks clamped at zero.   The square wave is of sufficient magnitude
to cut off the tube during the negative part of the cycle.   An
inverted but amplified form of the input signal will appear at the
plate of the tube, and will be differentiated by the very short time
constant circuit $R_4 C_2$.   However, the plate wave form will not be a
perfect square wave due to the finite length of time required to
charge C_2.   When the narrow peaks of voltage across R_4 are added
to the trapezoidal wave form, small pulses of current occur in the
plate circuit of the sawtooth current generator.   If these current
pulses are of the correct size they will not contribute appreciably to

the coil current, but will, at the start of the sweep, help to charge the distributed capacitance of the coil. The voltage pulses from the circuit of Fig. 7-23 can be added to the trapezoidal wave form in

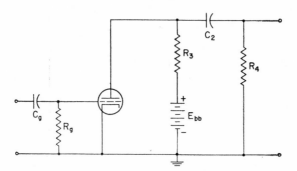

Fig. 7-23. Circuit to produce an approximate impulse for the current sweep system.

several different ways. For example, the two wave forms can be applied to the grid of two amplifiers which have a common load resistor. A second method is to return R_4 not to ground, but to the plate of the trapezoidal generator, causing both voltages to appear in the output. Such a circuit is shown in Fig. 7-24. Typical wave forms for this circuit are shown in Fig. 7-25.

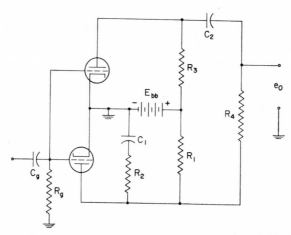

Fig. 7-24. Circuit to produce both the trapezoidal and impulse wave form.

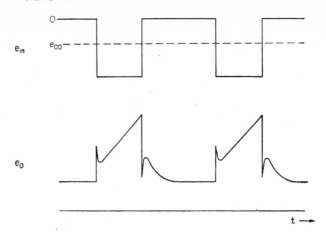

Fig. 7-25.   Wave forms for the circuit of Fig. 7-24.

Not only does the circuit of Fig. 7-24 add a positive "spike" at the start of the trapezoidal voltage, but it also places a negative pulse at the end.   This negative pulse can be eliminated by use of a circuit such as that of Fig. 7-26.

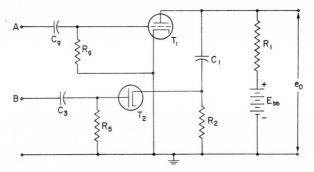

Fig. 7-26.   Circuit to produce a voltage wave form similar to that of Fig. 7-25 but without the negative pulse.

To initiate the sweep, a negative voltage is used to cut off the triode as in the previous case, while a positive square wave is applied to point B.   The rising voltage at B is differentiated by C_3 and R_5. The diode will then drive a positive pulse of current through R_2. Thus the output voltage will have a positive pulse at the start of the trapezoid, but will not have a negative pulse at the end, since the diode cannot conduct in both directions.

Another method of effectively adding a pulse to the leading edge of the trapezoidal wave form is to place a small capacitor across the cathode resistor of the sawtooth current amplifier tube.   When the initial jump of the trapezoidal wave form is applied between grid and ground, the full change appears between grid and cathode, since the cathode capacitor cannot change potential instantaneously. However, the capacitor will charge rapidly and reduce the grid-cathode voltage.   In effect, the system has negative current feedback at all times except when instantaneous changes in the input signal occur.

7-9 Feedback Sweep Systems

A sawtooth voltage of small amplitude may be easily formed, but the analogous problem of forming a sawtooth of current has been seen to be more difficult.   If a small sawtooth of voltage is amplified and then impressed across the series combination of a deflection coil and a resistor, a sawtooth current will not result.   However, if a voltage proportional to the current is fed back to the input of the amplifier, the tendency is to make the output current similar to the driving voltage.   Consider the generalized system shown in Fig. 7-27.

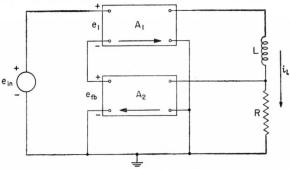

Fig. 7-27.   Generalized feedback system to produce a sawtooth current.

The input signal e_{in} is applied to a class A amplifier having a gain of A_1.   Part of the output voltage $i_L R$ is amplified by an amount A_2 and fed back to the input of the first amplifier.   From Fig. 7-27,

$$A_1 e_1 = L \frac{di_L}{dt} + R i_L \qquad (7\text{-}57)$$

but
$$e_1 = e_{\text{in}} - e_{fb} = e_{\text{in}} - A_2 R i_L \tag{7-58}$$

Substituting into Eq. (7-57) and rearranging,

$$\frac{di_L}{dt} + \frac{R}{L}(1 + A_1 A_2) i_L = \frac{A_1 e_{\text{in}}}{L} \tag{7-59}$$

If the driving voltage is a sawtooth, that is

$$e_{\text{in}} = kt \tag{7-60}$$

the solution of Eq. (7-59) is

$$i_L = Be^{-(R/L)(1+A_1A_2)} + \frac{A_1(k/L)}{(R/L)^2(1 + A_1 A_2)^2}$$
$$+ \frac{A_1(k/L)}{(R/L)(1 + A_1 A_2)}\, t \tag{7-61}$$

The gain of the first amplifier can be made very large, in which case i_L becomes

$$i_L = \frac{k}{RA_2}\, t \tag{7-62}$$

Typical results for the generalized system are shown in Fig. 7-28.

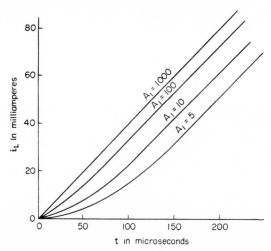

Fig. 7-28.   Current wave form for the circuit of Fig. 7-27.

A practical circuit is shown in Fig. 7-29. This circuit differs from the generalized case in that the feedback voltage is not ampli-

fied.   A simple way of amplifying the feedback voltage is shown in
Fig. 7-30.

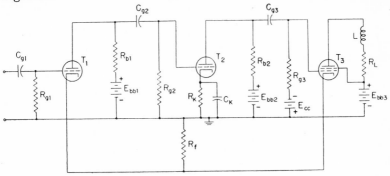

Fig. 7-29.   Circuit similar to that indicated in Fig. 7-27 except that the feedback
voltage is not amplified.

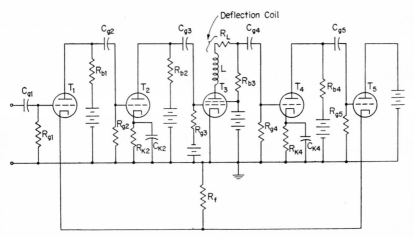

Fig. 7-30.   Circuit similar to that indicated in Fig. 7-27.   Feedback voltage is
amplified.

7-10 Blocking Grid Oscillator

The blocking grid oscillator is a type of relaxation oscillator which
is quite extensively used for the production of short voltage or current pulses.   Fundamentally it bears no relationship to a magnetic
sweep circuit, but since it is commonly used in conjunction with
various types of sweep circuits, it will be discussed in this chapter.

A complete mathematical analysis would be extremely complicated and will not be attempted here. This complexity is due to the fact that both the transformer and the tube used in the circuit may be operated under extreme nonlinear conditions. An approximate solution is given in *Principles of Radar*,[1] with a more comprehensive treatment given by Benjamin.[2]

One of the basic circuits is shown in Fig. 7-31. Assume that the

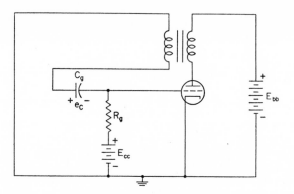

Fig. 7-31. Blocking oscillator.

capacitor C_g has somehow accumulated a charge of the polarity shown, and of sufficient magnitude to cut off the tube. The capacitor will then discharge through R_g and the secondary of the transformer. Eventually the grid voltage will reach the cutoff value, and a small plate current will result. A plate current increasing from zero to some very small value is indicative of an $L(di/dt)$ drop in the primary of the transformer, with a corresponding induced voltage in the secondary. The windings of the transformer must be connected in such a way that the induced voltage in the secondary will cause the grid to become more positive. This causes a further increase in plate current, with corresponding increases in grid voltage. Plate current and grid voltage will continue to increase very rapidly until the grid voltage reaches a small positive value. The time constant of the grid circuit is now relatively small, and the capacitor C_g will charge rapidly. This regenerative process may be terminated in several ways depending

[1] See reference 16 at end of chapter.
[2] See reference 3 at end of chapter.

upon the characteristics of the tube, the transformer, and the size of C_g.

When the grid of the tube takes current, the input resistance is decreased, causing heavy loading of the plate circuit. If the current demand of the grid circuit exceeds the plate current capabilities of the tube (the turns ratio of the transformer being considered), the peak plate current has been reached. For 6J5 tubes this peak plate current may approach 500 to 600 milliamperes.

A small capacitor in the grid circuit can cause a large capacitor voltage to be developed during the pulse. If this voltage starts to increase faster than the transformer voltage, the grid potential will be decreased. A decrease in the grid voltage causes a decrease in the plate current. This produces a further decrease in grid voltage, and reverse cumulative action takes place which can eventually cut off the tube. With the tube at cutoff, there can still be appreciable energy stored in C_g and the distributed capacitance of the transformer. There can also be some energy due to the capacitor discharge current in the transformer inductance.

A large capacitor in the grid circuit will not give sufficient voltage to cause the grid voltage to be limited. In this case, conduction will continue until an equilibrium condition is reached. As the equilibrium condition is approached, the induced voltage approaches zero, causing the grid voltage to decrease with resulting cumulative action as in the previous case.

When the tube is cut off, the RLC circuit consisting of the windings, the distributed capacitance, and the grid resistance may be oscillatory, critically damped, or overdamped. Since C_g acquired a large negative charge while the grid was positive and taking current, a second transient superimposed upon the original exponential voltage will take place far below the cutoff potential. After this secondary transient has been damped out, the grid voltage will move exponentially back toward E_{cc}. When the grid voltage reaches cutoff, the entire cycle of operation is repeated.

The shape and the magnitude of the current pulses are nearly independent of the time between pulses and are a very complicated function of the circuit parameters. The duration of the pulse can be made less than one microsecond. Under these conditions, the average plate current is linearly dependent upon the frequency.

If the charge accumulated by C_g during the pulse makes the grid voltage equal to E_m at the end of the pulse, the grid voltage between pulses will be as indicated by Fig. 7-32. During the time Δt_2 the

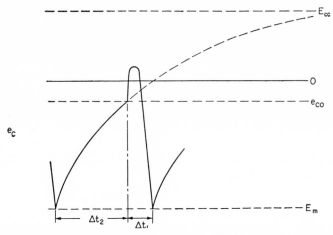

Fig. 7-32. Approximate grid wave forms for the blocking oscillator of Fig. 7-31.

grid voltage may be expressed as

$$e_c = E_m + (E_{cc} - E_m)(1 - e^{-t/R_g C_g}) \tag{7-63}$$

Substituting $e_c = e_{co}$ at $t = \Delta t_2$, and rearranging gives

$$\Delta t_2 = R_g C_g \ln \frac{E_{cc} - E_m}{E_{cc} - e_{co}} \tag{7-64}$$

If the pulse time is assumed constant and equal to Δt_1, the frequency will be

$$f = \frac{1}{\Delta t_1 + R_g C_g \ln (E_{cc} - E_m)/(E_{cc} - e_{co})} \tag{7-65}$$

It must be remembered that E_m and e_{co} are always negative quantities, thus negative numbers will be substituted for these terms in Eq. (7-65).

The frequency can be controlled by varying any of several parameters. A change in the time constant will change the frequency. This can best be done by altering R_g, since a change in C_g will affect more than one term in Eq. (7-65). The pulse shape, and thus Δt_1, will be affected if C_g is made sufficiently small, since the capacitor will then build up its voltage very rapidly. When C_g is increased, the time constant is increased, but the magnitude of E_m is decreased, so the denominator of Eq. (7-65) is not changed very much. A good way of changing the frequency uses the variation of the bias voltage. The fact that the grid is biased so that it tends to approach a positive voltage is not cause for alarm, since it never reaches the positive potential. The subject of positive grid return is treated in greater detail in Sec. 9-3. Typical wave forms for the blocking oscillator of Fig. 7-31 are shown in Fig. 7-33.

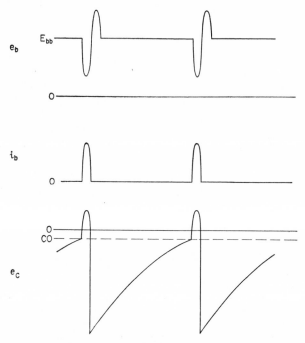

Fig. 7-33.   Approximate wave forms for the blocking oscillator of Fig. 7-31.

The blocking oscillator can operate as a free-running device, although it has perhaps its greatest value as a synchronized oscillator. The situation here is similar to the problem discussed in Sec. 6-10. Although it is possible to slow down a free-running blocking oscillator by application of a synchronizing signal, the usual, and more stable, procedure is to speed it up. The purpose of the synchronizing signal is then to bring the grid potential to the cutoff value at a time prior to its normal arrival.

One method by which the controlling signal can be introduced into the blocking oscillator is shown in Fig. 7-34.   This method is called

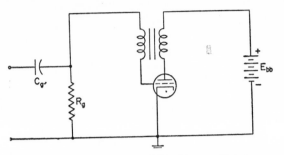

Fig. 7-34.   Synchronized blocking oscillator. .

series triggering, since the control signal is in series with the transformer.   The driving source must have a low impedance, since the feedback voltage is impressed across the series combination of the driver output impedance and the conducting grid resistance.

To produce *parallel triggering*, the input signal can be introduced directly on the plate of the tube, parallel with the transformer. Care must be taken to provide a pulse of such polarity that it will appear positive on the grid.

In the circuit of Fig. 7-34, a bias battery can be placed in series with R_g so that the tube will be normally at cutoff.   A pulse input to the circuit will then cause the system to go through one cycle of operation.

7-11 Application of Blocking Grid Oscillators to Complete Magnetic Sweep Systems

Consider the circuit of Fig. 7-35.   The tube T_1 along with its associated circuit is acting as a blocking grid oscillator as previously discussed.   If T_1 and T_2 are similar tubes, both will at the same time be either conducting or cut off, since the grid voltage will be of sufficient magnitude to allow for differences in the plate voltages. The second tube and its associated circuit will thus act as a trapezoidal generator.   Typical wave forms are shown in Fig. 7-36.   The resistance R_g is made variable in order to facilitate the synchronization of the oscillator.   In a commercial television receiver, R_g might be called the *hold* control.   The two resistors in the plate circuit of

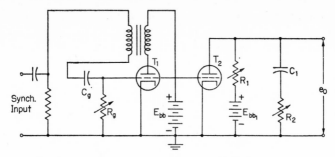

Fig. 7-35. Blocking oscillator used to operate trapezoidal voltage generator.

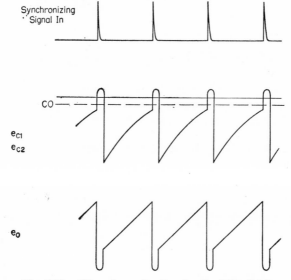

Fig. 7-36. Wave forms for the circuit of Fig. 7-35.

T_2 may also be made variable. The resistor R_1 will have the most effect on the amplitude of the linear portion of the trapezoidal wave form and thus may be called the *height* or *amplitude* control. The same effect can be achieved by using a potentiometer to control the effective plate supply voltage to T_2.

The resistance R_2 is sometimes called a *peaking* control since it will have its greatest effect upon the magnitude of the jump in the trapezoidal signal.

Actually it is not necessary to use both T_1 and T_2 since one tube will suffice. If T_2 were omitted, the charging capacitor could be made to discharge directly through the transformer into T_1. The wave forms would be similar to those of Fig. 7-36. A circuit is shown in Fig. 7-37. This circuit is a typical vertical deflection

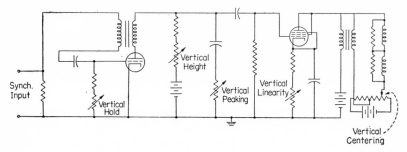

Fig. 7-37.   Vertical sweep system for television receiver.

system for a television receiver.   Several items not previously discussed have been included in this circuit.   For one thing, the cathode resistance of the sawtooth current generator has been made variable.   A change in this resistance will change the operating point of the tube, and thus the linearity of operation.   Since a change in the operating point may cause a change in the gain, the height control and the linearity control will not be independent.

In order to achieve higher deflection currents as well as a simple means of centering, a deflection transformer is often used.   The centering system need be only a center-tapped potentiometer, such that current can be sent either way through the deflection coils. Damping can usually be accomplished by shunting a resistor across the deflection coils.

The problem of damping in the horizontal deflection system of a television receiver is usually more involved than that for the vertical system.   The Federal Communications Commission regulations specify that the beam shall be blanked for 1250 microseconds while the spot is brought from the bottom of the screen back to the top. In a 525-line system, there are 525 horizontal sweeps every 1/30 second, or 15,750 horizontal sweeps per second.   At the same time there are only 60 vertical sweeps per second.   The time allowed for the vertical retrace is approximately the length of 20 complete horizontal sweeps.   Since the induced voltages in the transformer and deflection coils are proportional to the rate of change of current, the horizontal system will be in general more complicated than the vertical system.

Sometimes the faster sweep speeds of the horizontal system result in a simpler trapezoidal generator.   As the sweep speed is increased, the deflection coil inductance must decrease.   This necessitates larger output tubes and/or higher turns ratios in the transformer. The inductance may become so small that the $L(di/dt)$ term is small with respect to the Ri term, where R is the sum of the coil resistance, the transformer resistance, and the dynamic plate resistance.   Then the jump voltage component may be neglected, and only a sawtooth voltage need be applied to the sweep amplifier.

Since the retrace time of the horizontal system is short, very high potentials will be induced in the transformer and deflection coils.   These high potentials, if properly treated, may be very useful in supplying the accelerating potential needed for the cathode-ray tube.   Consider the horizontal deflection circuit and power supply of Fig. 7-38.

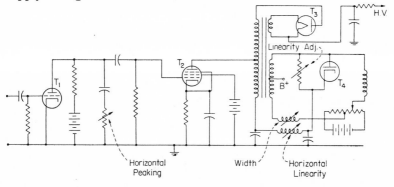

Fig. 7-38.   Horizontal sweep system and high voltage power supply for television receiver.

A complete horizontal scanning cycle must occur in 1/15,750 second, or 63.5 microseconds, of which the tube is blanked for approximately 11 microseconds.   During this 11 microseconds the horizontal retrace must take place.   The fastest possible retrace time is determined by the resonant frequency of the system; therefore the resonant frequency cannot be much less than 75 kilocycles per second.

When the input voltage to the sweep amplifier T_2 suddenly drops at the end of the sweep, the induced voltage is such as to keep the damping tube T_4 from conducting. Therefore there is a strong oscillation for half a cycle. At the end of this time, the current is maximum and is reversed in direction from the original value so the damping tube conducts. The retrace has now been completed, and the damping tube loads the system so heavily that no further oscillations are possible. Not only does the damping tube prevent any further oscillations, but it acts as a rectifier and puts energy into the LC pi filter. The effective plate supply voltage is then higher than the supply voltage. The inductance in this filter is variable, and thus by changing the ripple and supply voltages slightly, the characteristics of the output tube can be affected. If the energy in the deflection coils at the end of the sweep were dissipated in a resistor, the total power delivered to the system would be much greater than when a portion of the power is returned to the power supply.

The control on the variable inductance can be labeled *horizontal linearity*. The *horizontal width* control consists of an inductance shunted across the transformer. Changes in this shunt inductance will change the sweep current. Changing the *peaking* control will change the jump and slope voltages that are applied to the sweep amplifier. This control will not be independent with respect to the *horizontal width* control, since both affect the sweep length.

The high-voltage power supply using the rectifier T_3 derives its voltage from a winding on the deflection transformer. The pulse of extremely high voltage during the retrace is rectified by the pi RC combination. Due to the high frequency, the capacitor need not be very large. A 1-megohm, 500-micromicrofarad combination is usually quite satisfactory.

7-12 Miscellaneous Magnetic Tube Presentations

Generally speaking, any display that can be obtained on an electrostatic tube by application of a particular voltage can be obtained on a magnetic type tube by application of a similar deflection current. There are, however, some different possibilities available for magnetic type tubes.

For example, a plan-position-indicator form of display can be obtained by first providing a sweep from the center to the edge of the screen, and then rotating the whole set of deflecting coils mechanically around the neck of the tube.

A more elegant method of obtaining this display is similar to that used in the electric case. If the currents in the horizontal and vertical deflection coils are sinusoidal in form, and 90° apart in time, a circular trace will result. If the radius of the circle is changed as a linear function of time, and at a rate very large with respect to the sine wave frequency, a PPI type display will be obtained. Thus two sets of modulated current sawtooths are needed, the modulation being two sine waves 90° out of phase. If the radius of the circle is changed at a rate which is low compared to the sine wave frequency, spirals will result.

The system of Fig. 7-39 will provide the necessary rotating mag-

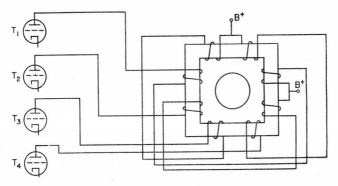

Fig. 7-39.   System to obtain circular sweep.

netic field. The tubes T_1, T_2, T_3, and T_4 are class A amplifiers which are to be driven by the trapezoidal wave form. The trapezoidal wave forms on all grids must start and stop together, but their sinusoidal envelopes must be 90° out of phase from tube to tube. It is possible to achieve the modulation by simultaneous variation of the screen voltages of the amplifiers, but this method may not provide linear modulation.

Another possibility of providing the modulated trapezoidal signal is by use of a rotary transformer as shown in Fig. 7-40. The input trapezoidal signal is fed to the rotor through slip rings, and the rotor is then rotated mechanically. This method is not suitable for accurate systems, as preservation of the wave form through the transformer is difficult.

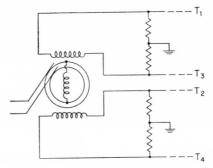

Fig. 7-40.   Rotating transformer used to obtain circular sweep.

REFERENCES

1. Arguimbau, Lawrence Baker, *Vacuum-Tube Circuits.* New York: John Wiley and Sons, Inc., 1948.
2. Baracket, A. J., "Television Synchronizing Signal Generator," *Electronics,* October, 1948, Vol. 21, p. 110.
3. Benjamin, R., "Blocking Oscillators," *Proc. IEE,* Radiolocation Conv., No. 1, Vol. 93, p. 309; No. 7, p. 1159.
4. Chance, Britton; Hughes, Vernon; MacNichol, Edward F.; Sayre, David; and Williams, Frederick C., *Waveforms,* New York: McGraw-Hill Book Co., Inc., 1949.
5. Cocking, W. T., "Electromagnetic Deflection," *Wireless World,* July, 1946, Vol. 52, p. 217; September, 1946, Vol. 52, p. 289.
6. Cocking, W. T., "Blocking Oscillators," *Wireless Engr.,* June, 1949, Vol. 26, p. 230.
7. Cruft Laboratory Electronics Training Staff, *Electronic Circuits and Tubes.* New York: McGraw-Hill Book Co., Inc., 1947.
8. Engstrom, E. W. and Holmes, R. S., "Television Deflection Circuits," *Electronics,* January, 1939, Vol. 12, p. 19.
9. Fink, Donald G., *Principles of Television Engineering.* New York: McGraw-Hill Book Co., Inc., 1940.
10. Friend, A. W., "Television Deflection Circuits," *RCA Rev.,* March, 1947, Vol. 8, p. 98.
11. Kiver, Milton S., "Modern Television Receivers," *Radio News,* August, 1949, Vol. 42, p. 41; September, 1949, Vol. 42, p. 62; October, 1949, Vol. 42, p. 59.

12. Kiver, Milton S., *Television Simplified*. New York: D. Van Nostrand Company, Inc., 1948.
13. Malling, Leonard R., "Triode Linear Saw-Tooth Current Oscillator," *Proc. IRE*, December, 1944, Vol. 32, p. 753.
14. Maloff, I. G. and Epstein, D. W., *Electron Optics in Television*. New York: McGraw-Hill Book Co., Inc., 1938.
15. McGregor, Robert B., "TV Reception Below Line of Sight," *Electronics*, November, 1949, Vol. 21, p. 90.
16. M.I.T. Radar School Staff, *Principles of Radar*. New York: McGraw-Hill Book Co., Inc., 1946.
17. Noll, Edward M., "Television Sweep Oscillators," *Radio News*, January, 1946, Vol. 35, p. 52.
18. Puckle, O. S., *Time Bases*. New York: John Wiley and Sons, Inc., 1943.
19. Rawcliffe, R. and Dressel, R. W., "Magnetic Focusing and Deflection," *Electronic Inds.*, October, 1946, Vol. 5, p. 51.
20. Schade, Otto, "Magnetic Deflection Circuits for Cathode Ray Tubes," *RCA Rev.*, September, 1947, Vol. 8, p. 506.
21. Schlesinger, Kurt, "Magnetic Deflection of Kinescopes," *Proc. IRE*, August, 1947, Vol. 35, p. 813.
22. Seeley, Samuel, *Electron-Tube Circuits*. New York: McGraw-Hill Book Co., Inc., 1950.
23. Seeley, S. W. and Kimball, C. N., "A New Method for Determining Sweep Linearity," *RCA Rev.*, January, 1940, Vol. 4, p. 338.
24. Soller, J. Theodore; Starr, M. A.; and Valley, George E., Jr., *Cathode Ray Tube Displays*. New York: McGraw-Hill Book Co., Inc., 1948.
25. Zeluff, Vin, "Television Remote Viewers," *Electronics*, December, 1948, Vol. 21, p. 90.
26. Zworykin, V. K. and Morton G. A., *Television*. New York: John Wiley and Sons, Inc., 1940.
27. Sziklai, G. C., "Current Oscillator for Television Sweep," *Electronics*, September, 1946, Vol. 19, p. 120.

PROBLEMS

7-1 A trapezoidal waveform $e_{in} = k_1 + k_2t$ is applied to a series RL circuit. Find the resulting current. Find the conditions under which the current will be a linear function of time if $i_L = 0$ at $t = 0$.

7-2 Show that the results of problem 7-1 agree with Eq. (7-22).

7-3 Find the input voltage necessary to give a coil current of the form $i_L = kt$. Assume the tubes to be identical and the time constants R_gC_g to be large with respect to the period of a sweep.

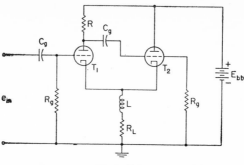

Prob. 7-3.

7-4 If the coil current in the circuit of problem 7-3 is to be of the form $i_L = A \sinh \beta t$ during the period of interest, calculate the input voltage.

7-5 Sketch and explain a trapezoidal voltage generator which would use a resistance-inductance circuit instead of a resistance-capacitance combination.

7-6 The linear amplifier shown is to use the initial part of a sine wave as a current sweep. A sinusoidal input voltage will be switched in and out of the circuit, giving intermittent operation. The current through the deflection coils is to be $i = I_0 + I_m \sin \omega t$ where t is measured from the instant of signal application. Only 10 per cent of the total magnitude of the sine wave is to be used for the sweep duration of 50 microseconds. If $R = 500$ ohms, $L = 0.1h$, $r_p = 1500$ ohms, and $\mu = 15$: (a) what must be the frequency of the applied sinusoid? (b) what must be the phase of the sinusoid at the instant of application? (c) what must be the amplitude of the input signal if the current is to go through a total change of 40 milliamperes during the sweep? Sketch and label the sweep current. The time constant $R_g C_g$ is large with respect to the period of the system.

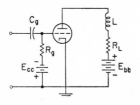

Prob. 7-6.

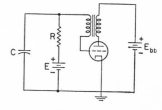

Prob. 7-7.

7-7 A blocking oscillator operates with the grid resistor returned to a source of fixed voltage as shown. When $E = E_1$ and $R = R_1$, the oscillator operates at a frequency f_1. If a second resistor R_2 is substituted for R_1 the frequency becomes f_2. When E is made equal to E_2 and R_1 is again used, the frequency becomes f_3. Assuming that for changes in either the grid resistor or the grid voltage, the only change in circuit operation will be in the RC transient of the grid circuit, calculate the voltage E_3 necessary to give a frequency f_4 if the resistor R_1 is used.

7-8 Sketch and label a generalized set of wave forms corresponding to the circuit of Fig. 7-26.

7-9 An input voltage of $e_{in} = kt$ is applied to the circuit of Fig. 7-29. Find the coil current in terms of the circuit parameters. The time constants $R_g C_g$ and $R_k C_k$ are all large with respect to a sweep period. The tubes T_1, T_2, and T_3 are operating as linear amplifiers with the characteristics r_{p1} and μ_1, r_{p2} and μ_2, and r_{p3} and μ_3. Let the parallel combinations of R_{b1}, R_{g2}, and R_{b2}, R_{g3} be termed R_1 and R_2, respectively.

7-10 Repeat problem 7-9 for the circuit of Fig. 7-30. Let

$$R_1 = \frac{R_{b1}R_{g2}}{R_{b1} + R_{g2}}; \qquad R_2 = \frac{R_{b2}R_{g3}}{R_{b2} + R_{g3}};$$

$$R_3 = \frac{R_{b3}R_{g4}}{R_{b3} + R_{g4}}; \qquad R_4 = \frac{R_{b4}R_{g5}}{R_{b4} + R_{g5}}$$

7-11 Verify the connections of Fig. 7-39.

CHAPTER EIGHT

TRIGGER CIRCUITS

The great majority of electric circuits can be shown to have a unique solution. However, one class of circuits may have more than one solution for every set of supply voltages and circuit parameters. Such circuits are called *trigger circuits*.

These circuits will not be stable at all possible operating points; between each pair of stable operating conditions, there will be an unstable condition. An unstable condition is a condition at which the circuit will operate only for a very small period of time, but the circuit will remain at a stable point for an indefinite time. If the circuit is disturbed only slightly it will return to the original stable point. However, it is possible to disturb the circuit to such an extent that it will seek a new stable point. This disturbance is said to "trigger" the circuit.

A circuit as described above can be made extremely versatile in application. A trigger circuit may serve as a pulse-controlled switch, as an information storage system, or as a counting circuit. It may also serve as a negative resistance, in which case it can form a steady-state oscillator. Many of these applications will be discussed in this chapter.

8-1 Basic Trigger Circuit

The simplest form of trigger circuit is that shown in Fig. 8-1. The resistance R shall be a simple linear resistance, while R_t must have a volt-ampere characteristic with some section having a negative slope. A simple possibility is shown in Fig. 8-2. The values of E and R shall be chosen such that there are three possible solutions, A, B, and C; each will be investigated in turn.

Let the system be operating with the current and voltages as

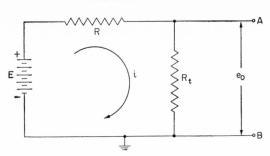

Fig. 8-1. Basic trigger circuit; see Fig. 8-2 for required characteristics of R_t.

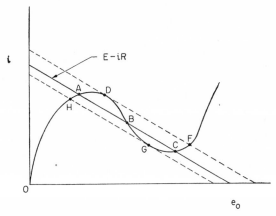

Fig. 8-2. Volt-ampere characteristic for R_t in the basic trigger circuit.

indicated by A.   If at this point the current should increase slightly, there will be a greater voltage drop across R_t; therefore the voltage across R must decrease.   This can be true only with a smaller current, since R is a linear resistor.   The tendency is thus for the operating point to be returned to A.   If the current is originally decreased slightly, the process would be reversed.   Point A is therefore a stable operating point.   By the same reasoning point C could also be shown to be stable.   If operation is at point B, a small increase in current will cause a decrease in the voltage across the linear portion of the circuit.   Applying this new voltage value to the negative resistance element would indicate a still larger current, and thus the point of operation would rapidly leave point B and approach a stable position.

The intersection of a load line and the negative slope of a volt-ampere characteristic does not in itself produce an unstable operating point. If the magnitude of the slope of the load line is greater than the magnitude of the slope of the volt-ampere characteristic at this intersection, the indicated operating point is stable. Such a condition could be obtained in Fig. 8-2 by choosing such values of E and R that the load line intersects the volt-ampere characteristic at two places in the region of negative slope.

The stability of a circuit similar to that of Fig. 8-1 can be most easily determined by examining the dynamic resistance looking back into the circuit (from terminals $A - B$). If this resistance is positive the system is stable, if negative, the circuit is unstable. Let the dynamic resistance of R_t at the point in question be given by ρ. The dynamic resistance looking back into the circuit is then

$$R_0 = \frac{\rho R}{\rho + R} \qquad (8\text{-}1)$$

If ρ is positive, R_0 must always be positive. If ρ is negative and $|\rho| > R$, the output resistance is positive and the circuit is stable. When ρ is negative and $|\rho| < R$, the output resistance is negative and the circuit is unstable.

It is impossible to examine the circuit of Fig. 8-1 and the characteristics of Fig. 8-2 and indicate specifically whether the operating point is at A or at C. It is necessary to have information pertaining to the past history of the circuit before the point of operation can be fixed. For example, let the supply voltage E be originally zero. It is then slowly increased, with the point of operation moving up the curve OHA. Knowing this, the operating point could be specified as A. As the $E - iR$ line moves just beyond the tangent point D, the point of operation must jump immediately to F, since that is the only solution available. If the supply voltage were now decreased, the operating point would move to C and then jump from G to H. This triggering phenomenon can be made to occur in a number of other ways. The value of R can be changed, or the characteristics of R_t can be displaced either vertically or horizontally. The usual form of trigger circuit will utilize high-vacuum or gas-filled tubes in such a manner that their characteristics may be changed by variation of the electrode voltages.

Any element that has a negative slope in a portion of its operating range may be used as the basis of a trigger circuit. It is impossible for this element to have a negative slope over an indefinitely large range, or in other words, no linear negative resistance can exist.

8-2 Means of Obtaining the Basic Trigger Circuit

There are many ways of obtaining a volt-ampere characteristic similar to that shown in Fig. 8-2. One of the more apparent methods is to utilize the volt-ampere characteristic of a tetrode which is being operated at a low value of plate voltage. This is shown particularly in the 24A, 32, 35, and 36 tubes. The plate characteristics for the type 32 tube are shown in Fig. 8-3. The

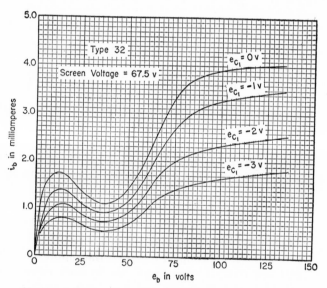

Fig. 8-3. Plate characteristics for type 32 vacuum tube.

trigger circuit of Fig. 8-1 is formed by using a battery and resistor in series with the plate-cathode circuit. The circuit can be most easily triggered by pulsing the control grid; however, a change in any electrode voltage or in the series resistance will allow triggering.

The slope of the negative resistance portion of the plate character-istics is dependent upon both the cathode emission and the secondary emission of the plate; thus the system is quite subject to aging effects.

The characteristics of Fig. 8-2 may be found also in the screen voltage-screen current relationship of a pentode operating under certain conditions.

The suppressor grid is connected to the screen grid in such a manner that a portion of the change in voltage at the screen will appear at the suppressor. The plate and screen should also be held positive and the suppressor always negative. A circuit is shown in Fig. 8-4.

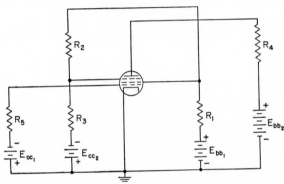

Fig. 8-4.   Pentode trigger circuit.

The resistance R_1 is the linear resistance in the trigger circuit. A voltage divider composed of R_2 and R_3 allows part of the changes in the screen voltage to be impressed upon the suppressor grid. Assume that the system is operating at the lower equilibrium value and that the screen voltage is then suddenly reduced by a small amount. This will tend to lower the screen current, but since the suppressor and screen are coupled together, the suppressor will also become more negative. If the suppressor becomes more negative the plate current will be reduced, and the screen current will tend to be increased again. Over some ranges of operating voltages the increased screen current caused by the reduction in suppressor voltage is greater than the loss caused by the lowering of the screen voltage. Since this increased screen current is accompanied by a further reduction in screen voltage due to the series resistance R_1, the process may become cumulative, with the screen moving to its higher equilibrium value.

At this point the plate current will be nearly zero, since the suppressor has decreased in potential until practically no electrons hit the plate. Since both stable combinations of screen and suppressor voltage give a definite plate current, there are two stable plate current values.

The complete process described here will be reversed if the current is originally at the upper equilibrium point and the change in screen voltage is upward.

The negative resistance characteristic necessary to form a trigger circuit can be found in the volt-ampere characteristic of several varieties of gas discharge systems. However, many of these systems are quite unstable and do not form satisfactory trigger circuits.

The desired characteristics can be found again in the volt-ampere characteristics of certain thermistors. Since the thermistor operates due to change in resistance caused by a change in temperature, the characteristic suffers from a serious thermal lag, possibly taking several seconds to reach an equilibrium condition. A typical thermistor characteristic is shown in Fig. 8-5. It is difficult to

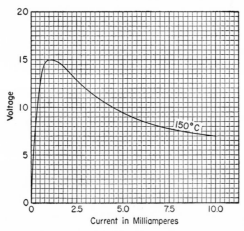

Fig. 8-5.   Typical thermistor characteristic.

obtain data for the portion of the curve to the right of the negative slope, since around this point the thermistor usually burns out.

It is also possible to connect a transistor so that a negative resistance characteristic can be obtained.[1]

A deflection system similar to that of a cathode-ray tube can be used as a form of trigger circuit. The sketch of Fig. 8-6 shows that

[1] See reference 75 at end of chapter.

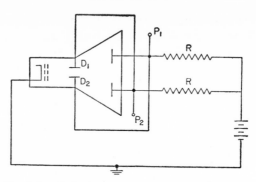

Fig. 8-6.   Cathode ray tube used as trigger circuit.

the tube shall consist of an electron source, a pair of deflection plates, and a pair of pickup elements.   If the potentials of P_1 and P_2 are equal, equal numbers of electrons will strike them.   However, if a few extra electrons strike P_1, its potential will be decreased, decreasing the potential of D_2 and causing still more electrons to strike P_1.   The process will be cumulative until the maximum possible number of electrons is striking P_1.   The negative resistance characteristic is symmetrical and appears between P_1 and P_2.

A second circuit which will provide a symmetrical volt-ampere characteristic is the Eccles-Jordan trigger circuit.   This is one of the most common and most useful of all the trigger circuits, and will be considered in detail through most of the remainder of this chapter.

As will be shown in the following section, the Eccles-Jordan circuit obtains the regeneration necessary to produce a negative resistance by the use of plate-to-grid coupling.   If both plate-to-grid coupling and cathode coupling are utilized, another trigger circuit is obtained.   This circuit is called the Schmitt trigger circuit.

It is also possible to obtain operation similar to that in a trigger circuit by the use of regeneration in a magnetic amplifier.   Such systems are usually characterized by relatively slow operation, although they have the advantages of long life with but little maintenance.

8-3 Eccles-Jordan Trigger Circuit

The Eccles-Jordan circuit is a two-tube system first described by Eccles and Jordan in the *Radio Review*.[2]   The basic form is shown

[2] See reference 27 at end of chapter.

in Fig. 8-7.   The resistance R_t with terminals P_1 and P_2 is enclosed
by the dotted line, with E and R comprising the rest of the trigger
circuit.

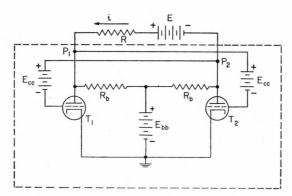

Fig. 8-7.   Basic Eccles-Jordan trigger circuit.

The volt-ampere characteristic for the terminals $P_1 - P_2$ is
shown in Fig. 8-8.   The shape of this curve is dependent upon the

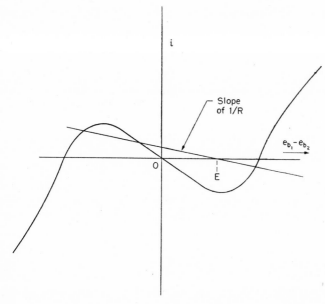

Fig. 8-8.   Volt-ampere characteristic for Eccles-Jordan trigger circuit.

magnitude of the parameters, and data for the curve may be obtained by the following procedure.

Summing the currents at P_1 gives

$$i_{b1} - i + \frac{e_{b1} - E_{bb}}{R_b} = 0 \tag{8-2}$$

The grid voltage of T_1 is

$$e_{c1} = e_{b2} - E_{cc} \tag{8-3}$$

An arbitrary value of i is now chosen. Using this value of i and the plate characteristics of T_1, a curve of e_{b1} versus e_{b2} may be obtained. The procedure is then repeated for T_2 where

$$i_{b2} + i + \frac{e_{b2} - E_{bb}}{R_b} = 0 \tag{8-4}$$

$$e_{c2} = e_{b1} - E_{cc} \tag{8-5}$$

For the assumed value of i, a second curve of e_{b1} versus e_{b2} is obtained which intersects with the first curve. This gives e_{b1} and e_{b2} for desired values of i. Thus a curve of $e_{b1} - e_{b2}$ versus i can be obtained. This curve is symmetrical if the corresponding sets of parameters are identical. The middle portion of the curve may be linear, and can represent the range where the characteristics of the tubes (g_m, μ, r_p) are equal and essentially constant. As the current in one tube decreases and the current in the other increases, both tubes are driven into nonlinear regions where they have no gain. This condition defines the limits of the negative resistance range. The Eccles-Jordan trigger circuit is usually constructed so that a stable state will exist with one tube completely cut off, although this is not necessary for correct operation.

The slope of the center of the negative resistance part of the characteristic may be approximated by assuming equal and constant dynamic values for the tubes. The equivalent circuit can then be drawn as shown in Fig. 8-9. Let $\mu = \mu_1 = \mu_2$ and $r_p = r_{p1} = r_{p2}$. An external generator e_0 will be applied between P_1 and P_2, and the quotient of e_0 and the resulting current i_0 will be the input resistance. Summing currents at the plate of T_1,

$$\frac{e_1 + \mu(e_1 - e_0)}{r_p} + \frac{e_1}{R_b} + \frac{e_1 - e_0}{R_b} + \frac{e_1 - e_0 + \mu e_1}{r_p} = 0 \tag{8-6}$$

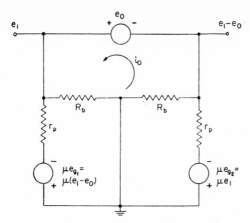

Fig. 8-9.   Dynamic equivalent circuit for basic Eccles-Jordan trigger circuit.

$$e_1 \left(\frac{2}{r_p} + \frac{2\mu}{r_p} + \frac{2}{R_b} \right) = e_0 \left(\frac{1}{r_p} + \frac{\mu}{r_p} + \frac{1}{R_b} \right) \tag{8-7}$$

or

$$e_1 = \frac{e_0}{2} \tag{8-8}$$

$$i_0 = \frac{e_1}{R_b} + \frac{e_1 + \mu(e_1 - e_0)}{r_p} \tag{8-9}$$

$$= e_0 \left\{ \frac{r_p + R_b(1 - \mu)}{2r_p R_b} \right\} \tag{8-10}$$

$$R_{\text{in}} = \frac{e_0}{i_0} = \frac{2r_p R_b}{r_p + R_b(1 - \mu)} \tag{8-11}$$

This value of R_{in} is the input dynamic resistance at the center of the curve.   It will be negative when

$$r_p + R_b < \mu R_b \tag{8-12}$$

or the minimum allowable value of R_b is

$$(R_b)_{\text{min}} = \frac{r_p}{\mu - 1} \tag{8-13}$$

If R_b is less than this value, the characteristic of Fig. 8-8 will have only a positive slope, and no trigger action could ever take place. The sketch of Fig. 8-10 shows this possibility.

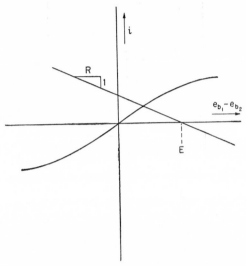

Fig. 8-10.   Degenerate volt-ampere characteristic for the Eccles-Jordan circuit; triggering cannot take place.

8-4 Schmitt Trigger Circuit

The basic form of the Schmitt trigger circuit is shown in Fig. 8-11.[3]

If suitable values for the supply voltages are used, the desired negative resistance characteristic can be found between the points $P_1 - P_2$. Although two stable points and one unstable point can be obtained, the volt-ampere characteristic is not necessarily symmetrical.

To find the negative resistance at the center of the characteristic, an external generator can be used as was done in the circuit of Fig. 8-9. However in this particular case, the conditions necessary to achieve a negative resistance can be found in a simpler way. An external generator will be applied to the grid of T_1 and the total grid voltage of T_1 will then be calculated.

[3] See reference 77 at end of chapter.

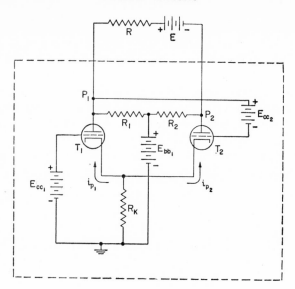

Fig. 8-11.　Schmitt trigger circuit.

Summing dynamic currents at the cathode,

$$\frac{e_k}{R_k} + i_{p1} + i_{p2} = 0 \tag{8-14}$$

However i_{p1} will be proportional to e_{g1} and i_{p2} proportional to e_{g2}. Using the symbols g_{m1}' and g_{m2}' for these constants of proportionality gives

$$\frac{e_k}{R_k} + g_{m1}'e_{g1} + g_{m2}'e_{g2} = 0 \tag{8-15}$$

If T_1 has a gain A,

$$e_{g1} = e_{\text{in}} - e_k$$

$$e_{g2} = Ae_{g1} = A(e_{\text{in}} - e_k) \tag{8-16}$$

Substituting these equations into Eq. (8-15) gives

$$\frac{e_k}{R_k} + g_{m1}'(e_{\text{in}} - e_k) + g_{m2}'A(e_{\text{in}} - e_k) = 0 \tag{8-17}$$

Solving for e_k and then eg_1,

$$e_k = \frac{(g_{m1}' + Ag_{m2}')e_{\text{in}}}{g_{m1}' + Ag_{m2}' - 1/R_k} \tag{8-18}$$

$$e_{g1} = \frac{e_{\text{in}}}{1 - R_k(g_{m1}' + A g_{m2}')} \qquad (8\text{-}19)$$

Equation (8-19) shows that it is possible to obtain changing potentials all through the circuit even though no input signal is applied. This is the condition necessary in general for an oscillator, or in this particular case, the condition that will give an infinite input impedance to $P_1 - P_2$. If the denominator of Eq. (8-19) is made negative, the input resistance will also be negative, the condition necessary to form a trigger circuit. Assuming T_1 and T_2 to be identical and operating in a region of constant μ and r_p, Eq. (8-19) can be written

$$e_{g1} = \frac{e_{\text{in}}}{1 + R_k\left[\dfrac{\mu(R_2 + r_p - \mu R_1)}{(r_p + R_1)(r_p + R_2) + R_k(r_p + R_2) + R_k(r_p + R_1) + \mu R_k r_p}\right]} \qquad (8\text{-}20)$$

8-5 Trigger Circuits as Oscillators

Since every trigger circuit has an unstable region which is essentially a region of negative dynamic resistance, a trigger circuit can be used to form an oscillator.

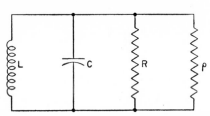

Fig. 8-12. *RLC* parallel circuit.

Any *RLC* circuit at one frequency can be drawn as the parallel combination of Fig. 8-12. If the parallel circuit is shunted with a negative dynamic resistance ρ, where $R = |\rho|$, the total circuit resistance is

$$R_0 = \frac{-(R)(|\rho|)}{R - |\rho|} = \infty \qquad (8\text{-}21)$$

Any variation of current or voltage in the remaining LC circuit will continue as an oscillation indefinitely, since there would be no damping. If $R < |\rho|$, the net resistance is positive with any existing oscillation being eventually damped out. If $R > |\rho|$, the amplitude of any oscillation will build up until the characteristics of the circuit producing the negative resistance have been altered so that $R = |\rho|$.

The tetrode trigger circuit may be made into an oscillator as shown in Fig. 8-13.[4]   Since negative dynamic resistance is developed

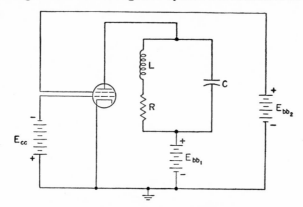

Fig. 8-13.   Dynatron oscillator.

between plate and cathode, the tuned circuit is connected to these points.   This oscillator was first studied by Hull, who called it the dynatron oscillator.   The amplitude of oscillation may be changed by variation of the control grid voltage, as this will change the slope of the negative resistance characteristic.   The system suffers from lack of stability due to variation in both the primary and secondary emitting surfaces.

If a tuned circuit is connected across the negative resistance of the pentode trigger circuit, the result is the transitron oscillator.[5]   A circuit is shown in Fig. 8-14.   A capacitor C_c is used to

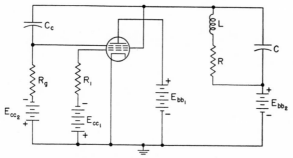

Fig. 8-14.   Transitron oscillator.

[4] See reference 40 at end of chapter.
[5] See reference 11 at end of chapter.

couple changes in the screen voltage to the suppressor grid.   The time constant $C_c R_g$ must be large with respect to the period of the oscillation.

The trigger circuit of Eccles and Jordan can also be used as the basis of a negative resistance oscillator.[6]   In this case the dynamic negative resistance is developed from plate to plate.   Again the grid-plate coupling batteries, or resistors, are replaced by capacitors. The circuit thus obtained, shown in Fig. 8-15, is very similar to a push-pull oscillator.

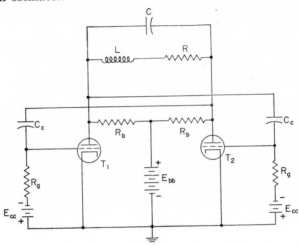

Fig. 8-15.   Push-pull negative resistance oscillator.

8-6 Static Solution of Eccles-Jordan Trigger Circuit

As was previously mentioned, the two-tube circuit of Eccles and Jordan seems to offer the greatest possibility for practical exploitation.   Consider the circuit of Fig. 8-7 with its characteristic of Fig. 8-8.   If the resistance R is made to approach infinity, the load line becomes horizontal.   This is equivalent to completely removing the external circuit of R and E.   However, there are still three possible points of operation, one of which is unstable and two of which are stable.   Any volt-ampere characteristic which crosses the $i = 0$ line in three or more places does not need an external circuit to form a trigger circuit.   If suitable supply voltages are used, the two

[6] See reference 70 at end of chapter.

stable points for the circuit of Fig. 8-7 will occur when one tube is at
cutoff and the other is conducting heavily. This can be shown
in another way. Assume the tubes are operating with equal plate
currents. A small increase in the emission of T_1 will cause its plate
voltage to decrease. A decrease in the plate voltage of T_1 will be
coupled through E_{cc} to the grid of T_2. The plate current of T_2
will then decrease and the plate potential of T_2 will rise. This
in turn will raise the grid voltage of T_1, which will cause still more
current in T_1. The process is cumulative until the tubes are driven
into nonlinear regions with T_1 conducting heavily, and T_2 at or
near cutoff.

The circuit of Fig. 8-7 can be modified into that of Fig. 8-16 in

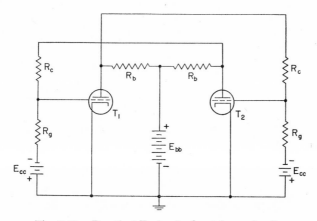

Fig. 8-16.   Practical Eccles-Jordan trigger circuit.

order to obtain a more practical device. The voltage changes on
the plates of the tubes are usually too great in magnitude to apply
directly to the grids, so a voltage divider consisting of R_c and R_g
is used. In addition, the grids are usually driven positive, causing
them to conduct. This would cause excessive loading on the
opposite plate circuits if a limiting resistance were not used. Bias
batteries will still be used to place the grid voltage in the proper
operating range. However, the two bias batteries have a common
connection allowing a single source to be used.

EXAMPLE: The circuit of Fig. 8-16 will be further investigated with the
aid of a numerical example. Let $R_b = 50,000$ ohms, $R_c = 500,000$ ohms,

R_g = 500,000 ohms, E_{bb} = 250 volts, and E_{cc} = 100 volts. The tubes will be of the 6J5 type. As previously explained, the circuit will seek a stable position, with one tube carrying the greater percentage of the total current. It will be assumed that T_1 is driven to full conduction and that T_2 is cut off. This is a stable condition which will continue to exist until some variation of

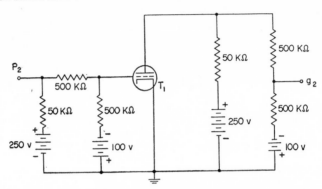

Fig. 8-17.   Circuit equivalent to that of Fig. 8-16 when T_1 is conducting and T_2 is cut off.

sufficient magnitude occurs to transfer the circuit to the other stable state. If T_1 is conducting and T_2 is cut off, the circuit of Fig. 8-17 can be drawn. Both the plate circuit and the grid circuit can be further simplified as shown by Fig. 8-18.   For the plate circuit,

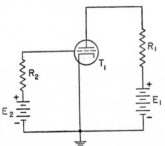

Fig. 8-18.   Circuit equivalent to that of Fig. 8-17.

$$\frac{e_{b1} + 100}{1000} + i_{b1} + \frac{e_{b1} - 250}{50} = 0 \quad (8\text{-}22)$$

where the currents are in milliamperes and the resistances are in thousands of ohms.   Simplifying Eq. (8-22) gives

$$e_{b1} + 47.6i_{b1} = 238 \quad (8\text{-}23)$$

or

$$E_1 = 238 \text{ volts}$$
$$R_1 = 47,600 \text{ ohms} \quad (8\text{-}24)$$

For the grid circuit,

$$\frac{e_{c1} + 100}{500} + i_{c1} + \frac{e_{c1} - 250}{550} = 0 \quad (8\text{-}25)$$

$$e_{c1} + 262i_{c1} = 66.6 \quad (8\text{-}26)$$

or $\qquad\qquad E_2 = 66.6$ volts

$$R_2 = 262{,}000 \text{ ohms} \qquad\qquad (8\text{-}27)$$

In writing Eq. (8-25), it has been assumed that the grid is taking current. If i_{c1} is made zero, e_{c1} will be positive; therefore the assumption is correct. The grid-cathode conducting resistance can be treated in either of two ways. The approximate method is to assume the grid conducting resistance to be equal to a constant, independent of grid voltage or plate voltage. For small receiving type tubes this resistance can be considered to be approximately 1000 ohms. In this case,

$$e_{c1} = 0.254 \text{ volt}$$
$$i_{c1} = 0.254 \text{ milliampere} \qquad\qquad (8\text{-}28)$$

After plotting Eq. (8-23) on the 6J5 plate characteristics, the plate voltage and plate current can be found:

$$e_{b1} = 48 \text{ volts}$$
$$i_{b1} = 4 \text{ milliamperes} \qquad\qquad (8\text{-}29)$$

The more accurate way of treating the conducting grid is to use the grid-voltage, grid-current curves and make a graphical solution. A probable value of plate voltage is chosen, which fixes an $e_c - i_c$ curve. Then a value for e_c can be found and carried over to the plate characteristics to find a corresponding value for the plate voltage. If this value of plate voltage is equal to the original value, the magnitudes of e_{c1}, i_{c1}, and e_{b1} are correct. In general however, the process must be repeated several times until values are obtained which check in both sets of curves. In the particular problem at hand, a grid voltage of 0.22 volt is obtained. This value is not sufficiently different from the original value of 0.254 volt to cause any appreciable change in the previously calculated plate potential.

It is now necessary to find out if the original assumptions are justified, that is, if T_2 is cut off. It has already been shown that T_1 is conducting. From Fig. 8-17,

$$\frac{e_{b2} - 250}{50} + \frac{e_{b2} - 0.25}{500} = 0 \qquad\qquad (8\text{-}30)$$

$$e_{b2} = 227 \text{ volts} \qquad\qquad (8\text{-}31)$$

$$\frac{e_{c2} - 48}{500} + \frac{e_{c2} + 100}{500} = 0 \qquad\qquad (8\text{-}32)$$

$$e_{c2} = -26 \text{ volts} \qquad\qquad (8\text{-}33)$$

With a plate voltage of 227 volts and a grid voltage of -26 volts, T_2 will be at cutoff.

8-7 Modifications of the Eccles-Jordan Circuit

In the symmetrical two-tube circuit of Fig. 8-16, either one tube or the other is at, or close to, cutoff at all times. With the usual symmetrical circuit the total cathode current is then constant. This makes possible the use of cathode bias as shown in Fig. 8-19. A capacitor is sometimes added to stabilize the cathode potential during the switching operation.

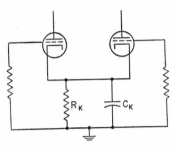

Fig. 8-19. Eccles-Jordan circuit with cathode bias.

Pentode-type tubes can also be used to form several modifications of the basic Eccles-Jordan circuit. One way of employing pentodes would be to use the plate, control grid, and cathode in the normal manner, with the screen grid connected to a constant high potential and the suppressor grid returned to the cathode.

A second way of using pentodes is shown in Fig. 8-20. In this circuit the first grid is used exclusively for control purposes, with

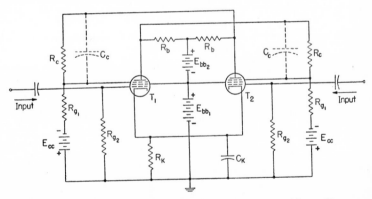

Fig. 8-20. Pentode trigger circuit with suppressor-grid coupling.

the suppressor grid performing the same function as the control grid in the triode. The tube that is at cutoff will have such a high negative suppressor voltage that the application of positive pulses to its control grid will have no effect. However, negative pulses applied to the control grid of the conducting tube will trigger the system. If the functions of the suppressor and control grids are interchanged, the circuit can be made to respond to pulses of either polarity. The use of the coupling capacitors C_c will be treated in the following section.

If the actual cathode, control grid, and screen grid of the pentode are treated as the effective cathode, control grid, and plate, respectively, a trigger circuit will be formed from which an electron coupled output can be obtained.

Another pentode trigger circuit which resembles the Eccles-Jordan circuit, is shown in Fig. 8-21.[7] This circuit has an advantage in that

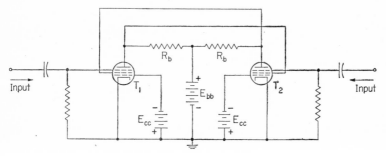

Fig. 8-21.   Pentode trigger circuit with screen-grid coupling.

it uses fewer parts than the preceding circuits. It can be controlled by the application of a negative pulse to the suppressor of the conducting tube.

It is possible to form trigger circuits from gas tubes. The simplest configurations are shown in Figs. 8-22a and 8-22b. In Fig. 8-22a, assume that T_1 is conducting and that T_2 is at cutoff, a stable operating point. A negative input pulse to either tube will not affect the system, since one tube is already at cutoff, and the grid has lost control in the other. A short positive pulse, however, will cause the nonconducting tube to conduct. When it does so, its plate drops in potential, and this drop is transmitted through C to the plate of T_1. If the plate supply voltage is greater than twice the conducting potential of the tube, the drop transmitted to the plate of T_1 is sufficient to cause T_1 to become nonconducting. The plate

[7] See references 5 and 67 at end of chapter.

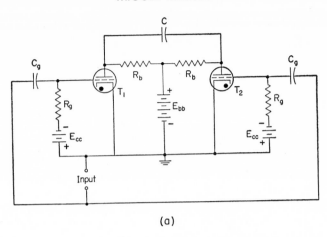

(a)

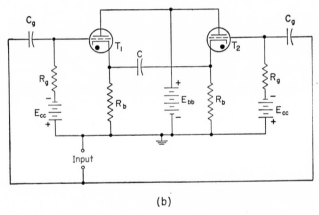

(b)

Fig. 8-22.   Thyratron trigger circuit: (a) coupling capacitor in plate circuit;
(b) coupling capacitor in cathode circuit.

voltage of T_1 will then rise exponentially toward the supply voltage
with a time constant $\tau = R_b C$.   Care must be taken that this time
constant is longer than the deionization time of the tube, or T_1
will not be cut off.

If the resistor-capacitor combination is placed in the cathode
circuit as shown in Fig. 8-22b, the form of operation is essentially
the same as just discussed.

The chief disadvantage of thyratron trigger circuits is their relative slowness of operation. The deionization time may range from 5 to 50 microseconds for small gas triodes and tetrodes.

8-8 Methods of Triggering the Eccles-Jordan Circuit

Any small change of voltage and current can be tolerated in the circuit of Fig. 8-16 without causing the tubes to transfer conduction. However, the Eccles-Jordan trigger circuit can be used advantageously only when the system is driven back and forth from one stable position to the other, these reversals being under the definite control of some external signal. Methods of triggering the circuit will therefore be studied.

In either of the two stable positions, the nonconducting tube has an effective g_m of zero. In order to transfer conduction from one tube to the other, the grid voltage of the off tube must be raised sufficiently to allow regeneration to take place. Once the regenerative process starts, it will be continued until the originally conducting tube is driven to cutoff. If the triggering signal is not of sufficient magnitude to bring the g_m of the off tube to the critical value, the circuit will drop back to its original state when the signal is removed.

One way of triggering the circuit is to apply a negative pulse through a small capacitor to one of the grids. Since the capacitor cannot change its voltage instantaneously, the potential of the grid will drop. If the negative pulse is applied to the tube at cutoff, nothing will happen, since a negative grid pulse will not disturb a tube which already has its grid below the cutoff potential. However, if the pulse is applied to the conducting tube, the reduction in its positive, or near zero, grid potential will cause a rapid drop in plate current, accompanied by a simultaneous rise in the plate current of the formerly nonconducting tube. If the input pulse is of sufficient magnitude to raise the g_m to the critical point, the tubes will transfer conduction.

Failure to trigger the circuit may actually be due to two causes. First, the input signal may be of insufficient magnitude; second, the wave form of the signal may have too gradual a slope, which allows the voltage of the input capacitor to change during a pulse. The voltage actually available at the grid of the tube has thus been reduced. Under some conditions, this second fault might be partially overcome by using a larger coupling capacitor to the grid.

The Eccles-Jordan trigger circuit can also be triggered by application of a positive pulse to the grid of the nonconducting tube. In general, the magnitude of the positive pulse needed to transfer conduction will be greater than the magnitude of the required negative pulse. The negative pulse is aided initially by the gain of a tube, while the positive pulse may have to overcome a considerable amount of bias to bring the nonconducting tube to partial conduction.

The trigger circuit cannot be controlled by applying to one tube a series of positive pulses only, or a series of negative pulses. If one negative pulse causes the tubes to transfer conduction, application of further negative pulses will have no effect. Similarly, the series of positive pulses can cause no more than one transfer of conduction. Thus to obtain complete control of the trigger circuit, two alternatives seem to be available. A pulse of the same polarity can be applied to each grid in turn, or alternate positive and negative pulses can be applied to the same grid. For most applications, both of these solutions are impractical. To gain control of the trigger circuit with pulses which are either all positive or all negative, a symmetrical triggering system must be used. One example of such a system is shown in Fig. 8-23. This system however, is

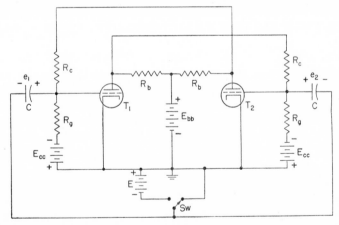

Fig. 8-23. Circuit used to study the triggering action of the Eccles-Jordan circuit.

not a practical solution, but is merely treated as an introduction to a better but more complicated circuit.

The trigger source is composed of the battery E and the switch Sw. The trigger pulse will be applied to the two grids through the small capacitors whenever the switch Sw is moved from ground to the battery E. It will be assumed that the resulting negative pulse is sufficiently great in magnitude to cut off both tubes. The problem then becomes that of determining which tube will first return to conduction.

Assume that the circuit is originally in a stable state with T_1 conducting. The grid-cathode potential of T_1 can then be considered to be approximately zero. The voltage e_1 across the grid capacitor of T_1 will be zero, while the other capacitor will have a voltage e_2, where

$$e_2 = \frac{(e_{b1} + E_{cc})R_g}{R_c + R_g} - E_{cc} \qquad (8\text{-}34)$$

and e_{b1} is the voltage across the conducting tube.

The switch Sw is now operated, applying the negative pulse to the circuit. If both tubes are cut off by the negative pulse, the circuits of Fig. 8-24 can be drawn. Except for the initial charges on the

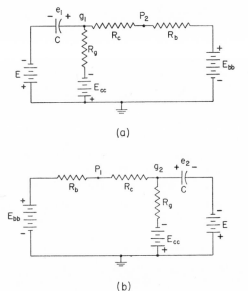

(a)

(b)

Fig. 8-24. Circuits equivalent to the circuit of Fig. 8-12 when both tubes are cut off.

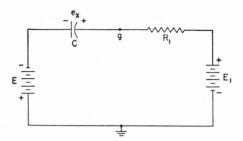

Fig. 8-25.   Circuit equivalent to that of either Fig. 8-24(a) or Fig. 8-24(b).

capacitors, the circuits are identical and may be reduced to the circuit of Fig. 8-25.   With respect to Fig. 8-25,

$$E_1 = -E_{cc} + \frac{(E_{cc} + E_{bb})R_g}{R_g + R_c + R_b} \tag{8-35}$$

$$R_1 = \frac{R_g(R_c + R_b)}{R_g + R_c + R_b} \tag{8-36}$$

From this circuit the grid voltage of each tube can be written as a function of time.   For T_1, and $e_x = e_1 = 0$,

$$e_{c1} = -E + (E_1 + E)(1 - e^{-t/R_1 C}) \tag{8-37}$$

For T_2, and $e_x = e_2$,

$$e_{c2} = -E - E_{cc} + \frac{(e_{b1} + E_{cc})R_g}{R_g + R_c}$$

$$+ \left[E_1 + E + E_{cc} - \frac{(e_{b1} + E_{cc})R_g}{R_g + R_c} \right] (1 - e^{-t/R_1 C}) \tag{8-38}$$

The grid voltage of both tubes is sketched in Fig. 8-26.   Both circuits have the same time constant, both grids approach the same final voltage, but the grid of T_1 starts at a higher potential than that of T_2.   The grid of T_1 therefore reaches the cutoff potential first, and T_1 comes back into conduction, holding T_2 at cutoff.   Thus the negative input pulse *did not* transfer conduction from one tube to the other.   The presence of a small amount of inductance, along with circuit unbalance, may sometimes cause the tubes to transfer conduction, but such action is not dependable.   Changes in the static condition of the trigger source will change the original voltages on the coupling capacitors, but the general relationship of the curves shown in Fig. 8-26 will not be altered.

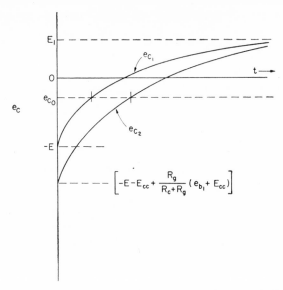

Fig. 8-26.   Grid voltages after triggering for the circuit of Fig. 8-23.

The circuit of Fig. 8-23 will now be modified into that of Fig. 8-27 by addition of small capacitors (C_c) in parallel with the coupling resistors.

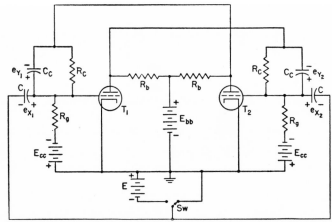

Fig. 8-27.   Eccles-Jordan circuit in which coupling capacitors have been added.

If T_1 is again conducting, with T_2 at cutoff, the capacitor voltages as labeled in Fig. 8-27 are

$$e_{y1} = \frac{-R_c}{R_b + R_c} E_{bb} \qquad \text{(a)}$$

$$e_{y2} = \frac{-R_c}{R_c + R_b + R_g} (E_{bb} + E_{cc}) \qquad \text{(b)}$$

$$e_{x1} = 0 \qquad \text{(c)}$$

$$e_{x2} = -E_{cc} + \frac{R_g(E_{bb} + E_{cc})}{R_g + R_c} \qquad \text{(d)}$$

(8-39)

The switch Sw is now operated, cutting both tubes off. Again two equivalent circuits can be drawn, which are similar except for the initial charges on the capacitors. The generalized equivalent circuit is shown in Fig. 8-28, where e_x and e_y are the initial voltages on the capacitors C and C_c, respectively.

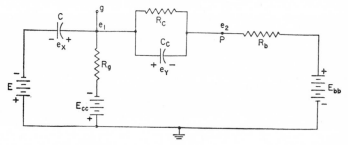

Fig. 8-28.   Circuit equivalent to those in Fig. 8-27 when both tubes are cut off.

The nodal equations for the circuit are

$$C \frac{d}{dt} (e_1 + E) + \frac{e_1 + E_{cc}}{R_g} + \frac{e_1 - e_2}{R_c} + C_c \frac{d}{dt} (e_1 - e_2) = 0 \quad \text{(8-40)}$$

$$C_c \frac{d}{dt} (e_2 - e_1) - \frac{e_2 - e_1}{R_c} + \frac{e_2 - E_{bb}}{R_b} = 0 \qquad \text{(8-41)}$$

The solution for the grid voltage e_1, is simple in form but rather cumbersome when expressed in terms of the original parameters.

$$e_1 = \frac{\tau_5 \tau_6}{\tau_2 \tau_3} + \frac{\dfrac{E_\alpha}{\tau_\alpha^2} - \dfrac{E_2}{\tau_1 \tau_\alpha} + \dfrac{E_3}{\tau_2 \tau_3}}{-\dfrac{1}{\tau_\alpha}\left(-\dfrac{1}{\tau_\alpha} + \dfrac{1}{\tau_\beta}\right)} e^{-t/\tau_\alpha} + \frac{\dfrac{E_\alpha}{\tau_\beta^2} - \dfrac{E_2}{\tau_\alpha \tau_\beta} + \dfrac{E_3}{\tau_2 \tau_3}}{-\dfrac{1}{\tau_\beta}\left(-\dfrac{1}{\tau_\beta} + \dfrac{1}{\tau_\alpha}\right)} e^{-t/\tau_\beta}$$

(8-42)

where

$$\frac{1}{\tau_\alpha} = \frac{1}{2}\left(\frac{1}{\tau_4} + \sqrt{\frac{1}{\tau_4{}^2} - \frac{4}{\tau_5\tau_6}}\right) \qquad (8\text{-}43)$$

$$\frac{1}{\tau_\beta} = \frac{1}{2}\left(\frac{1}{\tau_4} - \sqrt{\frac{1}{\tau_4{}^2} - \frac{4}{\tau_5\tau_6}}\right) \qquad (8\text{-}44)$$

$$E_\alpha = e_x - E \qquad (8\text{-}45)$$

$$\frac{E_2}{\tau_1} = \frac{e_x}{R_bC_c} - \frac{E_{cc}}{R_gC} - \frac{E}{R_bC_c} - \frac{E}{R_cC_c} + \frac{e_x}{R_cC_c} + \frac{e_y}{R_bC} + \frac{E_{bb}}{R_bC} \qquad (8\text{-}46)$$

$$\frac{E_3}{\tau_2\tau_3} = \frac{1}{CC_c}\left(\frac{E_{bb}}{R_cR_b} - \frac{E_{cc}}{R_gR_b} - \frac{E_{cc}}{R_gR_c}\right) \qquad (8\text{-}47)$$

$$\frac{1}{\tau_4} = \frac{1}{R_gC} + \frac{1}{R_bC} + \frac{1}{R_bC_c} + \frac{1}{R_cC_c} \qquad (8\text{-}48)$$

$$\frac{1}{\tau_5\tau_6} = \frac{1}{CC_c}\left(\frac{1}{R_gR_b} + \frac{1}{R_gR_c} + \frac{1}{R_cR_b}\right) \qquad (8\text{-}49)$$

For the two grid circuits under cutoff conditions, only the terms E_1 and E_2 are different. Thus the expression for each grid voltage contains two exponential terms, of identical time constant, but of different amplitudes. The time variation in the grid voltage for the two circuits may be quite different, however due to the complexity of the terms, it is difficult to state definitely whether or not the system has been improved. A numerical example will now be considered in order to see if the circuit of Fig. 8-27, using a typical set of parameters, has any improved characteristics.

EXAMPLE: In the circuit of Fig. 8-27 let $R_b = 50,000$ ohms, $R_c = 1$ megohm, $R_g = 1$ megohm, $C = 50\mu\mu f$, $C_c = 50\mu\mu f$, $E_{bb} = 250$ volts, $E_{cc} = 100$ volts, and $E = 50$ volts. A 6SN7 tube will be used. Then

$$\frac{1}{\tau_4} = 0.84 \times 10^6 \qquad \frac{E_3}{\tau_2\tau_3} = 1.16 \times 10^{12}$$

$$\frac{1}{\tau_5\tau_6} = 1.64 \times 10^{10} \qquad \frac{1}{\tau_\alpha} = 0.82 \times 10^6 \qquad \frac{1}{\tau_\beta} = 0.02 \times 10^6$$

The quiescent voltage across a tube during conduction will be approximately 50 volts. Then

$$e_{x1} = 0, \quad e_{x2} = -25 \text{ volts}, \quad e_{y2} = -171 \text{ volts}$$

$$E_{\alpha 1} = -50 \text{ volts}$$

$$E_{\alpha 2} = -75 \text{ volts}, \quad \left(\frac{E_2}{\tau_1}\right)_1 = -18.1 \times 10^6, \quad \left(\frac{E_2}{\tau_2}\right)_2 = 1.7 \times 10^6$$

If no coupling capacitors are used, $(C_c = 0)$, the expressions for the two grid voltages are

$$e_{c1} = 70.7 - 120.7e^{-0.391\times10^6 t} \tag{8-50}$$

$$e_{c2} = 70.7 - 145.7e^{-0.391\times10^6 t} \tag{8-51}$$

For the circuits with the coupling capacitors, the grid voltages are

$$e_{c1} = 70.7 - 26.9e^{-0.82\times10^6 t} - 93.8e^{-0.02\times10^6 t} \tag{8-52}$$

$$e_{c2} = 70.7 - 73.0e^{-0.82\times10^6 t} - 75.0e^{-0.02\times10^6 t} \tag{8-53}$$

All four curves are plotted in Fig. 8-29.

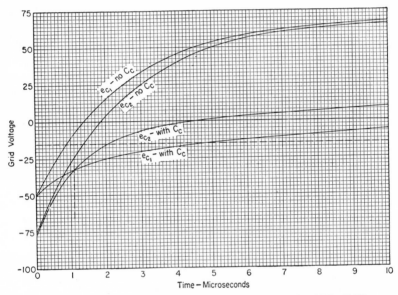

Fig. 8-29. Grid voltages after triggering for the circuit of Fig. 8-27.

Addition of the coupling capacitors results in a delay in the recovery time of the circuit, but the grid of the originally off tube now returns to the cutoff potential first. If the value of E changes, the change is instantaneously reflected to both grids, and if this change occurs after the crossover of the grid voltage at t_c, proper triggering will still result. If the magnitude of E decreases before t_c, however, the grid of the originally on tube will return to cutoff. The input pulse should therefore be of at least t_c duration.

It has been shown that a large negative pulse, applied to both

grids simultaneously through small capacitors, will trigger the
Eccles-Jordan circuit if suitable coupling capacitors are used.
However, the use of the input capacitors is inherently bad, since the
capacitors make it impossible to change the potential difference
between the two grids at a very high rate.   A better means of
triggering would be a symmetrical form which did not interrupt the
normal operation of the trigger circuit.   Three circuits of this type
are shown in Fig. 8-30.   Only the parts of the circuits pertaining to

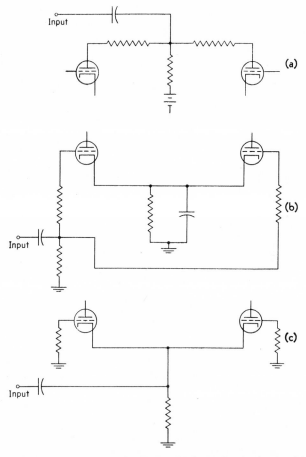

Fig. 8-30.   Means of triggering the Eccles-Jordan trigger circuit: (a) plate
triggering; (b) grid triggering; (c) cathode triggering.

the triggering system are shown. In Fig. 8-30a, a negative pulse is applied at the junction of R and the plate load resistors. For 6SN7 and 12AU7 tubes, the magnitude of resistance might range from 5000 to 50,000 ohms. An inductor might possibly be used to replace R, as the only requirement is that the junction be lowered in potential for the duration of the pulse. When the junction is lowered in potential, both grids are also lowered by an amount determined primarily by the voltage divider action of the plate and grid resistors. Thus the triggering action is approximately the same as that previously described. The circuit of Fig. 8-30b is also triggered by a negative pulse, while that of Fig. 8-30c must be triggered by a positive pulse.

A modification of the circuit of Fig. 8-30a is shown in Fig. 8-31.

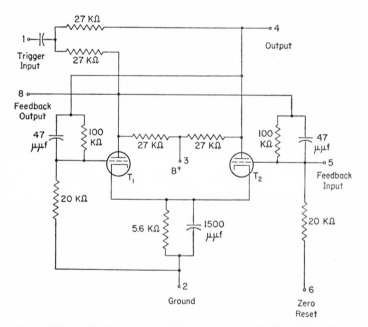

Fig. 8-31. Schematic diagram for trigger circuit shown in Fig. 8-32. (Courtesy General Electric Co.)

This particular circuit is manufactured as a plug-in unit by the General Electric Co. under the name "Binary Scaler, Model SN1A." A photograph of the complete unit is shown in Fig. 8-32.

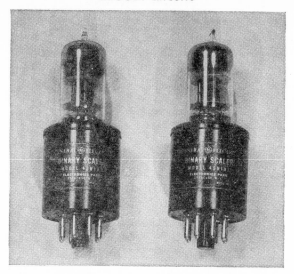

Fig. 8-32. Commercial binary scaler or trigger circuit. (Courtesy General Electric Co.)

8-9 Use of Trigger Circuits in Scaling Systems

A scaling circuit is a circuit which will produce a definite number of output pulses from a given number of input pulses. When trigger circuits are connected to form a scaling circuit, the number of these output pulses is equal to the number of input pulses divided by an integer.   In addition, the period of the input pulses need not be constant, and the "count-down ratio" of the circuit is completely independent of the period (assuming that there is sufficient time between pulses for the circuit to recover.)

Applications of such circuits can immediately be seen in the field of frequency measurement, the counting of relatively high-frequency pulses, and the construction of various forms of electronic computers.

If the trigger circuit of Fig. 8-27 were to be controlled by a series of negative pulses, the plate voltage of both tubes would be an approximate square wave.   If this square wave were then differentiated by a low time constant RC circuit, a new series of positive and negative pulses would result.

The output of the differentiating circuit will be applied to a network which will respond only to pulses of a given polarity.   The output of the network will consist of pulses of a single polarity, and if the system is arranged so that negative output pulses are obtained, they can be used to actuate a second trigger pair.

A circuit which will operate in the manner just described is shown in Fig. 8-33. The differentiating circuit is placed in the grid cir-

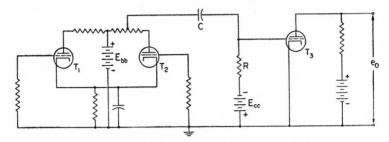

Fig. 8-33.   Trigger circuit and coupling network.

cuit of an overbiased amplifier. This amplifier will ignore all negative pulses, but will provide a negative output pulse for every positive input pulse. To minimize the effect of the differentiating circuit and amplifier on the trigger circuit, the output may be tapped down on the load resistor as shown. This will also allow a smaller bias voltage to be used in the following amplifier, but care must be taken that pulses of sufficient amplitude are still available. The same total resistance is kept in each plate circuit. The trigger circuit will usually perform properly if each component is within 10 per cent of the corresponding element.

A set of wave forms for the circuit of Fig. 8-33 is shown in Fig. 8-34. A typical input pulse train and the resulting plate voltage of one tube are given in Figs. 8-34a and 8-34b. The output of the differentiating circuit is shown in Fig. 8-34c with the corresponding grid voltage in Fig. 8-34d. The output pulses are shown in Fig. 8-34e.

The circuit of Fig. 8-33 has the disadvantage of requiring very careful adjustment of the bias. A simpler system would merely include a high-vacuum diode or crystal diode in series with the coupling capacitors. An adaptation of this method is shown in Fig. 8-35. No coupling capacitors have been added, but instead use is made of the already present grid-plate capacitors.

In many cases the circuits of Figs. 8-30a and 8-30b need no means

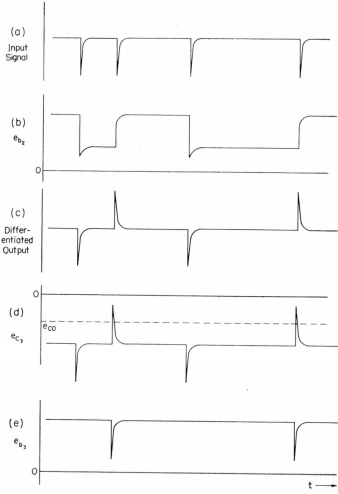

(a)
Input
Signal

(b)
e_{b_2}

O

(c)
Differ-
entiated
Output

O

(d)
e_{C_3}
e_{co}

(e)
e_{b_3}

O

t ⟶

Fig. 8-34.   Wave forms for the circuit of Fig. 8-33.

of eliminating the positive pulse in the coupling system between
cascaded pairs.   It has been shown that the amplitude of a positive
pulse needed for triggering is greater than that needed for a negative
pulse.   In addition, the instantaneous rise on the plate of a tube
which is being cut off is less than the drop on the plate of a tube
which is coming on.   The trigger circuits indicated will thus dis-

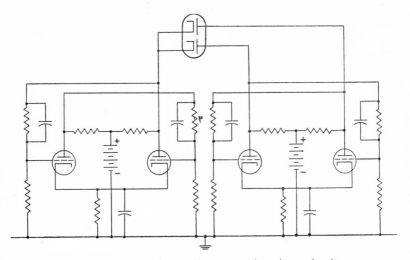

Fig. 8-35.   Diode coupling system for trigger circuit.

criminate against positive pulses, usually by a factor of about three to one.

The combined circuits which have been described in this section are actually counting down by a factor of two.   For every two input pulses, one negative output pulse is obtained.   There is nothing to prevent this output pulse from being used to initiate a similar cycle. Thus if N such combinations are cascaded, the input pulses will be scaled down by a factor of 2^N.   Such scaling circuits can have count-down ratios of 2, 4, 8, 16, etc.

8-10 Interpolation in Scaling Systems

The 2^N scaling circuit is frequently used to count down high-frequency pulses so that they may be recorded by mechanical counters.   For example, if a five-unit system were being used, it would take 32 input pulses before an indication would be observed on the mechanical counter.   However, if any number of pulses less than 32 have been applied, this fact could not be determined from the output register.   Some form of interpolation is thus very desirable.   Interpolation can be accomplished if two items of information can be made available.

First, it must be known in what state, conducting or nonconducting, was each of the trigger tubes before the pulses were started.

Second, as the counting progresses, continuous information must be available as to which tube in each trigger pair is conducting. The first requirement is easily satisfied by forcing a known tube to conduct in each trigger pair before the scaling or counting operation is begun. A means of doing this is shown in Fig. 8-36. Instead of directly grounding the grid resistors in all trigger pairs, one resistor in each pair is connected so that it can be tied momentarily to a positive potential. If the switch in Fig. 8-36 is thrown to position

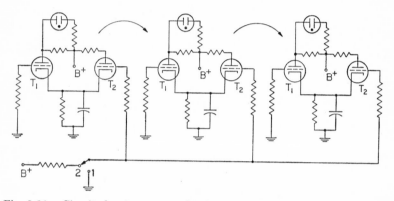

Fig. 8-36. Circuit showing reset and indicating systems for cascaded trigger pairs.

2 before the pulses are to be counted, each trigger pair will begin with the T_2 tube conducting. A switch of this type is usually called the *reset* in commercial scalers.

To find out which tube in each pair is conducting at any given time, ammeters could be placed in the plate or cathode circuits of the tubes, or voltmeters could be placed across the tubes. Perhaps the simplest voltmeter that can be used consists of a small gas diode in series with a large resistance. The gas diode, usually a neon tube, can be placed from plate to ground, or even across the plate load resistance of one tube. If placed across the plate load resistor, a glowing diode indicates a conducting tube. If placed from plate to cathode, an "on" diode indicates an "off" tube. It is not necessary to use two indicators per trigger pair, since under proper operation, if one tube is conducting, the other is not. An indicator system is shown in Fig. 8-36.

Consider the system of the five trigger pairs for which complete information is available as to which tubes are conducting and which tubes are not. They are cascaded in such a way that a negative output pulse from any pair will actuate the following pair. The neon indicators will be placed across the load resistors of the T_1 tubes. The output pulses will be taken from the plates of the T_2 tubes, while the reset system will allow the grid resistors of the T_2 tubes to be momentarily connected to a positive potential. The table of Fig. 8-37 shows which indicator lamp will be on after a

Number of Pulses	#1 Indicator	#2 Indicator	#3 Indicator	#4 Indicator	#5 Indicator
0	O	O	O	O	O
1	X	O	O	O	O
2	O	X	O	O	O
3	X	X	O	O	O
4	O	O	X	O	O
5	X	O	X	O	O
6	O	X	X	O	O
7	X	X	X	O	O
8	O	O	O	X	O
9	X	O	O	X	O
10	O	X	O	X	O
11	X	X	O	X	O
12	O	O	X	X	O
13	X	O	X	X	O
14	O	X	X	X	O
15	X	X	X	X	O
16	O	O	O	O	X
17	X	O	O	O	X
18	O	X	O	O	X
19	X	X	O	O	X

Fig. 8-37. Condition of the tubes in a system of five cascaded trigger pairs.

definite number of negative input pulses have entered the system. A circle indicates that the neon tube is off, a cross that the tube is on. If the indicator lights are numbered 1, 2, 4, 8, 16, respectively, the table shows that the total number of pulses at any time can be obtained by merely adding up the labeled number of the "on" tubes. This numbering system will be justified in the following section. The interpolating lights, however, can indicate only the number of pulses that have arrived since the system was last in the original, or reset, state. The number of times that the system has repeated can be determined by the number of output pulses from the last trigger pair.

8-11 Use of the Binary Number System

In the previous section, a numbering scheme for the interpolating lamps in a 2^N counter or scaler was given. The use of such a numbering system is an adaption of the binary number system. Before the operation of the cascaded trigger circuit is compared to the binary system, the more familiar decade system will be investigated.

In the familiar decade system of positional notation, ten numbers are used, that is, 0, 1, 2, 3, 4, 5, 6, 7, 8 and 9. Any number can be represented as the sum of the following terms:

$$S = k_n \times 10^n + k_{n-1} \times 10^{n-1} + \cdots$$
$$+ k_1 \times 10^1 + k_0 \times 10^0 \quad (8\text{-}54)$$

To write a number in the decade system, the coefficients k_n, k_{n-1}, $\cdots k_1$, k_0, are presented left to right, in the order given. All coefficients are less than 10, since 9 is the largest number in the decade system. Thus the number 26,743 is the sum of the following terms:

$$S = 2 \times 10^4 + 6 \times 10^3 + 7 \times 10^2 + 4 \times 10^1 + 3 \times 10^0 \quad (8\text{-}55)$$

Writing the coefficients in order gives 26743.

The binary system is treated in exactly the same manner, but now only two numbers are available, 0 and 1. Thus all coefficients must be either one or the other of these numbers. The number 863 in the decade system could be formed in the binary system by

$$S = 1 \times 2^9 + 1 \times 2^8 + 0 \times 2^7 + 1 \times 2^6 + 0 \times 2^5 + 1 \times 2^4$$
$$+ 1 \times 2^3 + 1 \times 2^2 + 1 \times 2^1 + 1 \times 2^0 \quad (8\text{-}56)$$

Writing the coefficients in order would give the binary form of the number, or 1101011111. For simplicity the decade system has been used to indicate the exponentials in the series of Eq. (8-56).

A comparison of the binary and decade systems for numbers between 0 and 10 is shown in Fig. 8-38. A study of this comparison

Decade	1	2	3	4	5	6	7	8	9	10
Binary	1	10	11	100	101	110	111	1000	1001	1010

Fig. 8-38. Relation between binary and decade systems.

and the table of Fig. 8-37 shows a very interesting comparison. The presence of a 0 in the table of Fig. 8-38 is analogous to a 0 in the table of Fig. 8-37, while an X in Fig. 8-37 is comparable to a 1 in the second table. If Fig. 8-37 is read from right to left, the indicating lights give the coefficients of the binary series. The reason for labeling or weighting the indicators by 1, 2, 4, 8, $\cdots$ is thus apparent.

The previous discussion is not restricted to the binary system, but can be applied to a number system of any base. In order to use the scheme just described, the basic scaling circuit must count down by a factor equal to the number base used. Thus if a basic unit could be found which would count down by a factor of P, a system of cascaded units would count down by P^N where N is the number of units. A more complex indicating method would also be necessary to obtain interpolation, because now P numbers are available to be used as coefficients instead of just 0 and 1 as was the case for the binary system.

The only systems in general use are the binary and decade systems. The binary system has the advantage of being economical in tubes and associated parts, but it does not conveniently fit in with the universally used decade system. It will be shown in the following section that count-down ratios of any integral value may be obtained if the expenditures of tubes and parts is warranted by the problem at hand.

8-12 Trigger Circuit Scaling System for Any Integral Value

Perhaps the most direct method of obtaining an arbitrary count-down ratio with cascaded trigger circuits is by use of a ring or closed loop system. This closed loop will contain P cascaded trigger pairs, with each pair effectively counting down by a factor of 2.

However, the output of the last trigger pair will be brought back to the input of the first. A reset system must be used which will initially make the right-hand tube in $P - 1$ pairs conduct. The grids of the left-hand tubes in each pair are also brought out to a common input through small capacitors. The first negative pulse

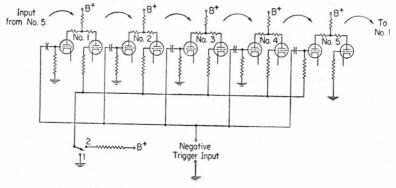

Fig. 8-39.   Closed ring system of cascaded trigger pairs.

Number of Input Pulses	Number 1 Pair	Number 2 Pair	Number 3 Pair	Number 4 Pair	Number 5 Pair
0	O X	O X	O X	O X	X O
1	X O	O X	O X	O X	O X
2	O X	X O	O X	O X	O X
3	O X	O X	X O	O X	O X
4	O X	O X	O X	X O	O X
5	O X	O X	O X	O X	X O

Fig. 8-40.   Condition of the tubes in the system of Fig. 8-39.

will trigger but one pair, since in all other pairs the negative pulse is applied to an "off" grid. When the one affected pair is triggered, the output pulse will be such as to trigger the following pair through the normal coupling system. The entire ring then remains stable until the next pulse comes along. Output can be taken from the trigger pair that did not have its right-hand tube conducting under reset conditions. The operation of a five-trigger-pair system is shown in Fig. 8-39. Only the pertinent parts of the trigger pairs have been shown, the feedback networks and the coupling systems having been omitted.

If an indicating lamp were placed on the corresponding tube in each pair, an "on" light could be made to "rotate" around the rings once for every five input pulses. Off-on conditions for each tube are indicated in Fig. 8-40.

8-13 Feedback in Cascaded Trigger Circuits

The circuit of Fig. 8-32 has two labeled terminals which have not been discussed. They are *feedback input* and *feedback output*. Their use will now be shown.

The theoretical possibilities of using a form of feedback on a system of cascaded trigger circuits will first be considered. A system of four trigger pairs as shown in Fig. 8-41 will be used as an

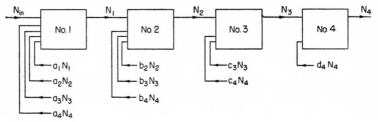

Fig. 8-41. Generalized system of feedback in cascaded trigger pairs.

example. With no form of feedback this system would have a count-down ratio of 2^4, or 16. Feedback can be applied in several ways. For example, the circuit may be altered so that the input to any trigger pair is the normal input plus the outputs of any or all of the following trigger pairs. To make the analysis more general, it will be considered that the input to each trigger pair consists of the sum of the normal input and all the subsequent outputs. The outputs of the No. 1, No. 2, No. 3, and No. 4 trigger pairs are N_1, N_2, N_3, and N_4, respectively, while N_{in} is the number of the input pulses. The input to the No. 1 pair is then

$$(N_{in})_1 = N_{in} + a_1 N_1 + a_2 N_2 + a_3 N_3 + a_4 N_4 \qquad (8-57)$$

The constants a_1, a_2, a_3, and a_4 are either zero or one, depending upon whether or not that particularly feedback line exists. The output of No. 1 can then be written

$$N_1 = \frac{1}{2}(N_{in} + a_1N_1 + a_2N_2 + a_3N_3 + a_4N_4) \qquad (8\text{-}58)$$

Similarly,

$$N_2 = \frac{1}{2}(N_1 + b_2N_2 + b_3N_3 + b_4N_4) \qquad (8\text{-}59)$$

$$N_3 = \frac{1}{2}(N_2 + c_3N_3 + c_4N_4) \qquad (8\text{-}60)$$

$$N_4 = \frac{1}{2}(N_3 + d_4N_4) \qquad (8\text{-}61)$$

Rewriting the previous equations gives

$$N_1(a_1 - 2) + N_2(a_2) + N_3(a_3) + N_4(a_4) = -N_{in} \qquad (8\text{-}62)$$

$$N_1(1) + N_2(b_2 - 2) + N_3(b_3) + N_4(b_4) = 0 \qquad (8\text{-}63)$$

$$0 + N_2(1) + N_3(c_3 - 2) + N_4(c_4) = 0 \qquad (8\text{-}64)$$

$$0 + 0 + N_3(1) + N_4(d_4 - 2) = 0 \qquad (8\text{-}65)$$

The count-down ratio is N_{in}/N_4. Solving for N_4,

$$D = \begin{vmatrix} (a_1 - 2) & a_2 & a_3 & a_4 \\ 1 & (b_2 - 2) & b_3 & b_4 \\ 0 & 1 & (c_3 - 2) & c_4 \\ 0 & 0 & 1 & (d_4 - 2) \end{vmatrix} \qquad (8\text{-}66)$$

$$DN_4 = \begin{vmatrix} (a_1 - 2) & a_2 & a_3 & -N_{in} \\ 1 & (b_2 - 2) & b_3 & 0 \\ 0 & 1 & (c_3 - 2) & 0 \\ 0 & 0 & 1 & 0 \end{vmatrix} \qquad (8\text{-}67)$$

$$N_4 = \frac{DN_4}{D} = \frac{N_{in}}{D} \qquad (8\text{-}68)$$

The count-down ratio can then be written as

$$\text{Count-down ratio} = \frac{N_{in}}{N_4} = D \qquad (8\text{-}69)$$

$$= \begin{vmatrix} (a_1 - 2) & a_2 & a_3 & a_4 \\ 1 & (b_2 - 2) & b_3 & b_4 \\ 0 & 1 & (c_3 - 2) & c_4 \\ 0 & 0 & 1 & (d_4 - 2) \end{vmatrix} \qquad (8\text{-}70)$$

The system can be easily extended for N cascaded trigger circuits, each with feedback as previously defined. However, the sign of the solution for DN_N is dependent upon whether N is odd or even, so the determinant giving the count-down ratio must be multiplied by $(-1)^N$.

$$\text{Count-down ratio} = (-1)^N \begin{vmatrix} (a_1-2) & a_2 & a_3 & \cdots & a_N \\ 1 & (b_2-2) & b_3 & \cdots & b_N \\ 0 & 1 & \cdot & & \cdot \\ \cdot & 0 & \cdot & & \cdot \\ \cdot & \cdot & \cdot & & \cdot \\ \cdot & \cdot & \cdot & & \cdot \\ \cdot & \cdot & \cdot & & \cdot \\ \cdot & \cdot & \cdot & & \cdot \\ 0 & \cdot & \cdot & & (N_N-2) \end{vmatrix}$$

$$(8\text{-}71)$$

It must be realized that the previous analysis has been only a theoretical approach to the problem. For any given circuit, most of the feedback coefficients must necessarily be zero, due to practical considerations. If all coefficients become zero, the count-down ratio will be 2^N. Also, as previously stated, the indicated system is but one of the ways to apply feedback to a series of cascaded trigger circuits. It would be impossible to use the type of feedback shown if action through the cascaded trigger circuits were instantaneous, that is, it is impossible to force a trigger circuit to change both ways at once. In some cases it may thus be necessary to delay, in some manner, the feedback pulses.

If all coefficients in the four-trigger-pair combination are made zero except b_4 and c_4, an interesting and useful result is obtained. A block diagram is shown in Fig. 8-42. Evaluating the determinant

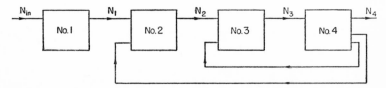

Fig. 8-42.   System of feedback in four trigger pairs to give a count-down ratio of ten.

to obtain the count-down ratio gives

$$\text{Count-down ratio} = \begin{vmatrix} -2 & 0 & 0 & 0 \\ 1 & -2 & 0 & 1 \\ 0 & 1 & -2 & 1 \\ 0 & 0 & 1 & -2 \end{vmatrix} \qquad (8\text{-}72)$$

The reason for selecting the particular coefficients b_4 and c_1 is to obtain the convenient count-down ratio of 10, which will allow decade systems to be devised. The $b_4 - c_4$ combination is not the only set which will give a decade scale; for example, b_3 and b_4, a_3 and c_4, and a_3 and b_3 will all give a scale of 10. Some of these combinations may be ruled out by undue complexity when an attempt is made to construct the physical circuit.

A physical system utilizing the $b_4 - c_4$ combination is shown in Fig. 8-43. The output of the plate of T_8 is applied through an RC

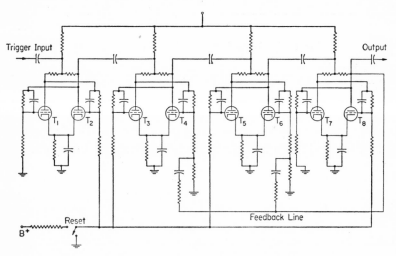

Fig. 8-43. Schematic diagram for the system of Fig. 8-42.

combination to the grids of T_4 and T_6. At the time this plate drops in potential, both feedback grids are high in potential, so the second and third trigger pairs are each triggered again. Thus the operation of the circuit fits the original mathematical description.

If the grids of T_2, T_4, T_6, and T_8 were tied into the reset system as previously explained (which they are not in Fig. 8-43), and if operation started from these reset conditions, the sketch of Fig. 8-44 could be drawn. The tubes T_2, T_4, T_6, and T_8 will be initially conducting, this being indicated by a minimum plate voltage in Fig. 8-44. Ordinary binary operation will take place until the six-

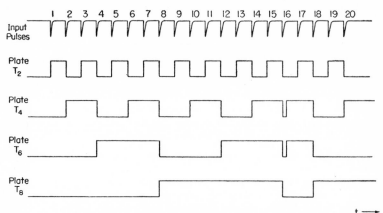

Fig. 8-44. Wave forms for the circuit of Fig. 8-43.

teenth pulse arrives. At this time feedback trips the second and third pairs again, and thus at the end of the sixteenth pulse all four trigger pairs are in the same condition as they were after the sixth pulse. From now on the system will operate between 6 and 16, with 1 output pulse for every 10 input pulses. By proper choice of the grids used for rest purposes, the initial condition can be made to represent any number between 1 and 16. The reset system of Fig. 8-43 sets up conditions similar to those that would normally exist after 6 pulses had arrived. Thus the circuit of Fig. 8-43 is a true decade scaling system.

By judicious use of a reset system in cascaded trigger circuits, predetermined counters can be devised; that is, the circuit can be made to give an indication after any desired number of pulses have been counted. This indication can be made to control automatically for many other purposes. A typical system might count pills going into a bottle until the required number has been supplied, whereupon the trigger circuit would cause a mechanism to remove the full bottle and supply an empty one.

If the original indicating system of four neon lights is used in the circuit of Fig. 8-43, the indicated count will always be too high by six. If the problem demands a better system, it is always possible to insert indicator lights into the circuit in such a manner that a true count is obtained. The count-down ratio of a series of cascaded trigger circuits is equal to the total number of stable states regardless of the type of feedback. For every stable state there is a set of voltages in the circuit which is unique to that state. Thus a light may be connected so that it is operated by that given combination of voltages and none other.

REFERENCES

1. Alfven, H., "A Simple Scale-Of-Two Counter," *Proc. Phys. Soc.*, May, 1938, Vol. 50, p. 358.
2. Astrom, Bjorn, "Decade Pulse Counter for Geiger-Muller Tubes," *Rev. Sci. Instruments*, April, 1950, Vol. 21, p. 323.
3. Baker, G. T., "Computation Problems in Circuit Design," *P.O. Elec. Eng. J.*, July, 1946, Vol. 39, p. 58.
4. Baker, G. T., "A Cyclic Electronic Counter," *J. Sci. Instruments*, April, 1948, Vol. 25, p. 127.
5. Blair, J. M., "An Improved Current Integrator," *Rev. Sci. Instruments*, March, 1943, Vol. 14, p. 64.
6. Bliss, Warren, H., "Electronic Digital Counters," *Elec. Eng.*, April, 1949, Vol. 68, p. 309.
7. Bliss, W. Roderick, "An Effective Diversity Adaptor," *CQ*, July, 1948, Vol. 4, p. 13.
8. Blume, Richard J., "Predetermined Counter for Process Control," *Electronics*, February, 1948, Vol. 21, p. 88.
9. Brown, Cyril, H., "Plug in Scaler for Industrial Counting," *Electronics*, July, 1948, Vol. 21, p. 90.
10. Brown, Sanborn C., "Theory and Operation of Geiger-Muller Counters, Part III," *Nucleonics*, October, 1948, Vol. 3, p. 46.
11. Brunetti, Cledo, "The Transitron Oscillator," *Proc. IRE*, February, 1939, Vol. 27, p. 88.
12. Brunetti, Cledo and Weiss, Eric, "Theory and Application of Resistance Tuning," *Proc. IRE*, June, 1941, Vol. 29, p. 333.
13. Brunetti, Cledo, "Characteristics of the Transitron Oscillator," *Communications*, June, 1944, Vol. 24, p. 40.
14. Burks, A. W., "Electronic Computing Circuits of the ENIAC," *Proc. IRE*, August, 1947, Vol. 35, p. 756.
15. Buys, W. L., "Analysis of Scale Units," *Nucleonics*, November, 1948, Vol. 3, p. 49.

16. Chance, Britton; Hughes, Vernon; MacNichol, Edward F.; Sayre, David; and Williams, Frederick C., *Waveforms*. New York: McGraw-Hill Book Co., Inc., 1949.

17. Chase, R. L., "Measuring Varying Frequency," *Electronics*, March, 1950, Vol. 23, p. 110.

18. Colebrook, F. M., "A Valve Voltmeter with Retroactive Direct-Voltage Amplification," *Wireless Engr.*, March, 1938, Vol. 15, p. 138.

19. Cooke-Yarborough, E. H., "A New Pulse Amplitude Discriminator Circuit," *J. Sci. Instruments*, March, 1949, Vol. 26, p. 96.

20. Cooke-Yarborough, E. H. and Putman, J. L., "A Simple Combined Coincidence and Anti-Coincidence Circuit," *J. Sci. Instruments*, July, 1949, Vol. 26, p. 240.

21. Corby Robert E., "Acoustic Anemometer-Anemoscope," *Electronics*, January, 1950, Vol. 23, p. 88.

22. Couch, Wm. F. Jr., "Scaler Circuits," *Radio News-Electronic Eng. Supplement*, June, 1948, Vol. 10, p. 3; August, 1948, Vol. 11, p. 10.

23. Degelmen, J., "Phototube Operated Trigger Circuit," *Electronics*, January, 1948, Vol. 21, p. 134.

24. DeVault, Don, "Vacuum Tube Scaling Circuit," *Rev. Sci. Instruments*, February, 1941, Vol. 14, p. 23.

26. Eberhard, E.; Endres, R. O.; and Moore, R. P., "Counter Circuits Using Transistors," *RCA Rev.*, December, 1949, Vol. 10, p. 459.

27. Eccles, W. H. and Jordan, F. W., "Trigger Relay Utilizing Three Element Thermionic Vacuum Tubes," *Radio Rev.*, October, 1919, Vol. 1, p. 143.

28. Elmore, William C. and Sands, Matthew, *Electronics—Experimental Techniques*. New York: McGraw-Hill Book Co., Inc., 1949.

29. Emery, W. L., *Ultra-High Frequency Radio Engineering*. New York: The Macmillan Company, 1944.

30. Fitch, Val, "A High Resolution Scale-of-Four," *Rev. Sci. Instruments*, December, 1949, Vol. 20, p. 942.

31. Fitzgerald, Alan S., "Feedback in Magnetic Amplifiers," *J. Franklin Inst.*, Part I, March, 1949, Vol. 247, p. 223; Part II, May, 1949, Vol. 247, p. 457.

32. Florman, E. F., and Tait, Andrew, "An Electronic Phasemeter," *Proc. IRE*, February, 1949, Vol. 37, p. 207.

33. Freas, R. R., "Direct-Reading Electronic Timer," *RCA Rev.*, December, 1949, Vol. 10, p. 554.

34. Giarratana, Joseph, "Scale of Eight Counting Circuit," *Rev. Sci. Instruments*, October, 1937, Vol. 8, p. 391.

35. Gossick, B. R., "Predetermined Electronic Counter," *Proc. IRE*, July, 1949, Vol. 37, p. 813.

36. Grosdoff, I. E., "Electronic Counters," *RCA Rev.*, September, 1946, Vol. 7, p. 438.

37. Herold, E. W., "Negative Resistance and Devices for Obtaining It," *Proc. IRE*, October, 1935, Vol. 23, p. 1201.

38. Higinbotham, W. A.; Gallagher, James; and Sands, Matthew, "Model 200 Pulse Counter," *Rev. Sci. Instruments*, October, 1947, Vol. 18, p. 706.

39. Howland, Bradford, "Scale of N Counting Circuit," *Electronics*, July, 1947, Vol. 20, p. 138.

40. Hull, A. W., "The Dynatron, A Vacuum Tube Possessing Negative Resistance," *Proc. IRE*, February, 1918, Vol. 6, p. 5.

41. Huntoon, R. D. and Strohmeyer, L. J., "A Hard Vacuum Tube Pulse Equalizing, Sharpening Circuit," *Rev. Sci. Instruments*, January, 1941, Vol. 12, p. 35.

42. Korff, Serge A., *Electron and Nuclear Counters*. New York: D. Van Nostrand Company, Inc., 1946.

43. Kretzmer, Ernest R., "Measuring Phase at Audio and Ultrasonic Frequencies," *Electronics*, October, 1949, Vol. 22, p. 114.

44. Kruse, O. E. and Watson, R. B., "Audio Frequency Phasemeter," *Audio Eng.*, February, 1950, Vol. 34, p. 9.

45. Lamb, James J. and Brustman, Joseph, A., "Polycathode Glow Tubes for Counters and Calculators," *Electronics*, November, 1949, Vol. 22, p. 92.

46. Leslie, C. B., "Megacycle Stepping Counter," *Proc. IRE*, August, 1949, Vol. 36, p. 1030.

47. Lewis, Clark, "An Instrument for the Measurement and Time Integration of Small Voltages and Currents," *J. Sci. Instruments*, March, 1949, Vol. 26, p. 80.

48. Lewis, W. B., *Electrical Counting*. New York: Cambridge University Press, 1942.

49. Lifshutz, H. and Lawson, J. L., "Triode Vacuum Tube Scale of Two Circuits," *Rev. Sci. Instruments*, March, 1938, Vol. 9, p. 83.

50. Lifshutz, Harold, "A Complete Geiger-Muller Counting System," *Rev. Sci. Instruments*, January, 1939, Vol. 10, p. 21.

51. Lifshutz, Harold, "New Vacuum Scaling Circuit of Arbitrary Integral or Fractional Scaling Ratio," *Phys. Rev.*, February, 1940, Vol. 57, p. 243.

52. Lowde, R. D., "A New Scale-of-Ten Recorder," *J. Sci. Instruments*, December, 1947, Vol. 24, p. 322.

53. Lurie, W. B., "High-Speed Trigger Circuits," *Electronics*, April, 1949, Vol. 22, p. 85.

54. Martens, Frederick H., "Differential Counting With Reversible Decade Counting Circuit," *Rev. Sci. Instruments*, June, 1949, Vol. 20, p. 424.

55. Martin, Thomas L., Jr., *Ultra High Frequency Engineering*. New York: Prentice-Hall, Inc., 1950.

56. McMaster, Herold, and Pool, M. L., "Some Improvements in a Geiger-

Muller Counting System," *Rev., Sci. Instruments*, June, 1940, Vol. 11, p. 196.

57. Middleton, D., "Spurious Signals Caused by Noise in Trigger Circuits," *J. Applied Phys.*, September, 1948, Vol. 19, p. 817.

58. Miller, C. F. and McLean, W. S., "New Design for a Secondary Emission Trigger Tube," *Proc. IRE*, August, 1949, Vol. 37, p. 452.

59. M.I.T. Radar School Staff, *Principles of Radar*. New York: McGraw-Hill Book Co., Inc., 1946.

60. Moerman, A. N., "Two Decade Electronic Counter," *Radio News-Electronic Eng. Supplements*, January, 1946, Vol. 35, p. 6.

61. Muehlhause, C. O. and Friedman, H., "Measurement of High Intensities With the Geiger-Mueller Counter," *Rev. Sci. Instruments*, November, 1946, Vol. 17, p. 506.

62. Neher, H. V., "High Speed Mechanical Recorder," *Rev. Sci. Instruments*, January, 1939, Vol. 10, p. 29.

63. Ostendorff, B., Jr., "A New Electronic Telegraph Regenerative Repeater," *Elec. Eng.*, March, 1950, Vol. 69, p. 237.

64. Page, C. H., "Digital Computer Switching Circuits," *Electronics*, September, 1948, Vol. 21, p. 110.

65. Phelps, Byron, E., "Dual-Triode Trigger Circuits," *Electronics*, July, 1945, Vol. 18, p. 110.

66. Potter, John T., "A Four-Tube Counter Decade," *Electronics*, June, 1944, Vol. 17, p. 110.

67. Regener, V. H., "Design and Use of Directly Coupled Trigger Pairs," *Rev. Sci. Instruments*, May, 1946, Vol. 17, p. 180.

68. Regener, V. H., "Decade Counting Circuits," *Rev. Sci. Instruments*, May, 1946, Vol. 17, p. 185.

69. Regener, V. H., "Reversible Decade Counting Circuit, *Rev. Sci. Instruments*, October, 1946, Vol. 17, p. 375.

70. Reich, Herbert J., "A Low Distortion Audio Frequency Oscillator," *Proc. IRE*, November, 1937, Vol. 25, p. 1387.

71. Reich, H. J., "A New Vacuum Tube Counting Circuit," *Rev. Sci. Instruments*, July, 1938, Vol. 9, p. 222.

72. Reich, H. J., "Trigger Circuits, *Electronics*, August, 1939, Vol. 12, p. 14.

73. Reich, Herbert J., "An Electronic Switch for the Simultaneous Observation of Two Waves with the Cathode-Ray Oscillograph," *Rev. Sci. Instruments*, April, 1941, Vol. 12, p. 191.

74. Reich, H. J., *Theory and Applications of Electron Tubes*. New York: McGraw-Hill Book Co., Inc., 1944.

75. Reich, Herbert J. and Ungrary, L., "A Transistor Trigger Circuit," *Rev. Sci. Instruments*, August, 1949, Vol. 20, p. 586.

76. Rotblat, J.; Sayle, E. A.; and Thomas, D. G. A., "Scale of Hundred Counting Unit," *J. Sci. Instruments*, February, 1948, Vol. 25, p. 33.
77. Schmitt, O. H., "A Thermionic Trigger," *J. Sci. Instruments*, January, 1938, Vol. 15, p. 24.
78. Seren, L., "Decade Ring Scaling Circuit," *Rev. Sci. Instruments*, September, 1947, Vol. 18, p. 654.
79. Sharpless, T. K., "High Speed N-Scale Counters," *Electronics*, March, 1948, Vol. 21, p. 122.
80. Shea, Gregory, "Electronic True Decade Counters," *Elec. Ind.*, September, 1946, Vol. 5, p. 82.
81. Shepherd, W. G. and Haxby, R. O., "Scale of Eight Impulse Counter," *Rev. Sci. Instruments*, November, 1936, Vol. 7, p. 425.
82. Starr, A. T., "A Trigger Peak Voltmeter Using Hard Valves, "*Wireless Engr.*, November, 1935, Vol. 12, p. 601.
83. Stevens, Louis D., Jr., "A Wide Range Pulse Shaper," *Radio News- Electronic Eng. Supplement*, September, 1949, Vol. 13, p. 15.
84. Stevenson, E. C. and Getting, I. A., "A Vacuum Tube Scaling Circuit for Scaling Down Counting Rates," *Rev. Sci. Instruments*, November, 1937, Vol. 8, p. 417.
85. Tombs, D. Martineau, "Negative and Positive Resistance," *Wireless Engr.*, August, 1942, Vol. 19, p. 341.
86. Toomin, Hershel, "Switching Action of the Eccles-Jordan Trigger Circuit," *Rev. Sci. Instruments*, June, 1939, Vol. 10, p. 191.
87. Urban, John V., "Electronic Counting," *Radio News- Electronic Eng. Supplement*, August, 1947, Vol. 38, p. 8.
88. van der Pol, Balth, "On Relaxation Oscillations," *Phil. Mag.*, November, 1926, Vol. 2, p. 978.
89. Watkins, Dean A., "The Ten Channel Electrostatic Pulse Analyzer," *Rev. Sci. Instruments*, July, 1949, Vol. 20, p. 495.
90. Weissman, Richard, "Stable Ten-Light Decade Scaler," *Electronics*, May, 1949, Vol. 22, p. 84.
91. Wellman, B. and Roeder, K., "Electronic Counter for Rapid Impulses," *Electronics*, October, 1942, Vol. 15, p. 74.
92. Wild, J. J., "Predetermined Counters," *Electronics*, March, 1947, Vol. 20, p. 121.
93. Wolfe, A. E., Jr., and Steele, F. G., "Direct Reading Electronic Clock," *Electronics*, December, 1949, Vol. 22, p. 75.
94. Wynn-Williams, C. E., "The Use of Thyratrons for High Speed-Automatic Counting of Physical Phenomena," *Proc. Roy. Soc.*, July, 1931, Vol. 132, p. 295.
95. Wynn-Williams, C. E., "Thyratron Scale of Two Automatic Counter," *Proc. Roy. Soc.*, May, 1932, Vol. 136, p. 312.

96. Yu, Y. P., "Regenerative Amplifiers," *Proc. IRE,* September, 1949, Vol. 37, p. 1046.

97. Zuharis, G., "Television Synchronizing Generator," *Electronics,* May, 1950, Vol. 23, p. 92.

PROBLEMS

8-1 A gas discharge tube has a volt-ampere characteristic which can be approximately represented over part of its range by the following equations

$$i = 0.8e \qquad 0 < e < 50$$

$$i = \frac{2000}{e} \qquad 50 < e < 250$$

where i is in milliamperes and e is in volts. For values of e greater than 250 volts, i again increases. If a constant voltage of 300 volts and a linear resistor of 10,000 ohms are placed in series with this gas tube, find the possible points of operation and show whether they are stable or unstable.

8-2 Using the symmetrical circuit of Fig. 8-7 and neglecting the resistance R and the voltage E, show that the relationship necessary to have changing voltages and currents in the system without any driving signal is similar to that of Eq. (8-12). (See the technique of Sec. 8-4.)

8-3 Derive Eq. (8-20).

8-4 Find the resistance looking into the points $P_1 - P_2$ in the circuit of Fig. 8-11, assuming a linear dynamic circuit. Consider the tubes to be identical. Show that the condition necessary to have a negative input resistance is similar to Eq. (8-20).

8-5 Calculate the steady-state grid and plate potentials for both tubes in

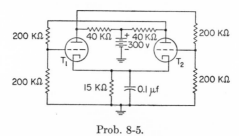

Prob. 8-5.

the trigger circuit shown. The tube is a 6SN7.

8-6 Calculate the steady-state grid and plate potentials in the circuit of Fig. 8-31. The tube is a 12AT7. The supply voltage is 300 volts.

8-7 In the circuit of Fig. 8-22b, R_b = 500,000 ohms, C = 0.1 microfarad, R_g = 100,000 ohms, C_g = 50 micromicrofarads, E_{bb} = 300 volts, and E_{cc} = −100 volts. The tubes are both 884's. Find the amplitude of a square wave needed to trigger the system. Sketch and label the cathode voltage for such an input signal.

8-8 Estimate the amplitude of the input signal needed to trigger the circuit of Fig. 8-31.

8-9 Write the number 109.64 (decade system) in the binary system.

8-10 Devise a feedback arrangement which will enable three cascaded trigger pairs to give a count-down ratio of five.

8-11 A decade scaler similar to that of Fig. 8-43 has been constructed. It is desired to use a system of 10 neon lights as indicators such that the lights will directly indicate the state of the scaler, that is, the No. 1 light alone is to be lit after the first pulse, the No. 2 light alone after the second pulse, etc. Show how these lights may be connected.

8-12 Calculate the upper and lower critical values for the grid voltage of

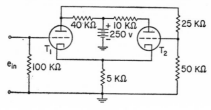

Prob. 8-12.

T_1 in the circuit shown.

8-13 The circuit of problem 8–12 is driven by a 100-volt rms, 60-cycle sine wave. Sketch and label a complete set of grid, plate, and cathode wave forms.

8-14 In the square wave shown f is constant at 60 cycles per second. While Δt may range from 400 to 5000 microseconds in length, it will remain at any given value for several seconds at a time. It is necessary to measure

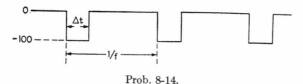

Prob. 8-14.

the value of Δt to an accuracy of 1 microsecond and have the results of this measurement presented visually. Sketch and explain a system to provide the desired measurement.

8-15 The coil shown can be used as a component in a scaling circuit if the core has the indicated hysteresis characteristic. Sketch and explain a

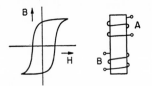

Prob. 8-15.

system which will allow such components to be cascaded for scaling operation. Consider the A and B windings to be used for the output and input circuits, respectively. A current of 100 milliamperes in either winding is sufficient to cause saturation. It may be necessary to use unilateral elements as coupling devices.

CHAPTER NINE

MULTIVIBRATORS

The first mention of the term *multivibrator* was by Abraham and Bloch in several French government publications during the period 1917–1919.[1] These authors considered the multivibrator as an oscillator which is extremely rich in harmonics, and thus one which is valuable for various forms of frequency measurement. Their name "multivibrateurs" was suggested by this abundance of harmonics.

The multivibrator can also be synchronized at a submultiple of a driving signal and thus can be used to count down in frequency as well as to supply higher harmonics.

Perhaps the greatest use of the multivibrator lies in its capabilities of supplying many different voltage and current wave forms. For example, multivibrators, can be devised which will supply pulse voltages, trapezoid voltages, or sawtooth sweep voltages.

9-1 General Discussion

Multivibrators may be classified in two different ways. The first way refers to the form of operation, that is, a multivibrator may be a free-running oscillator, or may require an external signal to drive it into a form of oscillation. In order to have operation of either type, there must be some means of positive feedback or regeneration. The second method of classification refers to the method by which this feedback is obtained.

Multivibrators which have a stable or nonoscillatory state, but which can be driven into an unstable state by an external signal, are quite commonly called single-cycle multivibrators. When an input signal is applied, such a multivibrator goes through a single cycle of

[1] See reference 3 at end of chapter.

operation, eventually returning to the initial state. Other names for this type of multivibrator are *start-stop*, *one-shot*, or *mono-stable* multivibrator.

The free-running type of multivibrator is quite often synchronized with a driving signal, but, differing from single-cycle operation, the oscillation does not stop when the signal is removed.

Feedback can be obtained by coupling from the plates to the grids of the tubes as is done in the Eccles-Jordan trigger circuit, or it can be obtained by cathode coupling as used in the Schmitt trigger circuit. Actually, the Schmitt circuit uses a combination of plate and cathode coupling.

Perhaps the easiest way to begin a study of multivibrators is by comparison with the Eccles-Jordan circuit. This trigger circuit was found to have two stable operating conditions. If, in this funda-

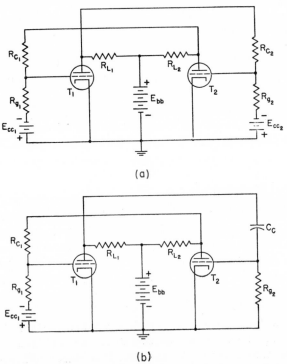

(a)

(b)

Fig. 9-1. (a) Eccles-Jordan trigger circuit. (b) Single-cycle, plate-coupled multivibrator.

mental trigger circuit, one coupling resistor is replaced by a capacitor, and the bias is also removed from that side, a completely different form of operation will result.   Such a circuit is shown in
Fig. 9-1b, with the original trigger circuit given in Fig. 9-1a.

In the original trigger circuit, a drop in potential at one plate
caused the opposite grid potential to drop to a low value.   This
value was usually below cutoff or at least sufficiently low to prevent
any further regeneration.   Thus a stable state resulted, with the
grid maintaining its high negative voltage.   This type of operation
is represented by the sketch of Fig. 9-2a.   In the modified circuit of

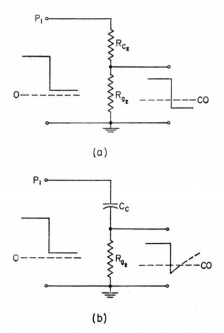

(a)

(b)

Fig. 9-2.   (a) Resistance coupling in trigger circuit.   (b) Capacitance coupling
in multivibrator.

Fig. 9-1b, the drop in potential of plate P_1 causes a corresponding
drop in the grid potential of tube T_2.   However, the grid circuit of
T_2 is now not a simple resistance voltage divider, but is a resistance-capacitance circuit, so that the grid voltage of T_2 returns
toward zero as the coupling capacitor charges.   When the grid
voltage comes up to the cutoff value, T_2 will conduct slightly.

This will lower the plate potential of T_2 and the grid potential of T_1, whereupon the familiar cumulative action will occur, with conduction being transformed back to T_2. The new circuit thus has but one stable condition. If some external signal should cause conduction to be transferred to T_1, the circuit will eventually return, without any further external disturbance, to the condition with T_2 conducting. The time required for this return will depend upon the effective time constant of the circuit, the voltages applied to the circuit, and the tube characteristics.

The circuit of Fig. 9-1b is called a plate-coupled, single-cycle multivibrator. If both coupling resistors in the basic Eccles-Jordan circuit are replaced by capacitors, a free-running, plate-coupled multivibrator will result. This is the circuit originally described by Abraham and Bloch. The circuit can be considered a combination of two single-cycle multivibrators with operation alternating back and forth between the two semistable states. No external signal is needed to cause this alternation, although one may be used to influence the rate of change.

Each basic form of multivibrator also has numerous modifications. Some of the more important of these modifications and their uses will be discussed in detail in the following sections.

9-2 Single-Cycle, Plate-Coupled Multivibrator

The Eccles-Jordan trigger circuit as modified into a single-cycle, plate-coupled multivibrator is shown in Fig. 9-3. This circuit will

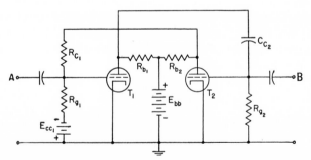

Fig. 9-3. Single-cycle, plate-coupled multivibrator.

have but one stable state, in which T_2 is conducting and T_1 is nonconducting. Under these conditions the circuit of Fig. 9-4 may be

drawn. If the circuit of Fig. 9-3 and Fig. 9-4 has been at rest for a
long time, the capacitor C_{c2} will have a potential of E_{bb} across its
terminals. The term E_{cc1} will be treated as a positive quantity;

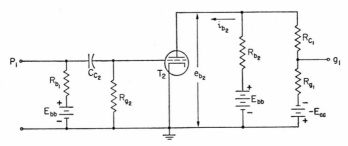

Fig. 9-4. Circuit equivalent to that of Fig. 9-3 when T_2 is conducting and T_1 is
cut off.

thus if R_{g1} is returned to a potential which is negative with respect to
ground, a negative number must be used in place of E_{cc1}. The
following equations can then be written. For the plate circuit,

$$(i_{b2})_0 + \frac{(e_{b2})_0 - E_{bb}}{R_{b2}} + \frac{(e_{b2})_0 - E_{cc1}}{R_{c1} + R_{g1}} = 0 \qquad (9\text{-}1)$$

$$\text{or } (e_{b2})_0 + (i_{b2})_0 \left[\frac{R_{b2}(R_{c1} + R_{g1})}{R_{b2} + R_{c1} + R_{g1}} \right] = \frac{E_{bb}(R_{c1} + R_{g1}) + E_{cc1}(R_{b2})}{R_{b2} + R_{c1} + R_{g1}}$$
$$(9\text{-}2)$$

The external subscript $(\ )_0$ indicates the original steady-state
values. The coefficient of the $(i_{b2})_0$ term is the equivalent resistance
in the plate circuit, and the term on the right side of the equation is
the equivalent supply voltage. Also, under steady-state conditions,
the grid voltage of T_2 will be zero.

If Eq. (9-2) is plotted on the plate characteristics of T_2, the intersection of this equation and the zero grid voltage curve will give
$(e_{b2})_0$ and $(i_{b2})_0$.

The grid voltage of T_1 is

$$(e_{c1})_0 = \frac{R_{g1}(e_{b2})_0 + R_{c1}E_{cc1}}{R_{c1} + R_{g1}} \qquad (9\text{-}3)$$

and the plate voltage is

$$(e_{b1})_0 = E_{bb} \qquad (9\text{-}4)$$

In order that the original assumptions be justified, $(e_{c1})_0$ must be negative and sufficiently great in magnitude to keep T_1 cut off for a plate voltage of E_{bb} volts.

The circuit can now be triggered in either of two general ways. A positive pulse can be applied to point A or a negative pulse can be applied to point B. The positive pulse at A must be sufficiently large to bring the grid of T_1 to a point just above the cutoff potential in order that regeneration can occur.

The amplitude of the negative pulse needed to trigger the system can only be approximated, but will be nearly that value which will cause a change of voltage at the plate of T_2 such that

$$\frac{R_{g1}}{R_{g1} + R_{c1}} \Delta e_{b2} = e_{co1} - (e_{c1})_0 \tag{9-5}$$

or
$$\Delta e_{b2} = \frac{R_{g1} + R_{c1}}{R_{g1}} [e_{co1} - (e_{c1})_0] \tag{9-6}$$

The equivalent circuit of Fig. 9-4 can be used in conjunction with the plate characteristics of T_2 to find the change in grid voltage needed to cause a change in plate voltage of Δe_{b2} volts.

It will now be assumed that conduction is instantaneously transferred from T_2 to T_1. The new equivalent circuit is shown in Fig. 9-5. For the instant just following the transfer of conduction,

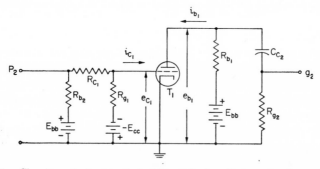

Fig. 9-5. Circuit equivalent to that of Fig. 9-3 when T_1 is conducting and T_2 is cut off.

but for no other time, the capacitor will have a terminal voltage of E_{bb}, and Eq. (9-7) may be written

$$(i_{b1})_1 + \frac{(e_{b1})_1 - E_{bb}}{R_{b1}} + \frac{(e_{b1})_1 - E_{bb}}{R_{g2}} = 0 \tag{9-7}$$

Rewriting Eq. (9-7),

$$(e_{b1})_1 + (i_{b1})_1 \left(\frac{R_{b1}R_{g2}}{R_{b1} + R_{g2}} \right) = E_{bb} \qquad (9\text{-}8)$$

The external subscript ( )$_1$ refers to conditions existing just after conduction has been transferred to T_1. Since there are no capacitors in the grid circuit, an equation can be written which will be correct so long as T_1 is conducting.

$$(i_{c1})_1 + \frac{(e_{c1})_1 - E_{cc1}}{R_{g1}} + \frac{(e_{c1})_1 - E_{bb}}{R_{c1} + R_{b1}} = 0 \qquad (9\text{-}9)$$

or $(e_{c1})_1 + (i_{c1})_1 \left[\dfrac{R_{g1}(R_{c1} + R_{b1})}{R_{c1} + R_{g1} + R_{b1}} \right] = \dfrac{E_{bb}R_{g1} + E_{cc1}(R_{c1} + R_{b1})}{R_{c1} + R_{g1} + R_{b1}}$

$$(9\text{-}10)$$

If $E_{bb}R_{g1} < |E_{cc}(R_{c1} + R_{b1})|$, $(e_{c1})_1$ will be negative and $(i_{c1})_1$ will be zero. If $(e_{c1})_1$ is negative and greater in magnitude than the cutoff potential for a plate voltage of E_{bb}, T_1 will not be conducting, and the circuit of Fig. 9-5 can never exist. Practically, such a situation will be evinced by an inability to trigger the circuit away from its normal steady-state condition where T_2 is conducting.

It is possible to trigger the circuit if $(e_{c1})_1$ is negative, but a more stable action will result if $(e_{c1})_1$ is made positive. In such a case, $(i_{c1})_1$ exists. To find the exact operating conditions just after conduction has been transferred to T_1, a set of grid-current, grid-voltage curves for various values of plate voltage is needed. A likely value of $(e_{c1})_1$ is then assumed, and by the use of plate characteristics and Eq. (9-8), a corresponding value of $(e_{b1})_1$ is found. The grid-current, grid-voltage curve for this value of $(e_{b1})_1$ is then used in conjunction with Eq. (9-10) to find a new value of $(e_{c1})_1$. The process is repeated until consistent values of $(e_{c1})_1$ and $(e_{b1})_1$ are obtained.

A simplifying approximation can again be made in the case where $(e_{c1})_1$ is positive. For most small receiving-type tubes, little error will result if the grid-current, grid-voltage characteristic is assumed linear. For tubes like 6J5, 6SN7, or 12AU7, the slope of the characteristic is approximately 1000 ohms in the region of low positive e_{c1}. If $\bar{r}_{g1}$ is assumed constant, $(e_{c1})_1$ is calculated from Eq. (9-10), and then $(e_{b1})_1$ and $(i_{b1})_1$ are found from the plate characteristics and Eq. (9-8).

The initial voltage on the grid of T_2 is

$$(e_{c2})_1 = (e_{b1})_1 - E_{bb} \tag{9-11}$$

while the voltage on the plate of T_2 is

$$(e_{b2})_1 = \frac{(e_{c1})_1 R_{b2} + E_{bb} R_{c1}}{R_{c1} + R_{b2}} \tag{9-12}$$

Once the initial conditions for the circuit of Fig. 9-5 have been found, the subsequent transient can be calculated. The capacitor C_{c2} will discharge until the grid voltage of T_2 reaches the cutoff value. Over this period of time the plate of T_2 and the grid of T_1 do not change appreciably in potential, the only variation at all being caused by a small change in $\bar{r}_{g1}$ which is due in turn to the changing plate potential of T_1. The time constant of the grid circuit of T_2 does change during the discharge, since the voltage across the tube changes and the static resistance of the tube is not constant.

It is quite possible to solve the circuit under these conditions by the use of the method outlined in Sec. 2-2. In general, however, such accuracy is not warranted, due to the labor involved. Again an approximation can be made, in this case with respect to the linearity of the plate-current, plate-voltage characteristic. Over the operating range an approximate average value of $\bar{r}_{p1}$ can be determined. One extreme of the operating range is given by the solution of $(e_{b1})_1$ and $(i_{b1})_1$ from Eq. (9-8), while the other extreme may be found by applying a supply voltage of E_{bb} and a load resistance of R_{b1} to the plate characteristics. For small values of grid voltage, the tube types previously mentioned have an $\bar{r}_p$ which can be assumed to be nearly 10,000 ohms.

The effective resistance in the grid circuit of T_2 is

$$R = \frac{\bar{r}_{p1} R_{b1}}{\bar{r}_{p1} + R_{b1}} + R_{g2} \tag{9-13}$$

The time constant is

$$\tau = \left(\frac{\bar{r}_{p1} R_{b1}}{\bar{r}_{p1} + R_{b1}} + R_{g2} \right) C_{c2} \tag{9-14}$$

The duration of the time interval during which T_2 is cut off and T_1 is conducting can now be calculated. A sketch of the grid voltage of T_2 is shown in Fig. 9-6. From this figure,

$$\Delta t = \tau \ln \frac{(e_{c2})_1}{e_{co2}} \qquad (9\text{-}15)$$

During the time Δt, the grid voltage goes through $[(e_{c2})_1 - e_{co2}]/(e_{c2})_1$ of its total change; thus the plate potential of T_1 will go

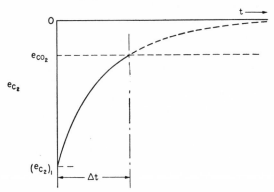

Fig. 9-6. Grid voltage of T_2 when T_2 is cut off.

through the same fraction of its total change. The final value of e_{b1} is that found from the application of E_{bb} and R_{b1} to the plate characteristics. If the final plate voltage of T_1 and the cutoff potential of T_2 are known, the final capacitor voltage may also be determined. The external subscript ( )₂ will be used to indicate conditions at this time, that is, the instant when the grid voltage of T_2 reaches the cutoff value.

When the grid potential of T_2 reaches the cutoff value, cumulative action will take place which will return T_2 to conduction and T_1 to cutoff. The equivalent circuit of Fig. 9-4 is now applicable, except that the capacitor C_{c2} does not originally have its steady-state terminal voltage of E_{bb}. The original capacitor voltage in the circuit of Fig. 9-4 is the final capacitor voltage in the circuit of Fig. 9-5. If this capacitor voltage is called $(e_c)_2$, and if the static grid resistance of T_2 is assumed constant as $\bar{r}_{g2}$,

$$(e_{c2})_3 = \frac{\bar{r}_{g2}R_{g2}[E_{bb} - (e_c)_2]}{R_{b1}R_{g2} + R_{b1}\bar{r}_{g2} + \bar{r}_{g2}R_{g2}} \qquad (9\text{-}16)$$

Quite commonly $\bar{r}_{g2} \ll R_{g2}$, in which case

$$(e_{c2})_3 = \frac{\bar{r}_{g2}[E_{bb} - (e_C)_2]}{R_{b1} + \bar{r}_{g2}} \tag{9-17}$$

The initial potential of P_1 is

$$(e_{b1})_3 = (e_{c2})_3 + (e_C)_2 \tag{9-18}$$

The external subscript ( )$_3$ indicates conditions existing just after conduction has been transferred from T_1 to T_2. Since the grid of T_2 will usually be driven quite positive, the plate of T_2 will drop to a very low value. This value is found by the intersection of the line given by Eq. (9-2) and the plate characteristic for the grid voltage of Eq. (9-17). The original grid voltage of T_1 is

$$(e_{c1})_3 = \frac{R_{g1}(e_{b2})_3 + R_{c1}(E_{cc1})}{R_{g1} + R_{c1}} \tag{9-19}$$

The time constant of the grid circuit of T_2 is

$$\tau = \left(\frac{\bar{r}_{g2} R_{g2}}{\bar{r}_{g2} + R_{g2}} + R_{b1} \right) C_{c2} \tag{9-20}$$

In approximately four time constants the circuit will be back in the steady-state condition.

The poorest approximation in the solution just given is in the assumption of a constant static resistance for T_1 when it is conducting. However, a considerable error in $\bar{r}_{p1}$ may be tolerated without greatly affecting the results. The initial and final values of e_{b1} were calculated from the plate characteristics and not from the assumed static plate resistance. The assumed value was used in the calculation of the time constant, but in this case it was added in parallel to a resistance of comparable size, the result then being added in series to a large resistance.

The assumption of a constant static grid resistance is justified by the fact that the plate characteristics are very closely spaced for positive values of grid voltage. Thus a small change in grid voltage does not cause a very large change in plate voltage.

EXAMPLE: In the circuit of Fig. 9-3, let $R_{g1} = R_{g2} = 100,000$ ohms, $R_{b1} = R_{b2} = 50,000$ ohms, $R_{c1} = 250,000$ ohms, $C_{c2} = 0.001\mu f$, $E_{cc1} = -75$ volts, $E_{bb} = 300$ volts, and let the tube be a 6SN7.

With T_2 initially conducting, Eq. (9-2) may be used and written as

$$(e_{b2})_0 + (43,800)(i_{b2})_0 = 253$$

Plotting this equation on the plate characteristics and using $(e_{c2})_0 = 0$, $(i_{b2})_0$ is found as 4.5 ma and $(e_{b2})_0$ as 56 volts. From Eq. (9-3), the quiescent grid voltage of T_1 is -37.5 volts. This is sufficiently large to keep T_1 cut off at a plate voltage of 300 volts.

To trigger the system with a positive pulse at A, a magnitude of $37.5 - 18$, or 19.5 volts is needed. To calculate the magnitude of the negative pulse needed at B, Eq. (9-6) is used.

$$\Delta e_{b2} = \frac{R_{c1} + R_{g1}}{R_{g1}} [e_{co1} - (c_{c1})_0] = 68.3 \text{ volts}$$

The change in the grid voltage of T_2 needed to achieve a plate voltage change of 68.3 volts is approximately 4.2 volts.

When conduction is transferred to T_1, the circuit of Fig. 9.5 becomes applicable. Rewriting Eq. (9-8),

$$(e_{b1})_1 + (33,300)(i_{b1})_1 = 300$$

Also $$(e_{c1})_1 + (75,000)(i_{c1})_1 = 18.75$$

If a completely graphical solution is made for $(e_{c1})_1$, a value of 0.37 volt is obtained. However, if the static grid resistance of T_1 is assumed to be 1000 ohms, the grid voltage is found as 0.25 volt. Either value will provide sufficient accuracy.

A value of $(e_{b1})_1 = 70$ volts is then found from the T_1 plate characteristics. Since the grid of T_2 must have dropped in potential by the same amount as did the plate of T_1, $(e_{c2})_1 = -230$ volts. From Eq. (9-12), the plate voltage of T_2 is

$$(e_{b2})_1 = \frac{(0.25)(10,000) + (300)(250,000)}{250,000 + 50,000} = 250 \text{ volts}$$

The assumptions that T_1 is conducting and that T_2 is at cutoff after the pulse has been applied are seen to be justified.

With T_1 conducting, the time constant of the grid circuit of T_2 is, from Eq. (9-14),

$$\tau = \left[100,000 + \frac{(10,000)(50,000)}{60,000} \right] (0.001 \times 10^{-6}) = 108.33 \text{ microseconds}$$

The value of $\bar{r}_{p1}$ has been assumed to be 10,000 ohms. From Eq. (9-15), Δt may be found as

$$\Delta t = 108.33 \ln \frac{230}{15} = 294 \text{ microseconds}$$

At the end of the Δt period, the grid voltage of T_2 has gone through $(230 - 15)/(230)$, or 93.5 per cent of its total possible change. Thus the plate voltage at the end of the period will be

$$(e_{b1})_2 = 70 - (0.935)(14) = 56.9 \text{ volts}$$

The voltage on the capacitor at this time will be $(56.9 + 15) = 71.9$ volts.

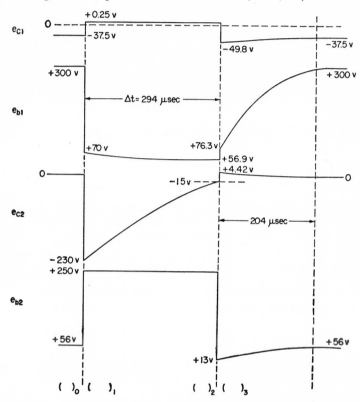

Fig. 9-7. Wave forms for the single-cycle multivibrator of Fig. 9-3.

Using Eq. (9-16), the grid voltage of T_2 is calculated for the time just after T_2 has returned to conduction.

$$(e_{c2})_3 = \frac{(1000)(100,000)(300 - 71.9)}{(50,000)(100,000) + (50,000)(1000) + (1000)(100,000)} = 4.42 \text{ volts}$$

From Eq. (9-18), $(e_{b1})_3 = 4.42 + 71.9 = 76.3$ volts, and from the plate characteristics, $(e_{b2})_3 = 13$ volts. The grid voltage of T_1 is calculated from Eq. (9-19).

$$(e_{c1})_3 = \frac{(100,000)(13) - (250,000)(75)}{(100,000 + 250,000)} = -49.8 \text{ volts}$$

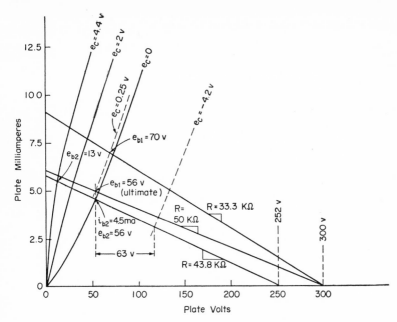

Fig. 9-8. Graphical solution for the single-cycle multivibrator of Fig. 9-3.

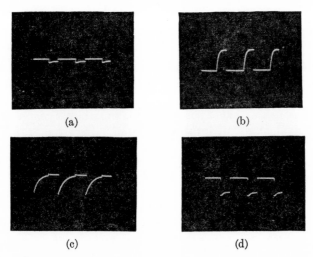

(a)   (b)

(c)   (d)

Fig. 9-9. Photographs showing the wave forms of the single-cycle multivibrator
of Fig. 9-3: (a) e_{c1}; (b) e_{b1}; (c) e_{c2}; (d) e_{b2}.

The time required for the circuit to return to steady-state conduction is

$$4\tau = 4\left[\frac{(1000)(100,000)}{101,000} + 50,000\right](0.001 \times 10^{-6}) = 204 \text{ microseconds}$$

A complete set of analytical wave forms is shown in Fig. 9-7, while the graphical solutions are shown in Fig. 9-8.

The corresponding photographs for a particular circuit of this type are shown in Fig. 9-9.

9-3 Single-Cycle, Plate-Coupled Multivibrator with Positive Grid Return

Several modifications of the circuit of Fig. 9-3 are possible, with some of these modifications having definite practical value. One of these is shown in Fig. 9-10. The grid of T_2 is now returned through

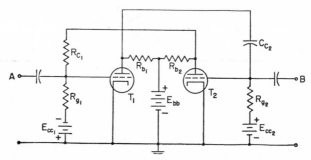

Fig. 9-10. Single-cycle, plate-coupled multivibrator with positive grid return.

the grid resistor R_{g2} to a positive source E_{cc2}, instead of to ground as was done in Fig. 9-3. The analysis of the new circuit will be similar to that of Sec. 9-2.

Assume again that T_1 is at cutoff and that T_2 is conducting. The equivalent circuit for this condition is the same as that shown in Fig. 9-4 except for the positive source in the grid circuit of T_2. The conditions in the plate circuit of T_2 can be represented by Eq. (9-2), which is repeated here as Eq. (9-21).

$$(e_{b2})_0 + (i_{b2})_0\left[\frac{R_{b2}(R_{c1} + R_{g1})}{R_{b2} + R_{c1} + R_{g1}}\right] = \frac{E_{bb}(R_{c1} + R_{g1}) + E_{cc1}(R_{b2})}{R_{b2} + R_{c1} + R_{g1}}$$

$$(9-21)$$

As was previously shown, a constant static grid resistance $\bar{r}_{g2}$ may be chosen without undue error. The grid of T_2 will not be at zero in steady state as in the original case, but will be at a potential $(e_{c2})_0$ where

$$(e_{c2})_0 = \frac{\bar{r}_{g2}E_{cc2}}{\bar{r}_{g2} + R_{g2}} \tag{9-22}$$

The steady-state operating conditions for T_2 can now be obtained from the plate characteristics.

The driving pulse is then applied to the circuit. The amplitude of this pulse can be found as discussed for the circuit of Fig. 9-4. If conduction is instantaneously transferred from T_2 to T_1, the equivalent circuit for the period when T_1 is conducting is shown in

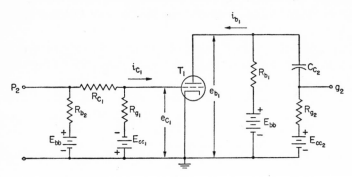

Fig. 9-11.   Circuit equivalent to that of Fig. 9-10 when T_1 is conducting and T_2 is cut off.

Fig. 9-11.   The grid circuit of Fig. 9-11 is similar to that of Fig. 9-5, so with the assumption of a constant $\bar{r}_{g1}$,

$$(e_{c1})_1 = \frac{\bar{r}_{g1}[R_{g1}E_{bb} + (R_{c1} + R_{b2})E_{cc1}]}{R_{g1}(R_{c1} + R_{b2}) + \bar{r}_{g1}(R_{c1} + R_{b2}) + \bar{r}_{g1}R_{g1}} \tag{9-23}$$

Theoretically the value of $(e_{c1})_1$ will have changed from the previous circuit, since the plate voltage of T_1 has been changed. The capacitor voltage just prior to the transfer of conduction is

$$(e_c)_0 = E_{bb} - (e_{c2})_0 \tag{9-24}$$

For the instant immediately following the transfer of conduction to T_1, Eq. (9-25) may be written.

$$(e_{b1})_1 + (i_{b1})_1\left\{\frac{R_{g2}R_{b1}}{R_{g2} + R_{b1}}\right\} = \frac{E_{bb}[R_{g2} + R_{b1}] + E_{cc2}R_{b1} - (e_{c2})_0R_{b1}}{R_{g2} + R_{b1}} \tag{9-25}$$

The use of Eq. (9-23), Eq. (9-25), and the plate characteristics fixes $(e_{b1})_1$, $(i_{b1})_1$, and $(e_{c1})_1$. If $(e_{c2})_0$ and E_{cc2} are made zero in Eq. (9-25), the equation is similar to Eq. (9-10).

Since $(e_{b1})_1$ can now be found, $(e_{c2})_1$ can be calculated. The plate of T_1 has dropped instantaneously by $[E_{bb} - (e_{b1})_1]$ volts, so the grid of T_2 drops by the same amount. The value of $(e_{b2})_1$ has not changed from the original example.

With or without the battery E_{cc2}, the final value of the plate voltage of T_1, if the circuit did not change, is that found from the plate characteristics using only R_{b1} and E_{bb}. The average static resistance can still be assumed to be approximately 10,000 ohms; thus the time constant of the circuit has not changed from its original value.

During the time that T_2 is cut off, the grid of T_2 is returning from $(e_{c2})_1$ to the cutoff potential. However, the grid voltage is not

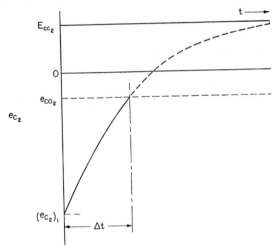

Fig. 9-12. Grid voltage of T_2 when T_2 is cut off.

approaching a zero potential as before, but is approaching E_{cc2}. This is shown in Fig. 9-12. The time Δt is

$$\Delta t = \tau \ln \frac{E_{cc2} - (e_{c2})_1}{E_{cc2} - e_{co2}} \qquad (9-26)$$

At the end of the Δt interval, the plate potential of T_1 will be

$$(e_{b1})_2 = (e_{b1})_1 - \frac{(e_{c2})_1 - e_{co2}}{(e_{c2})_1 - E_{cc2}} [(e_{b1})_1 - e_{b1}'] \qquad (9\text{-}27)$$

where e_{b1}' is the value of e_{b1} which would be reached if T_1 continued to conduct indefinitely.

The voltage on the capacitor $(e_c)_2$ when e_{c2} reaches the cutoff potential will be equal to $(e_{b1})_2$, as calculated from Eq. (9-27), minus e_{co2}. Conduction will now be transferred back to T_2, giving the equivalent circuit of Fig. 9-13. If the static resistance of T_2

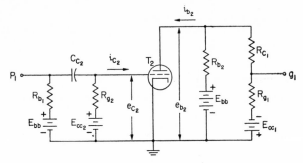

Fig. 9-13.   Circuit equivalent to that of Fig. 9-10 when T_2 is conducting and T_1 is cut off.

is assumed constant, the grid voltage of T_2 immediately subsequent to its return to conduction is

$$(e_{c2})_3 = \frac{\bar{r}_{g2}R_{b1}E_{cc2} + \bar{r}_{g2}R_{g2}[e_{co2} + E_{bb} - (e_{b1})_2]}{R_{g2}R_{b1} + \bar{r}_{g2}R_{b1} + \bar{r}_{g2}R_{g2}} \qquad (9\text{-}28)$$

The relationship between $(e_{b2})_3$ and $(i_{b2})_3$ is similar to that of Eq. (9-2), or

$$(e_{b2})_3 + (i_{b2})_3 \left[\frac{R_{b2}(R_{g1} + R_{c1})}{R_{b2} + R_{g1} + R_{c1}} \right] = \frac{E_{bb}(R_{c1} + R_{g1}) + E_{cc1}R_{b2}}{R_{b2} + R_{c1} + R_{g1}} \qquad (9\text{-}29)$$

The values of $(e_{b2})_3$ and $(i_{b2})_3$ can be found by using Eq. (9-28), Eq. (9-29), and the plate characteristics of T_2. To find the new value of $(e_{c1})_3$, Eq. (9-19) may be used. Since the grid of T_2 jumped upwards by an amount $(e_{c2})_3 - e_{co2}$, the new value of e_{b1} is

$$(e_{b1})_3 = (e_{b1})_2 + (e_{c2})_3 - e_{co2} \qquad (9\text{-}30)$$

The time constant of the circuit has not changed, and is given by Eq. (9-20).

Application of a positive voltage to the grid of T_2 has caused minor changes in the voltages present on all elements in the circuit. However, the major change is that the grid potential of T_2 is now returning toward the positive voltage instead of toward zero. The time constant, the starting voltage, and the final voltage have not changed appreciably, but the time interval required to accomplish the same voltage change is quite different. A comparison is shown in Fig. 9-14.

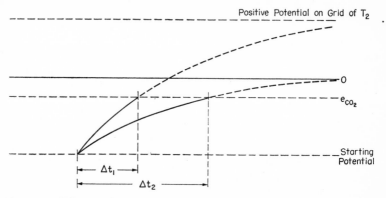

Fig. 9-14. Effect of the positive grid return on the grid voltage of T_2 during the off time.

The time interval during which T_2 is cut off, following the input pulse, is quite often the most important consideration in the practical application of a single-cycle multivibrator. Under these circumstances, the positive grid connection offers a definite advantage. With the grid returned to ground, the grid voltage approaches zero from a large negative value. The voltage difference between zero and the cutoff potential is a small part of the total grid voltage change, so the grid voltage approaches the cutoff value at a small angle. If the applied voltages or the characteristics of the tube change slightly, the cutoff potential will change, giving a correspondingly large change in the time that T_2 is cut off. With the grid returned to a high positive potential, the grid voltage curve intersects the cutoff line at a large angle. Small changes in the cutoff value will then cause only small changes in the delay time. Thus the circuit is more stable when the grid is returned to a positive

potential.   If a definite time interval is desired, the time constant
can be decreased as the positive grid voltage is increased.

EXAMPLE: A numerical example of the single-cycle, positive-grid multivibrator will be shown.   The parameters and circuit configuration used in
this example will be exactly the same as the example in the preceding section
except for the inclusion of $E_{cc2} = 100$ volts.

Assuming a static resistance of $\bar{r}_{g1} = 1000$ ohms will give $(e_{c2})_0 = 1$ volt.
The voltage across the capacitor will be 299 volts, and $(e_{b2})_0$ will be 40
volts.   The plate voltage of T_1 at this time is 300 volts, while

$$(e_{c1})_0 = \frac{R_{g1}(e_{b2})_0 + R_{c1}E_{cc1}}{R_{g1} + R_{c1}} = -42.1 \text{ volts}$$

The positive bias has no effect on the grid voltage of T_1 for the time immediately subsequent to the transfer of conduction to that tube, so $(e_{c1})_1 = 0.25$
volt.   Equation (9-25) may be written

$$(e_{b1})_1 + (33,000)(i_{b1})_1 = 333.3 \text{ volts}$$

Plotting this equation on the T_1 plate characteristics gives $(e_{b1})_1 = 76$
volts.   The plate voltage of T_1 has dropped instantaneously by $(300 - 76)$
or 224 volts, so

$$(e_{c2})_1 = -224 + 1 = -223 \text{ volts}$$

The value of $(e_{b2})_1$ is the same as in the previous example, or 250 volts.
The time constant is also unchanged at 108.3 microseconds.

The time that T_2 is cut off may be calculated from Eq. (9-26) as

$$\Delta t = 108.3 \ln \frac{100 - (-223)}{100 - (-15)} = 112 \text{ microseconds}$$

From Equation (9-27),

$$(e_{b1})_2 = 76 - \frac{-223 - (-15)}{-223 - 100} (76 - 56) = 63.1 \text{ volts}$$

The voltage on the capacitor at this time is $15 + 63.1$ or 78.1 volts.   Letting T_2 return to conduction, $(e_{c2})_3$ can be calculated from Eq. (9-28).

$$(e_{c2})_3 = \frac{(100)(50,000)(100) + (1000)(100,000)(-78.1 + 300)}{(100,000)(50,000) + (1000)(50,000) + (1000)(100,000)} = 5.29 \text{ volts}$$

Using Eq. (9-29) and the plate characteristics, $(e_{b2})_3$ may be determined as
approximately 8 volts.   Also

$$(e_{b1})_3 = 63.1 + 5.29 + 15 = 83.4 \text{ volts}$$

$$(e_{c1})_3 = \frac{(100,000)(8) + (250,000)(-75)}{(100,000 + 250,000)} = -51.3 \text{ volts}$$

As before, the circuit will return to a steady-state condition in four time constants, or 204 microseconds.

Wave forms are shown in Fig. 9-15, with the graphical solutions indicated in Fig. 9-16.

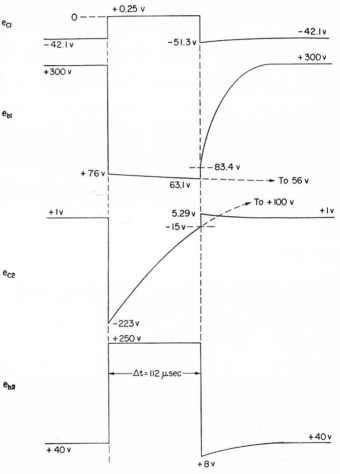

Fig. 9-15.   Wave forms for the circuit of Fig. 9-10.

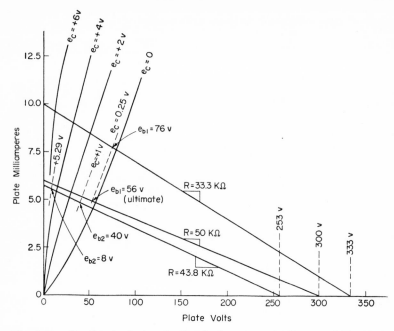

Fig. 9-16. Graphical solution for the single-cycle multivibrator of Fig. 9-10.

9-4 Single-Cycle, Plate-Coupled Multivibrator with Inductive Grid Circuit

Another modification of the circuit of Fig. 9-3 is shown in Fig. 9-17. The operation of this circuit differs in one important detail from those previously discussed. The tube T_2 is normally conducting, and when the circuit is triggered by application of a positive pulse at A or a negative pulse at B, T_2 is cut off by the large negative voltage appearing at its grid. In the two previous examples, the variation of the grid voltage between this large negative voltage and the cutoff value was an exponential function. This is not the case in the circuit of Fig. 9-17. The exact form of the grid voltage will be determined.

The quiescent conditions for this circuit are the same as for the circuit of Fig. 9-3. When conduction is transferred to T_1 by the driving pulse, the circuit of Fig. 9-18 may be used. Just before conduction was transferred to T_1, the current through the inductor was zero, so immediately after the transfer of conduction, the cur-

rent is still zero. Similarly, the voltage across the capacitor
remains unchanged at the supply potential.

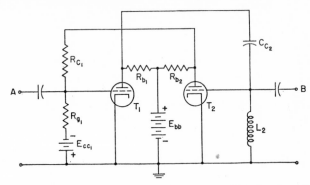

Fig. 9-17.   Single-cycle, plate-coupled multivibrator with inductive grid circuit.

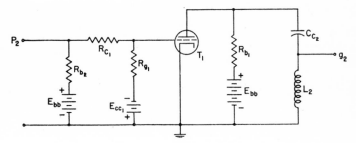

Fig. 9-18.   Circuit equivalent to that of Fig. 9-17 when T_1 is conducting and T_2
is cut off.

For the instant following the transfer, the operating conditions of
T_1 can be found by using a load line
which is determined only by R_{b1} and
E_{bb}.   The value of $(e_{c1})_1$ is fixed by
Eq. (9-23).   The voltage across the
inductor just after transfer is

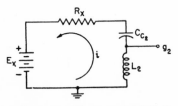

Fig. 9-19.   Equivalent RLC circuit found in the plate circuit of T_1
when conducting.

$$(e_{c2})_1 = -E_{bb} + (e_{b1})_1 \quad (9\text{-}31)$$

If the static conducting resistance of T_1 is assumed to be con-
stant, the circuit of Fig. 9-19 can be drawn.   In this series RLC
circuit

$$E_x = \frac{\bar{r}_{p1}E_{bb}}{\bar{r}_{p1} + R_{b1}} \qquad (9\text{-}32)$$

and
$$R_x = \frac{\bar{r}_{p1}R_{b1}}{\bar{r}_{p1} + R_{b1}} \qquad (9\text{-}33)$$

The solution of this circuit can be obtained by reference to Sec. 2-5, and can be written

$$i = Ae^{-R_xt/2L_2} \sinh \left(\sqrt{\left(\frac{R_x}{2L_2}\right)^2 - \frac{1}{L_2C_{c2}}} \right) t \qquad (9\text{-}34)$$

In order to have the grid voltage return to the cutoff potential at a steep angle, it is desirable to have the system oscillatory, that is,

$$\frac{1}{L_2C_{c2}} > \left(\frac{R_x}{2L_2}\right)^2 \qquad (9\text{-}35)$$

Even if the inequality of Eq. (9-35) is satisfied, the system will be oscillatory for only a little less than a quarter of a cycle, since at that point the circuit will again be changed. The grid voltage of T_2 during its "off" time is then

$$e_{c2} = -L_2 \frac{di}{dt} = -Ae^{-R_xt/2L_2} \left(\omega L_2 \cos \omega t - \frac{R_x}{2} \sin \omega t \right) \quad (9\text{-}36)$$

$$e_{c2} = Be^{-R_xt/2L_2} \cos (\omega t + \theta) \qquad (9\text{-}37)$$

where
$$\theta = \text{arc tan} \frac{R_x}{2\omega L_2} \qquad (9\text{-}38)$$

and
$$B = \frac{(e_{c2})_1}{\cos \theta} \qquad (9\text{-}39)$$

In many circuits the damping is sufficiently small so that it may be neglected over a quarter of a cycle. In this case, the time that T_2 will be cut off is equal to

$$\Delta t = \frac{1}{\omega} \text{arc cos} \frac{e_{co2}}{-E_{bb} + (e_{b1})_1} \qquad (9\text{-}40)$$

If the damping is high, Δt must be calculated from Eq. (9-37).

A sketch of the grid voltage of T_2 is shown in Fig. 9-20. The advantage of the inductive grid multivibrator is evident from this

sketch. As in the positive grid case, the grid voltage curve intersects the cutoff value at a sharp angle, contributing to an increase
in stability.

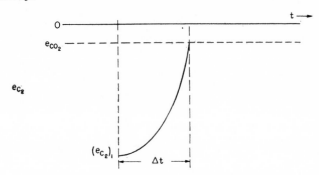

Fig. 9-20.   Grid voltage of T_2 when T_2 is cut off.

When the grid voltage of T_2 reaches the cutoff potential, conduction will be transferred back to T_2. If instantaneous transfer
of conduction is assumed, the voltage on the capacitor the instant
after the transfer is the same as that just prior to the transfer.
Similarly, the inductor currents before and after transfer will be
considered identical. These values of voltage and current will now
be found.

The value of the current at the end of the Δt period will be

$$(i)_2 = - \left[\frac{-E_{bb} + (e_{b1})_1}{\omega L_2} \right] e^{-R_x \Delta t / 2L_2} \sin \omega \Delta t \qquad (9\text{-}41)$$

The current as shown in Fig. 9-19 and given by Eq. (9-41) will be
positive. The voltage drop on the capacitor (voltage drop from
plate of T_1 to grid of T_2) at this time is

$$(e_C)_2 = (i)_2 R_x + E_x - e_{co2} \qquad (9\text{-}42)$$

With T_2 again conducting and T_1 cut off, the equivalent circuit is
shown in Fig. 9-21. The initial value of (e_{c2}) is

$$(e_{c2})_3 = \frac{\bar{r}_{g2}[E_{bb} - (e_C)_2 + R_{b1}(i)_2]}{R_{b1} + \bar{r}_{g2}} \qquad (9\text{-}43)$$

Using $(e_{c2})_3$ from Eq. (9-43), along with the plate circuit of Fig. 9-21,
the initial plate voltage of T_2, $(e_{b2})_3$, and the initial grid voltage of

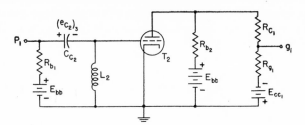

Fig. 9-21. Circuit equivalent to that of Fig. 9-17 when T_2 is conducting and T_1 is cut off.

T_1, $(e_{c1})_3$, may be determined. The initial plate voltage of T_1, $(e_{b1})_3$, is then equal to the sum of $(e_{c2})_3$ and $(e_C)_2$. Eventually the plate of T_1 will return to the supply potential and the grid of T_2 will return to zero. To find the time necessary for this return necessitates solution of two simultaneous differential equations. Due to low conducting grid resistance of T_2, the solution will invariably be of the overdamped form.

EXAMPLE: For the circuit of Fig. 9-17 let $R_{b1} = R_{b2} = 50,000$ ohms, $C_{c2} = 0.001$ microfarad, $R_{c1} = 250,000$ ohms, $R_{g1} = 100,000$ ohms, $E_{cc1} = -75$ volts, $E_{bb} = 300$ volts, and $L_2 = 0.5$ henry. The tube will be a 6SN7. This circuit is then the same as that used in the previous example except for the inductor in the grid circuit of T_2.

The quiescent conditions will be unchanged, that is, $(e_{c2})_0 = 0$, $(e_{b2})_0 = 56$ volts, $(e_{c1})_0 = -37.5$ volts, and $(e_{b1})_0 = 300$ volts. Just after conduction has been transferred to T_2, the grid potential of T_1 and the plate potential of T_2 will be the same as that of the previous example, that is, $(e_{c1})_1 = 0.25$ volt and $(e_{b2})_1 = 250$ volts. Using a load line determined by a 50,000 ohm resistor and a 300-volt supply fixes the plate voltage of T_1, $(e_{b1})_1$ at 56 volts. Then $(e_{c2})_1 = -244$ volts.

If $\bar{r}_{p1}$ is assumed to be 10,000 ohms, $E_x = 50$ volts, and $R_x = 8330$ ohms. The value of $1/L_2C_{c2}$ is 2×10^9 while $(R_x/2L_2)^2$ is 6.9×10^7. Thus the grid circuit of T_2 is oscillatory with a frequency of 7110 cycles per second. Substituting -15 volts for e_{c2} in Eq. (9-36) allows Δt to be calculated as 29.3 microseconds. A full quarter cycle is 35.2 microseconds in length.

From Eq. (9-41), the inductor current at the end of the Δt period is found to be 8.24 ma, while Eq. (9-42) gives the capacitor voltage as 133.6 volts. The plate voltage of T_1 at this time is then $133.6 - 15$, or 118.6 volts.

After T_2 has again returned to conduction, the potential of the grid of T_2 is calculated from Eq. (9-43) as 11.35 volts. Since the plate of T_1 will have the same jump in potential as the grid of T_2, it will rise instantaneously to a value of 145 volts. The plate potential of T_2 will drop to a value somewhat less than 10 volts, while the grid of T_1 will go down to approximately -51 volts. A sketch of the wave forms is shown in Fig. 9-22.

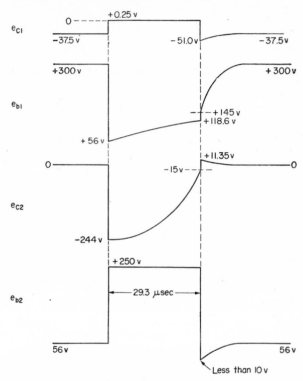

Fig. 9-22.　Wave forms for the circuit of Fig. 9-17.

9-5 Series Grid Resistance in Single-Cycle Multivibrator

In several applications, it is desirable to obtain from the single-cycle multivibrator a wave form which is as rectangular as possible. The plate voltage of T_2 in the circuit of Fig. 9-3 is a near approximation to this shape. However, it is sometimes possible to improve the wave form. The very low plate voltage which occurs as T_2 returns to conduction is caused by the positive grid voltage at that time. A review of Chapter 5 indicates what may be done to eliminate the positive grid swing. If a large resistance is inserted in series with the grid as shown in the circuit of Fig. 9-23, it will be impossible to drive the grid of T_2 very far into the positive region. This will then decrease the negative plate voltage swing.

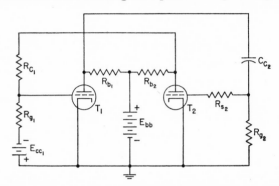

Fig. 9-23. Single-cycle, plate-coupled multivibrator with series grid resistance.

The steady-state operating conditions for the circuit of Fig. 9-23 will be the same as for the circuit of Fig. 9-3. There will also be no difference in the electrode voltages during the time that T_2 is cut off, since the initial conditions are the same, and the series grid resistor can have no effect on a nonconducting grid circuit. However, as T_2 returns to conduction, there will be considerable difference in the electrode voltages as compared with the original circuit.

After transfer of conduction to T_2, the circuit of Fig. 9-24 may be

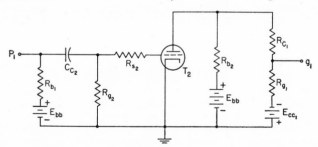

Fig. 9-24. Circuit equivalent to that of Fig. 9-23 when T_2 is conducting and T_1 is cut off.

drawn. The initial voltage on the grid of T_2 will be

$$(e_{c2})_3 = \frac{\bar{r}_{g2}R_{g2}[E_{bb} - (e_{b1})_2 + e_{co2}]}{(R_{b1} + R_{g2})(\bar{r}_{g2} + R_{s2}) + R_{g2}R_{b1}} \tag{9-44}$$

If $\bar{r}_{g2}$ is small with respect to R_{s2}, $(e_{c2})_3$ will usually be only a fraction of a volt. The initial plate potential of T_1 is

$$(e_{b1})_3 = \frac{E_{bb}R_{g2}(R_{s2} + \bar{r}_{g2}) + R_{b1}[(e_{b1})_2 - e_{co2}](R_{g2} + R_{s2} + \bar{r}_{g2})}{R_{g2}(R_{s2} + \bar{r}_{g2}) + R_{b1}(R_{g2} + R_{s2} + \bar{r}_{g2})} \quad (9\text{-}45)$$

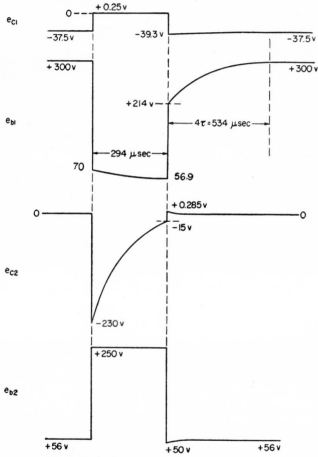

Fig. 9-25. Wave forms for the circuit of Fig. 9-23.

The values of $(e_{b2})_3$ and $(e_{c1})_3$ can be found from the same load line used in Sec. 9-2, if the new value of $(e_{c2})_3$ is observed.

The circuit will now reach the quiescent conditions in about four time constants, but this time constant is larger than in the original case due to the inclusion of R_{s2}. The new time constant is

$$\tau = \left[R_{b1} + \frac{R_{g2}(R_{s2} + \bar{r}_{g2})}{R_{g2} + R_{s2} + \bar{r}_{g2}} \right] C_{c2} \qquad (9\text{-}46)$$

EXAMPLE: The example given in Sec. 9-2 will be repeated, except for the addition of a 500k resistor in the grid circuit of T_2. The quiescent conditions and the conditions during the conduction time of T_1 will be unchanged. As T_2 comes back into conduction, the initial grid voltage can be calculated from Eq. (9-44) as 0.285 volt. Then from Eq. (9-45), $(e_{b1})_3 = 214$ volts. From the 6SN7 plate characteristics, $(e_{b2})_3 = 50$ volts and $(e_{c1})_3 = -39.3$ volts. From Eq. (9-46) the time required for the circuit to become quiescent is 4τ, or 534 microseconds. A sketch of the wave forms is shown in Fig. 9-25.

Fig. 9-26. Photograph showing the grid voltage of T_2 in the circuit of Fig. 9-23.

A photograph of the wave form of T_2 is shown in Fig. 9-26 and can be compared with that of Fig. 9-9c.

There are many minor modifications and combinations of the basic single-cycle, plate-coupled multivibrators other than those which have been treated in the past few sections. Most of these circuits may be solved by methods which have been demonstrated.

9-6 Single-Cycle, Cathode-Coupled Multivibrator

The development of the single-cycle, plate-coupled multivibrator from the Eccles-Jordan trigger circuit has been discussed in Sec. 9-1. Similarly, a single-cycle multivibrator can be derived from the Schmitt trigger circuit of Sec. 8-4. One example of this type of multivibrator is given in Fig. 9-27.

Under steady-state conditions, T_2 will have zero grid voltage. With a small plate resistor, T_2 can then draw sufficient current to keep T_1 cut off, as the bias on T_1 is determined by the common cathode resistance.

A sufficiently positive input pulse to the grid of T_1 will cause a small current in T_1, resulting in a decrease in the plate-ground voltage of T_1. This causes a corresponding decrease in the potential of the grid of T_2 with respect to ground. The tube T_2 then sends

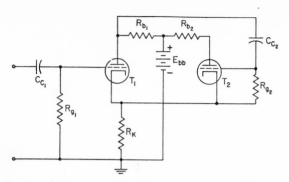

Fig. 9-27. Single-cycle, cathode-coupled multivibrator.

less current through the cathode resistor, while T_1 tends to cause more. However, if the grid of T_1 is at constant potential with respect to ground, and the grid voltage of T_2 is decreasing with respect to the same reference, the total cathode current must decrease, since changes in the cathode voltage of T_2 cannot exceed changes in the grid voltage. This process continues until T_2 is completely cut off. The instability can also be shown by the appearance of a negative dynamic resistance from plate to plate or, as was done in Sec. 8-4, by the possibility of a change in grid voltage of T_2 with a zero change in input voltage.

Once T_2 has been made nonconducting by the input pulse, the capacitor C_{c2} will discharge until the grid of T_2 reaches the cutoff potential. The increase in total cathode current then decreases the grid potential of T_1, which in turn raises the plate potential of T_1 and the grid potential of T_2. This process ends as the system approaches its original steady state.

If it is assumed that T_2 is conducting and that T_1 is cut off, the equivalent circuit of Fig. 9-28 is applicable. The grid-cathode potential of T_2 will be zero under steady-state conditions. Using a supply voltage of E_{bb} and a resistance of $R_{b2} + R_k$, a load line can be drawn which will give $(e_{b2})_0$ and $(i_{b2})_0$, where $(e_{b2})_0$ is the plate-cathode voltage of T_2. The cathode potential $(e_k)_0$ is also fixed as $(i_{b2})_0 R_k$. The plate-cathode voltage of T_1, $(e_{b1})_0$, will be $(e_{b1})_0 = E_{bb} - (e_k)_0$. This voltage is also equal to the capacitor voltage.

A positive pulse will now be applied to T_1. This pulse must be large enough to cause T_1 to draw a small amount of current. With conduction transferred to T_1, the circuit of Fig. 9-29 may be

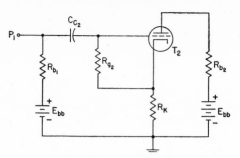

Fig. 9-28.   Circuit equivalent to that of Fig. 9-27 when T_2 is conducting with zero grid voltage and T_1 is cut off.

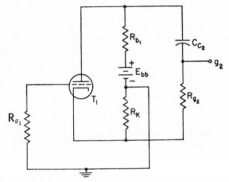

Fig. 9-29.   Circuit equivalent to that of Fig. 9-27 when T_1 is conducting and T_2 is cut off.

drawn.   Using the cathode as a reference, currents are summed at the plate, giving

$$(i_{b1})_1 + \frac{(e_{b1})_1 - E_{bb}}{R_{b1} + R_k} + \frac{(e_{b1})_1 - E_{bb} + (e_k)_0}{R_{g2}} = 0$$

or $(e_{b1})_1 + (i_{b1})_1 \left[\frac{R_{g2}(R_{b1} + R_k)}{R_{g2} + R_{b1} + R_k} \right] = E_{bb} - \frac{(R_k + R_{b1})(e_k)_0}{R_{g2} + R_{b1} + R_k}$

$$(9\text{-}47)$$

With respect to the cathode, the ground potential is

$$e_{\text{gnd}} = \frac{R_k[(e_{b1})_1 - E_{bb}]}{R_k + R_{b1}}.$$

Since the grid of T_1 is at ground potential, $(e_{c1})_1$ can be substituted for e_{gnd}. If the expression for $(e_{b1})_1$ from Eq. (9-47) is substituted into the expression for e_{gnd}, and equation for $(e_{c1})_1$ in terms of $(i_{b1})_1$ is obtained.

$$(e_{c1})_1 = -\left[\frac{R_k(e_k)_0}{R_{g2} + R_{b1} + R_k} + \frac{R_k R_{g2}(i_{b1})_1}{R_{g2} + R_{b1} + R_k} \right] \quad (9\text{-}48)$$

To find the values of $(i_{b1})_1$, $(e_{c1})_1$ and $(e_{b1})_1$, Eqs. (9-47) and (9-48) are plotted on the plate characteristics. The intersection of the two plotted lines gives the desired values. The grid voltage of T_2 is

$$(e_{c2})_1 = (e_{b1})_1 - E_{bb} + (e_k)_0 \quad (9\text{-}49)$$

If the circuit of Fig. 9-27 did not change (T_1 conducting indefi-

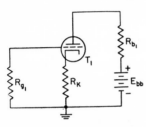

Fig. 9-30. Circuit equivalent to that of Fig. 9-29 when T_1 is conducting under steady-state conditions and T_2 is cut off.

nitely), eventually the capacitor current would be zero and the circuit could be given as that of Fig. 9-30. Using the plate characteristics and this circuit, values for the static plate resistance of T_1 may be found. If these resistances are averaged over the operating range, a useable value is obtained. In general, this value of $\bar{r}_{p1}$ will be much larger than that obtained for tubes with zero or positive values of grid voltage. The time constant is then

$$\tau = \left[R_{g2} + \frac{\bar{r}_{p1}(R_{b1} + R_k)}{\bar{r}_{p1} + R_{b1} + R_k} \right] C_{c2} \quad (9\text{-}50)$$

The grid voltage of T_2 can be sketched as shown in Fig. 9-31. The

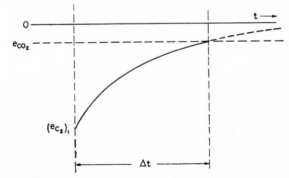

Fig. 9-31. Grid voltage of T_2 when T_2 is cut off.

time Δt that T_2 is cut off is

$$\Delta t = \tau \ln \frac{(e_{c2})_1}{e_{co2}} \qquad (9\text{-}51)$$

During this time, the grid voltage goes $[(e_{c2})_1 - e_{co2}]/(e_{c2})_1$ of its total possible excursion. The grid voltage of T_1 would eventually be at the negative of the cathode potential e_{c1}' as given by Fig. 9-30. Thus at the end of the Δt period, $(e_{c1})_2$ would be

$$(e_{c1})_2 = (e_{c1})_1 + \frac{(e_{c2})_1 - e_{co2}}{(e_{c2})_1} [e_{c1}' - (e_{c1})_1] \qquad (9\text{-}52)$$

Also at the end of the period,

$$(e_{b1})_2 = E_{bb} + \frac{R_k + R_{b1}}{R_k} (e_{c1})_2 \qquad (9\text{-}53)$$

$$(e_C)_2 = (e_{b1})_2 - e_{co2} \qquad (9\text{-}54)$$

Assume that conduction is now transferred back to T_2. The operating conditions immediately after the transfer of conduction can be found by the same process as was used before, if the grid-cathode static conducting resistance is assumed to be constant.

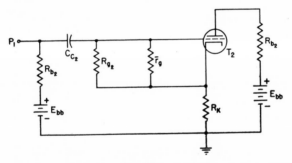

Fig. 9-32. Circuit equivalent to that of Fig. 9-29 when T_2 is conducting with a positive grid voltage and T_1 is cut off.

As far as the plate circuit is concerned, the circuit of Fig. 9-32 could be used, where

$$R_x = \frac{R_k(R_{b1}\bar{r}_{g2} + R_{b1}R_{g2} + \bar{r}_{g2}R_{g2})}{(R_k + R_{b1})(R_{g2} + \bar{r}_{g2}) + \bar{r}_{g2}R_{g2}} \qquad (9\text{-}55)$$

and

$$E_x = E_{bb} - R_k \left[\frac{E_{bb} - (e_{b1})_2 - e_{co2}}{R_k + R_{b1} + \dfrac{\bar{r}_{g2}R_{g2}}{\bar{r}_{g2} + R_{g2}}} \right] \qquad (9\text{-}56)$$

Writing equations from Fig. 9-32 gives

$$-(i_{b2})_3 + \frac{(e_k)_3}{R_k} - \frac{(e_{c2})_3(\bar{r}_{g1} + R_{g2})}{(\bar{r}_{g2})(R_{g2})} = 0 \qquad (9\text{-}57)$$

and
$$\frac{(e_{c2})_3(\bar{r}_{g2} + R_{g2})}{\bar{r}_{g2}R_{g2}} + \frac{(e_k)_3 + (e_{c2})_3 + (e_{b1})_2 - e_{co2} - E_{bb}}{R_{b1}} = 0$$

$$(9\text{-}58)$$

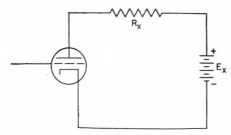

Fig. 9-33.   Circuit equivalent to that of Fig. 9-32.

Eliminating $(e_k)_3$ from these equations,

$$(e_{c2})_3 = \frac{\bar{r}_{g2}R_{g2}[E_{bb} - (e_{b1})_2 + e_{co2}]}{(R_{g2} + \bar{r}_{g2})(R_{b1} + R_k) + \bar{r}_{g2}R_{g2}}$$
$$- \frac{R_{g2}\bar{r}_{g2}R_k(i_{b2})_3}{(R_{g2} + \bar{r}_{g2})(R_{b1} + R_k) + \bar{r}_{g2}R_{g2}} \qquad (9\text{-}59)$$

A load line can be plotted on the plate characteristic by the use of Eqs. (9-55) and (9-56). A second line is given by Eq. (9-59), the intersection of these two lines giving the operating conditions.

After the circuit has again been undisturbed for a long time the capacitor current will be zero, with the operating conditions being the same as those found for the circuit of Fig. 9-28. The static plate resistance of T_2 can be averaged over the recovery time to give a satisfactory approximate value.

The time taken for the circuit to recover will be approximately four time constants, this time constant being determined from the circuit of Fig. 9-34.

$$\tau = C_{c2}\left[R_{b1} + \frac{(\bar{r}_{p2} + R_{b2})R_k}{R_k + \bar{r}_{p2} + R_{b2}} + \frac{\bar{r}_{g2}R_{g2}}{R_{g2} + \bar{r}_{g2}} \right] \qquad (9\text{-}60)$$

Several modifications of the cathode-coupled multivibrator just discussed are possible. Perhaps the most important of these is

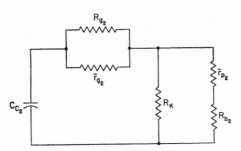

Fig. 9-34. Equivalent circuit from which time constant can be determined.

obtained by causing the grid of T_2 to be returned to a positive potential instead of to the cathode. The solution of such a circuit may be carried out in the same manner as the previous examples.

EXAMPLE: Let the parameters in the circuit of Fig. 9-27 have the following values: $R_{b1} = 50{,}000$ ohms, $R_{b2} = 20{,}000$ ohms, $R_{g2} = 250{,}000$ ohms, $R_{g1} = 250{,}000$ ohms, $R_k = 5000$ ohms, $C_{c2} = 0.001$ microfarad, and $E_{bb} = 250$ volts. The tube is a 6SN7.

By the use of the plate characteristics and the circuit of Fig. 9.28 $(e_{b2})_0$ is found to be 75 volts, with $(i_{b2})_0 = 7$ ma. The cathode voltage $(e_k)_0$ is thus 35 volts, giving a plate voltage for T_1 of 215 volts.

A positive pulse of approximately 22 volts amplitude will cause conduction to transfer to T_1. From Eq. (9-47),

$$(e_{b1})_1 + 45.1(i_{b1})_1 = 243.7$$

From Eq. (9-48),

$$(e_{c1})_1 = -4.1(i_{b1})_1 - 0.573$$

where $(i_{b1})_1$ is in milliamperes for both equations. The intersection of these two lines occurs at

$$(e_{c1})_1 = -7.3 \text{ volts} \quad \text{and} \quad (e_{b1})_1 = 165 \text{ volts}.$$

From Eq. (9-49),

$$(e_{c2})_1 = 165 - 250 + 35 = -50 \text{ volts}$$

The operating conditions of the circuit given in Fig. 9-30 are then

$$e_k' = 7.5 \text{ volts}$$

$$i_{b1}' = 1.5 \text{ ma}$$

$$e_{b1}' = 167.5 \text{ volts}$$

The average static conducting resistance is

$$r_{p1} = \frac{165 + 167.5}{(1.5 + 1.7)(10)^{-3}} = 104{,}000 \text{ ohms}$$

Using this value in Eq. (9-50) gives τ as 286 microseconds. Since the plate voltage of T_2 varies less than a volt from the original value of 242.7 volts, the cutoff potential may be taken as approximately -14 volts. This gives Δt as 364 microseconds.

The grid potential of T_2 goes $(50 - 14)/50$ or 72 per cent of its total

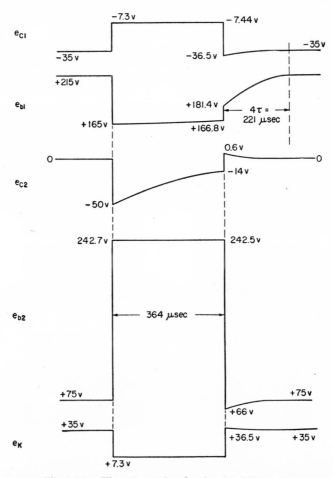

Fig. 9-35.   Wave forms for the circuit of Fig. 9-27.

possible excursion in the Δt period. The grid voltage of T_1 will then drop from a value of -7.3 volts to $-7.3 - 0.72$ (0.2) $= -7.44$ volts. Also at the end of the period

$$(e_{b1})_2 = 165 + (0.72)(2.5) = 166.8 \text{ volts}$$

$$(e_C)_2 = 166.8 + 14 = 180.8 \text{ volts}$$

Conduction is now transferred back to T_2. From Eq. (9-55), $R_x = 24{,}550$ ohms, and from Eq. (9-56), $E_x = 243.8$ volts. From Eq. (9-59),

$$(e_{c2})_3 = 1.23 - 0.089(i_{b2})_3$$

A plot of this equation intersects the load line at $(e_{c2})_3 = 0.6$ volt and $(i_{b2})_3 = 7.3$ ma. The plate voltage of T_2 must then have dropped instantaneously to 66 volts, while the plate voltage of T_1 increased to 181.4 volts.

Averaging the static plate resistance of T_2 over its recovery period gives

$$\bar{r}_p = \frac{75 + 66}{(7.0 + 7.3)(10)^{-3}} = 9850 \text{ ohms}$$

Then $4\tau = 221.2$ microseconds. A complete set of analytical wave forms is shown in Fig. 9-35. A corresponding set of photographs for a similar circuit is shown in Fig. 9-36.

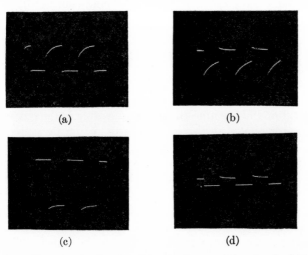

(a)   (b)

(c)   (d)

Fig. 9-36. Photographs showing the wave forms of the circuit of Fig. 9-27: (a) plate of T_1 to ground; (b) grid of T_2 to ground; (c) plate of T_2 to ground; (d) cathode to ground.

9-7 Application of the Single-Cycle Multivibrator

One of the more important applications of single-cycle multibrators is in the generation of positive or negative pulses of arbitrary duration.

For example, in the circuits previously discussed, a positive pulse could be obtained from the plate of T_2 for every input pulse. The circuit of Fig. 9-23 would be the most satisfactory as a source of rectangular pulses. The width of the positive pulses would be equal to the time that T_2 is cut off.

If the plate wave form of T_2 in these circuits were differentiated, two narrow output pulses could be obtained for every input pulse. The circuit of Fig. 9-23, if driven by a series of positive pulses, would give the output wave form shown in Fig. 9-37. The positive output pulses from the differentiating circuit could be eliminated, perhaps by a diode or an overbiased amplifier, giving one negative pulse for every positive input pulse. Then the system could serve as a delay circuit, since the negative output pulse will occur 294 microseconds after the positive input pulse.

Another use of the single-cycle multivibrator is that of pulse equalization. Suppose that pulses are being counted by a circuit which is very critical with respect to the size and shape of the input pulses. The pulses to be counted, however, are of many sizes and shapes, and thus some means of correction will be required in front of the counting system.

A single-cycle multivibrator can be used to provide this equalization. The irregular pulses can be used to trigger a single-cycle multivibrator, and the uniform pulses appearing in the output of the multivibrator may then be counted by the counting system. The multivibrator can be adjusted to provide the counting system with pulses of optimum size and shape.

There are several restrictions which must be considered with respect to the above process. The input pulses cannot be too closely spaced or the multivibrator will ignore some of them. Also, input pulses of different shapes may not trigger the multivibrator at exactly the same time after the start of the pulse. Thus with irregularly shaped pulses there may be unequal delays.

In a great number of cases, it is necessary to have a variable

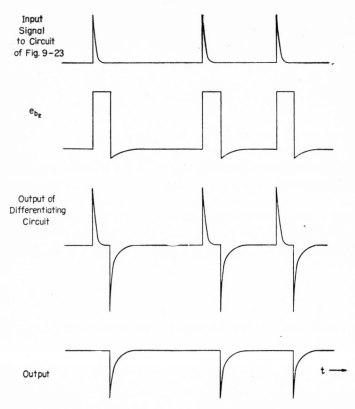

Fig. 9-37. Wave forms showing the use of the single-cycle multivibrator as a delay circuit.

pulse width at the plate of T_2, or in the case where the multivibrator is used as a delay system, a variable delay. In the circuit of Fig. 9-3, this can be accomplished by varying the grid resistance of T_2, R_{g2}.

  For every value of R_{g2}, a Δt can be determined by the same type of analysis which was used in the example to find the Δt for an R_{g2} of 100,000 ohms. After a value for R_{g2} has been selected, the equivalent plate load resistance R_{ep} is found by

$$R_{ep} = \frac{50,000(R_{g2})}{R_{g2} + 50,000} \tag{9-61}$$

Then the plate voltage is found by using a supply voltage of 300 volts, a load resistance of R_{ep}, and the $e_{c2} = 0.25$ volt line. The plate of T_1 has dropped from 300 volts to $(e_{b1})_1$; thus the grid voltage of T_2 has also dropped from zero to $-[300 - (e_{b1})_1]$. This grid voltage will return toward zero, but Δt is the time needed to reach the cutoff value, -15 volts. Then

$$\Delta t = RC \ln \frac{300 - (e_{b1})_1}{15} \qquad (9\text{-}62)$$

where $C = 0.001$ microfarad and $R = R_{g2} + 8330$ ohms. The time interval is

$$\Delta t = (R_{g2} + 8330)(0.001) \ln \frac{300 - (e_{b1})_1}{15} \text{ microseconds} \qquad (9\text{-}63)$$

A plot of this equation is shown in Fig. 9-38. For this curve,

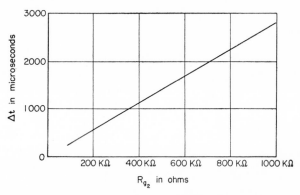

Fig. 9-38.   Delay time vs. R_{g2} for the circuit of Fig. 9-3.   All other parameters are the same as used in the example of Sec. 9-2.

R_{g2} has not been made small enough to cause the plate voltage to change appreciably. Therefore Δt is approximately a linear function of R_{g2}.

The circuit of Fig. 9-10 offers a very convenient method of varying the time during which T_2 is cut off. To accomplish this, it is necessary only to vary the positive voltage to which the grid of T_2 is returned. A plot of Δt as a function of this positive voltage is shown in Fig. 9-39.

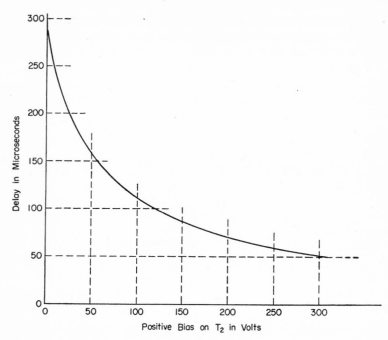

Fig. 9-39.   Delay time vs. positive grid bias on T_2 for the circuit of Fig. 9-10. All other parameters are the same used in the example of Sec. 9-3.

9-8 Basic Plate-Coupled, Free-Running Multivibrator

The multivibrator of Fig. 9-40 is very similar to that originally described by Abraham and Bloch.

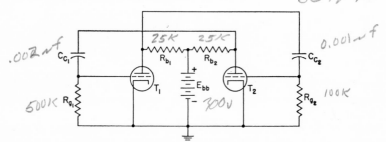

Fig. 9-40.   Plate-coupled, free-running multivibrator.

This particular circuit has been treated by some sources as a two-stage amplifier in which the output is returned to the input.

Each stage then supplies a phase shift of 180°.   If it is assumed that the voltage across the capacitor is relatively constant and that R_g is large with respect to R_b, a necessary condition for self-oscillation in a symmetrical circuit is

$$R_b > \frac{r_p}{\mu - 1} \tag{9-64}$$

As shown in Sec. 8-3, this condition is also that necessary to give an infinite plate-to-plate input resistance.

The oscillations which take place in the circuit of Fig. 9-40 are not sinusoidal in form but are actually a type of relaxation oscillations.   The voltage variations which are encountered are of such magnitude that the μ and r_p of the tubes have little meaning in the conventional sense.

Perhaps the easiest way to analyze the circuit of Fig. 9-40 is in a manner very similar to that used for the single-cycle multivibrator. However, several significant differences will be encountered.

In the single-cycle multivibrators previously discussed, a completely stable state was present, for which an analysis yielding initial conditions for the energy storage elements could be made. No such conditions exist in the free-running circuit.   It then becomes convenient to begin the study of the cycle just as a specified grid voltage approaches the cutoff value.   Since a conducting grid circuit time constant is usually much lower than the time constant of the nonconducting grid circuit, the grid voltage of the conducting tube can usually be assumed to have a zero value at this time.   If the grid voltage of the "on" tube is at zero, the plate voltage of the "off" tube is equal to the supply voltage.

Equations very similar to those of the single-cycle multivibrator will be derived for the circuit of Fig. 9-40.

Assume that T_1 is conducting, but that the grid of T_2 is just approaching the cutoff potential.   The circuit of Fig. 9-41 is applicable.   Conditions at this time will be designated with the subscript ( )$_0$.   Summing currents at the anodes gives

$$(i_{b1})_0 + \frac{(e_{b1})_0 - E_{bb}}{R_{b1}} + \frac{e_{co2}}{R_{g2}} = 0 \tag{9-65}$$

or $$(e_{b1})_0 + R_{b1}(i_{b1})_0 = E_{bb} - \frac{R_{b1}}{R_{g2}} e_{co2} \tag{9-66}$$

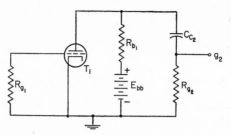

Fig. 9-41.　Circuit equivalent to that of Fig. 9-40 when T_1 is conducting with zero grid voltage and T_2 is cut off.

Since the grid voltage of T_1 is assumed to be zero, the intersection of the zero grid voltage curve with the line of Eq. (9-66) gives the values of $(e_{b1})_0$ and $(i_{b1})_0$. Also at this time, the capacitor voltages are

$$(e_{c1})_0 = E_{bb} \tag{9-67}$$

$$(e_{c2})_0 = (e_{b1})_0 - e_{co2} \tag{9-68}$$

Conduction will now be transferred to T_2, giving the circuit of Fig. 9-39. The subscript ( )$_1$ will be used to denote the time just following the transfer of conduction. Assuming a value of $\bar{r}_{g2}$ for the conducting grid resistance of T_2 gives

$$(e_{c2})_1 = \frac{R_{g2}\bar{r}_{g2}[E_{bb} + e_{co2} - (e_{b1})_0]}{R_{g2}\bar{r}_{g2} + R_{b1}(R_{g2} + \bar{r}_{g2})} \tag{9-69}$$

The plate circuit of T_2 at this time is specified by

$$(e_{b2})_1 + (i_{b2})_1 \left(\frac{R_{b2}R_{g1}}{R_{b2} + R_{g1}} \right) = E_{bb} \tag{9-70}$$

The value of $(e_{c2})_1$ from Eq. (9-69), the line of Eq. (9-70), and the plate characteristics will fix the value of $(e_{b2})_1$ and $(i_{b2})_1$. Knowing that the plate potential of T_2 has dropped from E_{bb} to $(e_{b2})_1$, the value of $(e_{c1})_1$ is

$$(e_{c1})_1 = (e_{b2})_1 - E_{bb} \tag{9-71}$$

The plate voltage of T_2 may be very low due to the high grid potential.

To calculate the time constant of the grid circuit of T_1, a constant static conducting resistance of $\bar{r}_{p2}$ is assumed for T_2. This time constant is

$$(\tau_{g1})_{\Delta t_1} = \left[R_{g1} + \frac{R_{b2}\bar{r}_{p2}}{R_{b2} + \bar{r}_{p2}} \right] C_{c1} \tag{9-72}$$

For the grid circuit of T_2,

$$(\tau_{g2})_{\Delta t_1} = \left(R_{b1} + \frac{\bar{r}_{g2}R_{g2}}{\bar{r}_{g2} + R_{g2}} \right) C_{c2} \tag{9-73}$$

As previously stated, $(\tau_{g2})_{\Delta t_1}$ is usually small compared to $(\tau_{g1})_{\Delta t_1}$, allowing the grid voltage of T_2 to reach zero before the grid of T_1 reaches the cutoff potential. If Δt_1 is the time that T_1 is cut off,

$$\Delta t_1 = (\tau_{g1})_{\Delta t_1} \ln \frac{(e_{b2})_1 - E_{bb}}{e_{co1}} \tag{9-74}$$

The second portion of the operational cycle is calculated in exactly the same way, giving

$$(e_{b2})_0 + R_{b2}(i_{b2})_0 = E_{bb} - \frac{R_{b2}}{R_{g1}} e_{co1} \tag{9-75}$$

$$(e_{c2})_0 = 0 \tag{9-76}$$

$$(e_{c1})_0 = (e_{b2})_0 - e_{co1} \tag{9-77}$$

$$(e_{C2})_0 = E_{bb} \tag{9-78}$$

$$(e_{c1})_1 = \frac{R_{g1}\bar{r}_{g1}[E_{bb} + e_{co1} - (e_{b2})_0]}{R_{g1}\bar{r}_{g1} + R_{b2}(R_{g1} + \bar{r}_{g1})} \tag{9-79}$$

$$(e_{b1})_1 + (i_{b1})_1 \left(\frac{R_{b1}R_{g2}}{R_{b1} + R_{g2}} \right) = E_{bb} \tag{9-80}$$

$$(e_{c2})_1 = (e_{b1})_1 - E_{bb} \tag{9-81}$$

With T_1 conducting,

$$(\tau_{g2})_{\Delta t_2} = \left(R_{g2} + \frac{R_{b1}\bar{r}_{p1}}{R_{b1} + \bar{r}_{p1}} \right) C_{c2} \tag{9-82}$$

$$(\tau_{g1})_{\Delta t_2} = \left(R_{b2} + \frac{R_{g1}\bar{r}_{g1}}{R_{g1} + \bar{r}_{g1}} \right) C_{c1} \tag{9-83}$$

The time that T_2 is cut off is

$$\Delta t_2 = (\tau_{g2})_{\Delta t_2} \ln \frac{(e_{b1})_1 - E_{bb}}{e_{co2}} \tag{9-84}$$

The frequency of the multivibrator may be calculated as

$$f = \frac{1}{\Delta t_1 + \Delta t_2} = \frac{1}{(\tau_{g1})_{\Delta t_1} \ln \dfrac{(e_{b2})_1 - E_{bb}}{e_{co1}} + (\tau_{g2})_{\Delta t_2} \ln \dfrac{(e_{b1})_1 - E_{bb}}{e_{co2}}} \tag{9-85}$$

or

$$f = \cfrac{1}{(C_{c1})\left(R_{g1} + \cfrac{R_{b2}\bar{r}_{p2}}{R_{b2} + r_{p2}}\right) \ln \cfrac{(e_{b2})_1 - E_{bb}}{e_{co1}} + (C_{c2})\left(R_{b2} + \cfrac{\bar{r}_{g1}R_{g1}}{\bar{r}_{g1} + R_{g1}}\right) \ln \cfrac{(e_{b1})_1 - E_{bb}}{e_{co2}}} \qquad (9\text{-}86)$$

For a completely symmetrical system,

$$f = \cfrac{1}{2C_c\left(R_g + \cfrac{R_b\bar{r}_p}{R_b + \bar{r}_p}\right) \ln \cfrac{(e_b)_1 - E_{bb}}{e_{co}}} \qquad (9\text{-}87)$$

Quite often the combination of the plate load resistance and the static resistance will be small as compared with the grid resistance. Then

$$f = \cfrac{1}{2C_cR_g \ln \cfrac{(e_b)_1 - E_{bb}}{e_{co}}} \qquad (9\text{-}88)$$

In some extreme cases calculation may show that the grid potential of a tube could not be quite zero just before the tube was cut off, even though this assumption was originally made. The new value of the grid potential can then be used to recalculate the entire cycle of operation, giving a third value for the grid potential. The process is then repeated until results are obtained which are sufficiently close to the starting point. It is also possible to write sufficient numbers of simultaneous equations to solve the system; however, this procedure is usually not very practical.

EXAMPLE: In the circuit of Fig. 9-40, let $R_{b1} = R_{b2} = 25,000$ ohms, $C_{c1} = 0.002$ microfarad, $C_{c2} = 0.001$ microfarad, $R_{g1} = 500,000$ ohms, $R_{g2} = 100,000$ ohms, and $E_{bb} = 300$ volts. The tube type will be a 6SN7.

If it is assumed that T_1 is conducting and has zero grid voltage, and that the grid of T_2 is at the cutoff value, the circuit of Fig. 9-41 may be used. When $(i_{b1})_0$ is in milliamperes, Eq. (9-66) is

$$(e_{b1})_0 + 25(i_{b1})_0 = 304.5$$

This line plotted on the plate characteristics intersects the $e_{c1} = 0$ curve at $(e_{b1})_0 = 89$ volts. From Eq. (9-67), the voltage on C_{c2} at this time is $89 + 18$, or 107 volts. The voltage on C_{c1} is 300 volts.

When conduction is instantaneously transferred to T_2, the circuit of

Fig. 9-42 is used.   Assuming $r_{g1} = 1000$ ohms gives, from Eq. (9-69),

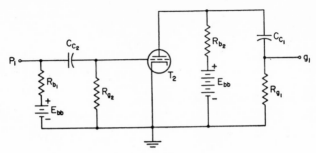

Fig. 9-42.   Circuit equivalent to that of Fig. 9-40 when T_2 is conducting and T_1 is cut off.

$(e_{c2})_1 = 7.35$ volts.   Equation (9-70) becomes

$$(e_{b2})_1 + (23.8)(i_{b2})_1 = 300$$

where $(i_{b2})_1$ is in milliamperes.   The value of $(e_{b2})_1$ is then found to be 287 volts.   Since the plate voltage of T_2 has dropped 287 volts, the grid voltage of T_1 will drop to -287 volts.   The grid voltage of T_2 and the plate voltage of T_1 have both instantaneously increased 25.35 volts.   Assuming $\bar{r}_{p2} = 10,000$ ohms in Eq. (9-72), and $\bar{r}_{g2} = 1000$ ohms in Eq. (9-73) gives

$$(\tau_{g1})_{\Delta t_1} = 26 \text{ microseconds}$$

$$(\tau_{g2})_{\Delta t_1} = 1014 \text{ microseconds}$$

From Eq. (9-74),

$$\Delta t_1 = 2805 \text{ microseconds}$$

Carrying through a set of similar calculations for the second half of the operating cycle gives the following results:

$$(e_{c2})_0 = 0$$

$$(e_{b2})_0 = 87 \text{ volts}$$

$$(e_{c1})_0 = 105 \text{ volts}$$

$$(e_{c2})_0 = 300 \text{ volts}$$

$$(e_{b1})_1 = 18 \text{ volts}$$

$$(e_{c2})_1 = -282 \text{ volts}$$

$$(\tau_{g2})_{\Delta t_2} = 107 \text{ microseconds}$$

$$\Delta t_2 = 295 \text{ microseconds}$$

The frequency of the multivibrator is $f = 1/(\Delta t_1 + \Delta t_2) = 322$ cycles per second.

A complete set of wave forms is shown in Fig. 9-43.

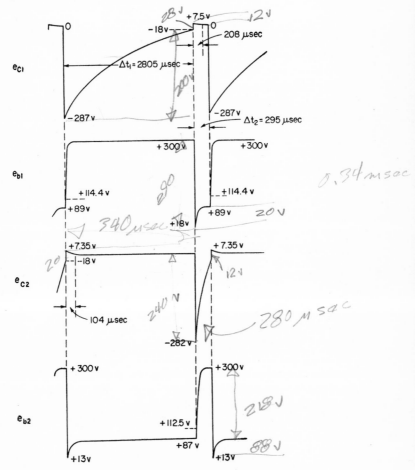

Fig. 9-43.   Wave forms for the circuit of Fig. 9-40.

9-9 Modifications of the Plate-Coupled Multivibrator

All the modifications of the basic single-cycle multivibrator which have been previously discussed can be applied to the free-running multivibrator.   For example, one or both grids may be returned to a positive potential instead of to ground. The results obtained in the single-cycle case will be obtained here, that is, in general the frequency and stability will be increased by the positive grid connection. Few other changes will be realized, and the circuit can be easily analyzed by methods already shown. Variation of the positive voltage to which the grids are returned offers a convenient method of varying the frequency.

In many applications of the multivibrator, it is desirable that the plate voltage wave form be as rectangular as possible. As was discussed with reference to the single-cycle multivibrator, this effect can be approached by use of a series grid resistor.

If these resistors are used, the negative dips will be removed from the plate voltage wave forms, because the grids cannot be driven appreciably positive. Also, since the grid side of the coupling capacitors are at higher resistance points, the initial jump in plate voltage of an "off-going" tube will be greater. However, even though the plate potential changes by a greater amount instantaneously, it will take a longer time to get back to the supply voltage, since the time constant has been increased.

The interelectrode capacitances of the tubes have been neglected up to this point, although it is realized that the speed with which the multivibrator can switch from one condition to the other is determined by the rate at which these capacitances can be charged and discharged. When the series grid resistors are added to improve the plate voltage wave forms, the time required to charge the input capacitance of a tube is increased, since the capacitance is charged through the added series resistor. This may have an undesirable effect on the leading edge of the voltage wave forms. The effect of the input capacitance may be minimized by shunting the series resistor by a small capacitor C_s where

$$C_s R_s = C_{in} \bar{r}_g \tag{9-89}$$

It is nearly impossible to obtain perfect compensation, since both C_{in} and $\bar{r}_g$ may not be constant during the time that the tube is driven positive. However, the wave form can usually be much improved.

The effects of the interelectrode capacitance can also be minimized by the use of pentodes instead of triodes. In particular, the reduced plate-grid capacitance will allow steeper wave fronts to be realized. Connected in a different manner, pentodes allow an output signal to be taken from an isolated circuit. To do this, the screen grids will be made to serve as the effective plates of the multivibrator circuit, and the actual tube plates, from which the output voltage is taken, are then electron-coupled to the multivibrator. This is shown in the circuit of Fig. 9-44.

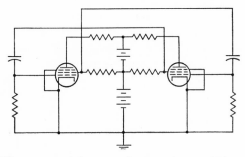

Fig. 9-44. Electron-coupled output, free-running, pentode multivibrator.

A sketch of the wave forms for one tube is shown in Fig. 9-45. It is to be noted that the rising edge of a plate voltage wave form does not have the exponential approach to the supply voltage as found in the triode multivibrator. The plate voltage becomes the supply voltage whenever the tube is cut off, even though the screen voltage is lowered because of the current taken by a charging capacitor.

A multivibrator circuit which is not too practical, but one which leads to an interesting solution if the usual approximations are made, is shown in Fig. 9-46. The circuit is similar to that of Fig. 9-40, except that a negative voltage, less than the cutoff potential, has been added to the grid circuit of T_1. The solution of the circuit is also similar to that of Sec. 9-8 with the exception of two changes.

When T_1 is cut off, the grid voltage of T_1 does not return toward zero but toward the negative value. Thus the return is slower and also more unstable, since the curve crosses the cutoff line at a very small angle.

When T_1 returns to conduction, the usual procedure is to assume a value for the conducting grid-cathode resistance which is small and constant when e_{c1} is greater than zero, and infinite when e_{c1} is less than zero. The volt-ampere characteristic under such an assump-

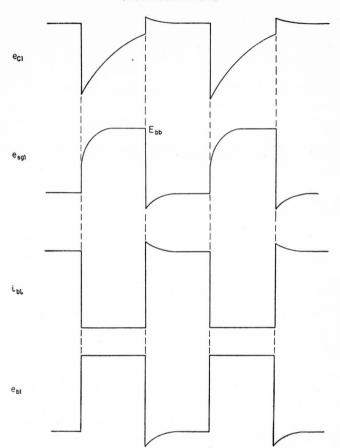

Fig. 9-45.   Wave forms for the circuit of Fig. 9-44.

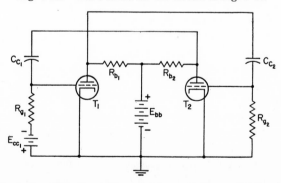

Fig. 9-46.   Negative grid return, free-running multivibrator.

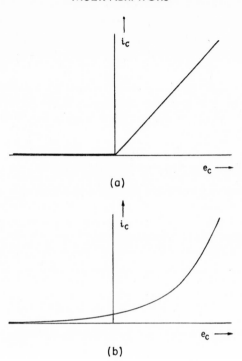

Fig. 9-47.   Grid-cathode characteristic for triode: (a) ideal; (b) practical.

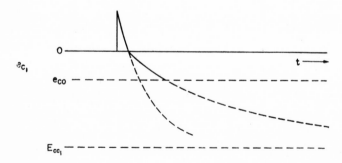

Fig. 9-48.   Grid voltage of T_1 when T_1 is cut off in the circuit of Fig. 9-46.

tion is shown in Fig. 9-47a. The grid-cathode voltage would follow a curve such as shown in Fig. 9-48. The initial part of the
curve is calculated on the basis that no further switching will take
place. In this case, the curve will approach a negative value which
is somewhat smaller than the bias voltage. Only the first part of

this curve will ever exist, however, since at zero it is assumed that the conducting grid-cathode resistance is removed. This causes the time constant to be increased, with a corresponding discontinuity in the slope of the curve. In any practical circuit this discontinuity will not appear, because there is no discontinuity in the slope of the curve as has been assumed. If the correct curve were used as shown in Fig. 9-47b the grid voltage of Fig. 9-48 would have no discontinuity in slope.

9-10 Cathode-Coupled, Free-Running Multivibrators

Several forms of the cathode-coupled multivibrator are possible. One type of single-cycle, cathode-coupled multivibrator was discussed in Sec. 9-6. This multivibrator can also be free-running if the parameters are chosen correctly.[2]

If the grid resistor of T_2 is returned to ground instead of to the common cathode connection, the circuit will still function as a free-running multivibrator.[3] Such a circuit is shown in Fig. 9-49.

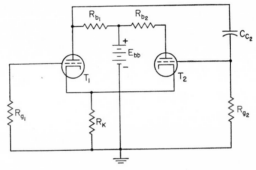

Fig. 9-49. Cathode-coupled, free-running multivibrator.

The time constants in the circuit of Sec. 9-6 can be adjusted so that the multivibrator is free-running in such a way that the current in T_2 consists of a series of narrow pulses. A parallel RC network in the cathode circuit of T_2 would then develop a sawtooth voltage, since the capacitor could be charged rapidly by the current pulse through the tube and discharged slowly through the shunting resistor. This voltage could be used as a sweep voltage. A circuit

---

[2] See reference 85 at end of chapter.
[3] See references 64 and 66 at end of chapter.

is shown in Fig. 9-50. The frequency of the circuit will depend primarily upon the $R_s - C_s$ and $R_{g2} - C_{c2}$ combinations. In

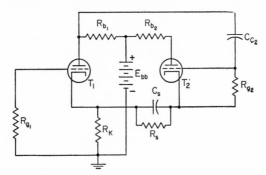

Fig. 9-50. Cathode-coupled, free-running multivibrator modified to produce a sweep voltage.

order to change frequency and still maintain a constant sawtooth voltage across the $R_s - C_s$ combination, both R_{g2} and R_s would have to be varied simultaneously. The difficulty can be obviated by elimination of R_{g2} and C_{c2} to obtain a completely new free-running multivibrator whose frequency is primarily determined by R_s and C_s. This is shown in Fig. 9-51. It may not be possible to connect the grid of T_2 directly to the plate of T_1, in which case a resistive voltage divider may be used.

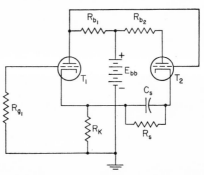

Fig. 9-51. Further modification of cathode-coupled, free-running multivibrator.

The circuit of Fig. 9-51 may again be modified in several ways to obtain other multivibrators. One modification is obtained by returning R_s to ground as shown in Fig. 9-52.

Another cathode-coupled multivibrator, similar to those previously discussed, is shown in Fig. 9-53. A brief description of the operation of this circuit will be given.

Assume that T_2 is conducting and that T_1 is at cutoff. This may or may not be a stable condition, depending upon the magni-

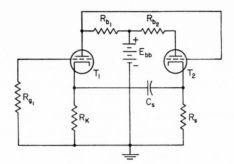

Fig. 9-52. Cathode-coupled, free-running multivibrator modified to produce a sweep voltage.

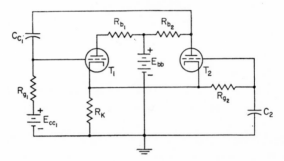

Fig. 9-53. Cathode-coupled multivibrator in which operation can be controlled by magnitude of d-c input voltage.

tude of E_{cc1}. If this is taken to be a stable state, that is, $e_{c2} = 0$, the operating conditions may be found from the plate characteristics. The plate-cathode potential of T_1 may also be found, which fixes the corresponding cutoff voltage. The value of E_{cc1} which is necessary to keep T_1 cut off can then be found. If the actual value of E_{cc1} is greater than this critical value, T_1 will start to conduct as soon as C_1 has discharged sufficiently. When T_1 starts to conduct, the grid-ground voltage of T_2 cannot change instantaneously; therefore the current through T_2 must decrease. This raises the plate voltage of T_2 and the grid voltage of T_1, causing a further increase of cathode voltage. The process continues until T_1 is conducting heavily and T_2 is cut off.

As C_2 then charges, the grid-cathode voltage of T_2 decreases toward zero, and T_2 eventually draws current. This lowers the grid voltage of T_1, and a process opposite to the previous one takes

place, bringing T_2 to conduction and cutting off T_1. The complete
cycle continues to repeat indefinitely.

A particular advantage of this circuit is that a state of oscillation
or nonoscillation can be easily selected by variation of the magnitude
of E_{cc1}. In other words, the multivibrator can be controlled by the
magnitude of the d-c potential applied to the grid of T_1.

Another interesting and useful multivibrator is shown in Fig.
9-54.[4] With the exception of the R_{g1}, C_1, and E_{cc1} combination in

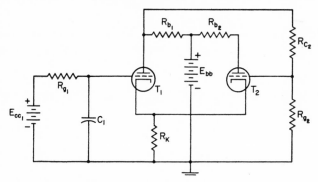

Fig. 9-54. Multivibrator derived from Schmitt trigger circuit.

the grid circuit of T_1, the circuit of Fig. 9-54 is identical to the
Schmitt circuit as discussed in Sec. 8-4.

A low value of voltage on the grid of T_1 will cause it to be cut off,
with T_2 conducting. If the grid voltage of T_1 is increased to the
critical value, conduction will be transferred to T_1. If the grid
potential is reduced to a second critical value, somewhat lower than
the first, conduction will be transferred back to T_2.

In the circuit of Fig. 9-54, the grid voltage of T_1 is increased when
the capacitor C_1 charges through R_{g1} from the source E_{cc1}. When
the capacitor voltage reaches the critical value, a small amount of
current flows through T_1. The plate potential of T_1 drops, and the
drop is directly coupled through the voltage-dividing resistor network to the grid of T_2. The current through T_2 decreases, the
cathode potential drops, and cumulative action occurs, causing the
cathode potential to drop still more. The grid of T_1 is thus driven
positive, and conduction occurs through the grid-cathode circuit,
discharging the capacitor. As this occurs, a point is reached where

[4] See reference 76 at end of chapter.

a rising potential at the plate of T_1 and a dropping cathode potential combine to bring T_2 back into conduction. The cycle is then repeated. A good sawtooth voltage may be obtained from the capacitor C_1, while a rectangular voltage appears at the plate of T_2. It may be shown that the sawtooth voltage appearing across the capacitor varies between two limits determined by the parameters of the circuit other than the charging resistance R_{g1}. If the value of R_{g1} becomes too large, however, the circuit will become inoperative.

9-11 Uses of Cathode Resistance in Multivibrators

Usually the output voltage of the multivibrator is taken from the plate or the grid circuit. It is possible, however, to insert a resistor in one or both cathode circuits and to take the output from this resistor. Such a circuit is shown in Fig. 9-55. There are two

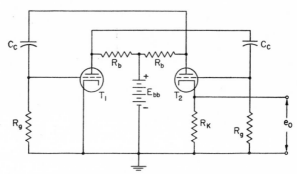

Fig. 9-55.   Cathode-output multivibrator.

principal advantages to this type of output coupling. The output resistance is quite low, and the output voltage is more nearly rectangular, since it depends only upon the plate current. The magnitude of the output voltage is much less than could be obtained from a plate or a grid circuit.

There is one major difference in the voltage wave forms of the multivibrator with cathode-coupled output as compared with the basic multivibrator. In the basic multivibrator, the grid voltage of a conducting tube relaxes toward zero. In the circuit of Fig. 9-55, however, the cathode voltage during this time is not zero, and the grid potential will relax toward a value which is negative with respect to the cathode. This tends to make the grid potential during the transient period in this circuit more negative than the grid potential of the basic multivibrator during the corresponding interval. The plate voltages of the circuit of Fig. 9-55 therefore rise to higher values during conduction than do the plate voltages of the basic multivibrator.

If the two grid resistors are returned to a positive potential, the frequency will be a function of the magnitude of this potential.[5] For most multivibrators, the relationship is linear over quite a range, tending to flatten out at both the high and low ends of the frequency scale. Inclusion of cathode resistors alters the relationship as shown in Fig. 9-56. Thus if it is desired to linearize the

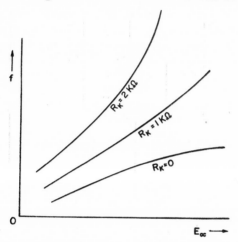

Fig. 9-56. Effect of cathode resistance on frequency-positive bias characteristic.

relationship in the neighborhood of a given frequency or bias voltage, an optimum value of R_k can usually be found.

9-12 Multivibrator Type Circuits Based on Miller Sweep Circuit

There is a class of circuits which, although not multivibrators, are very similar in some respects.[6] The most important of these circuits, which were originally developed in England, are the phantastron, sanatron, and sanaphant. These circuits differ from

[5] See reference 13 at end of chapter.
[6] See reference 18 at end of chapter.

the multivibrator in that the timing wave form is not an exponential voltage but is a linear voltage as developed by the Miller sweep circuit. Two of the more elementary examples of the phantastron type circuit will be briefly discussed.

The basic Miller sweep circuit is shown in Fig. 6-43. The screen grid voltage consists of a positive pulse lasting for the duration of the sweep. This positive pulse on the screen grid could be coupled to the suppressor grid, necessitating only an initiating pulse to be applied to the suppressor grid in order that the process be started. Such a circuit is called a screen-coupled phantastron and is shown in Fig. 9-57. The action in the circuit of Fig. 9-57 will cease when

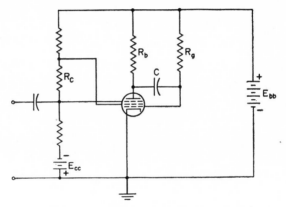

Fig. 9-57.   Screen-coupled phantastron.

the operation reaches the knee of the plate characteristic. At this point the screen current will increase, causing the screen voltage, and thus the suppressor voltage, to drop. The plate voltage also will rise, and this rise will be coupled to the grid to make the process regenerative. The circuit will then return to its original state. A square wave can be obtained from either the screen or the suppressor grid. The chief advantage of the circuit is derived from the fact that the timing wave is a linear function instead of an exponential function as obtained in the true multivibrator. The circuit is thus valuable as a variable time delay device.

The circuit of Fig. 9-57 may be modified in many different ways in order to produce either a free-running oscillator or a trigger circuit. It may be made free-running by merely replacing R_c with a coupling capacitor.

A phantastron type circuit which is remotely similar to a cathode-coupled multivibrator may also be devised. It is not necessary that the positive square wave be coupled back to the suppressor grid to maintain operation if the same effect can be obtained in another manner. A resistor inserted in the cathode circuit will produce, from cathode to ground, a negative square pulse, which will have the desired effect. Such a circuit is shown in Fig. 9-58.

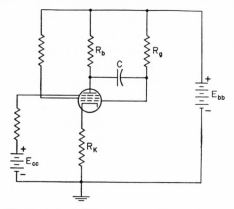

Fig. 9-58.   Phantastron analogous to cathode-coupled multivibrator.

9-13 Synchronization of the Multivibrator

The free-running multivibrator bears considerable resemblance to the gas-tube sweep circuit in that both are forms of relaxation oscillators. However, in the case of the multivibrator, the critical potentials are determined by the cutoff characteristics of high-vacuum tubes. The gas-tube relaxation oscillator could be synchronized by varying the effective critical potentials with some external signal. In the same manner, the free-running multivibrator can be synchronized. Each oscillator possesses a natural frequency which can be affected by application of an external signal.

The object of multivibrator synchronization is to produce a signal which is a subharmonic of the driving frequency. For most types of driving signals, sine waves for example, the frequency of the multivibrator can be controlled, but the phase of the output signal is hard to determine. Also, the wave form of the output signal is very nearly independent of the driving signal. Other forms of driving signals which have definite discontinuities in their makeup, such as pulses or square waves, can fix both the frequency and phase of the output signal, but the shape of the output wave form can still be independent of the driving signal.

Since the synchronization is to be obtained by alteration of the critical potentials, maximum sensitivity will usually be obtained if the driving signal is injected into one or both of the grid circuits. In effect, the driving signal will be added to the normal grid voltage, as shown by the sine wave example of Fig. 9-59.   Unless the grids

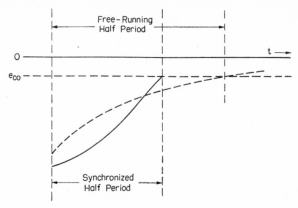

Fig. 9-59.   Effect of synchronizing signal on normal grid voltage.

have been returned to a high positive potential, or very small synchronizing voltages are applied, the grid voltage curve will intersect the cutoff line during the positive slope of the input signal.   In other words, it will be easier to synchronize a multivibrator at a frequency higher than its normal frequency, than to synchronize it at a lower-than normal frequency.

In general, the introduction of a voltage of frequency f into a multivibrator will provide an output voltage which has a frequency of $(m/n)f$, where m and n are integers. As explained above, $(m/n)f$ will usually be greater than the unsynchronized frequency. The most important case is where $m = 1$, and the multivibrator is operating as a count-down system with ratio n. This case will be discussed in more detail.

A symmetrical multivibrator will usually provide an m of unity. By proper choice of the injection system, odd or even values of n can be favored.   Consider the circuits of Fig. 9-60a, b, and c.   The

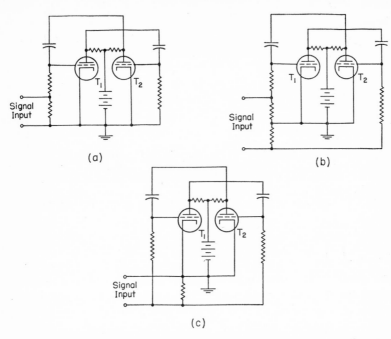

Fig. 9-60. Means of synchronizing the free-running, plate-coupled multivibrator: (a) control of grid only; (b) out-of-phase control on both grids; (c) in-phase control on both grids.

count-down characteristics can be determined by a system similar to that of Fig. 9-61. In this system, the multivibrator is synchronized by a sine wave oscillator. The same sine wave is also used to form Lissajous figures with the output of the multivibrator. From these figures, the ratio of the multivibrator frequency to the sine wave frequency can be determined.

The symmetrical circuit of Fig. 9-60a is being driven on one grid only, and does not favor either odd or even values of n. A characteristic similar to that of Fig. 9-62 would be obtained.

In the circuit of Fig. 9-60b, the grids are driven out of phase. As previously explained, it is not necessary that the grids alone be controlled. Out-of-phase voltages can be applied to any two symmetrical points in the circuit.

Assume that the symmetrical circuit of Fig. 9-60b is being synchronized, with an even number of half cycles occurring during each grid return period. Approximate sketches of the grid voltages of

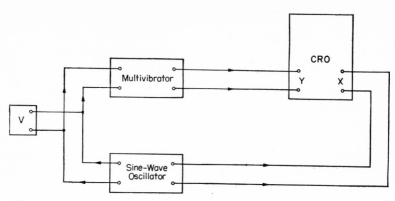

Fig. 9-61.   System to check synchronizing characteristics of multivibrator.

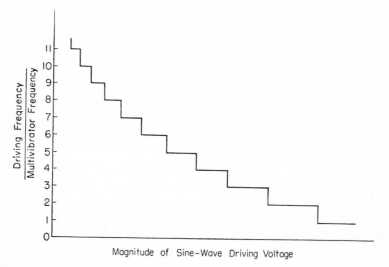

Magnitude of Sine-Wave Driving Voltage

Fig. 9-62.   Curve obtained by controlling symmetrical multivibrator from one grid.

T_1 and T_2 are shown in Fig. 9-63.   If the grid voltage of T_1 ends on a positive slope portion of the input signal, the grid voltage of T_2 must be at a negative slope position at the end of an identical period of time.   Thus an even number of half cycles on each grid wave form is inherently unstable.   Let the same circuit by synchronized with an odd number of half cycles on each grid wave form. This is shown in Fig. 9-64.   Both grid voltages can end on a positive

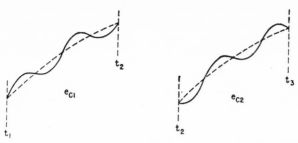

Fig. 9-63.   Grid voltage for the symmetrical circuit of Fig. 9-60(b) showing the probability of instability if an even number of half-cycles appears on each grid wave form.

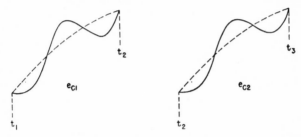

Fig. 9-64.   Grid voltage for the symmetrical circuit of Fig. 9-60(b) showing the probability of stability if an odd number of half-cycles appears in each grid wave form.

slope in this case.   The situation is thus a stable one, and the circuit of (b) tends to synchronize when there are an odd number of half cycles in each grid wave form, or when n is odd.   It is possible for the circuit to synchronize on even values, but the odd values are favored.   A typical control characteristic for the circuit of Fig. 9-60b is shown in Fig. 9-65.

By the same reasoning as discussed for the circuit of Fig. 9-60b, it can be found that the circuit of Fig. 9-60c will be most stable when an even number of half cycles are present in each grid return time.   Thus that particular circuit will favor even count-down ratios.   A typical control characteristic is shown in Fig. 9-66.

Values of m other than unity can be obtained by use of non-symmetrical multivibrators, but the principles of operation will be the same as previously discussed.   Small values of m and n give the most stable systems.   Generally, the product of m and n is kept below 10.

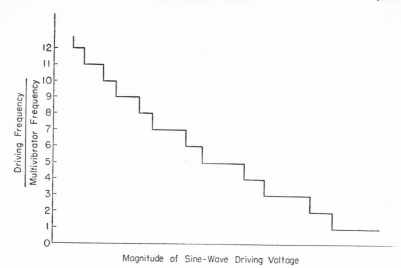

Fig. 9-65. Curve obtained by controlling symmetrical multivibrator with
out-of-phase sine waves on grids.

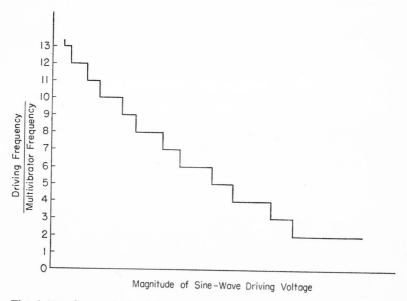

Fig. 9-66. Curve obtained by controlling symmetrical multivibrator with
in-phase sine waves on grids.

If it is desired to synchronize the multivibrator in such a way that the time of switching is definitely known, pulse-type synchronizing signals may be used. A grid wave form might then appear as shown in the sketch of Fig. 9-67.

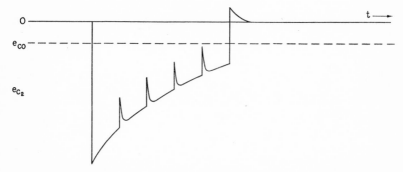

Fig. 9-67. Control of multivibrator frequency by pulse-type wave forms.

The stability of the system could be increased if a larger difference between the desired trigger pulse and the one just preceding it could be obtained. One way of doing this is by the use of resonant stabilization. Consider the circuit of Fig. 9-68. A parallel

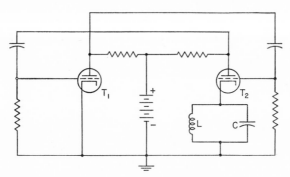

Fig. 9-68. System of resonant stabilization as applied to the control of a free-running multivibrator.

LC circuit has been inserted in the cathode of T_2. When T_2 conducts, the pulse of current excites the parallel combination. The grid-cathode voltage of T_2 during its off period will then look like the sketch of Fig. 9-69. The over-all stability of the system has been greatly increased, since the possibility of an earlier pulse intersecting the cutoff voltage has been lessened.   In general, the circuit of Fig. 9-68 will work best when the parallel LC circuit is excited by a narrow pulse of current.

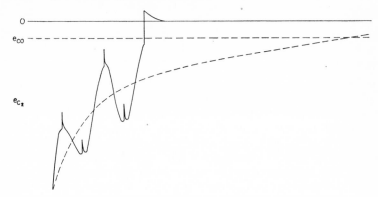

Fig. 9-69.   Grid voltage of T_2 in the circuit of Fig. 9-68.

9-14 Effect of Interelectrode Capacitance on the Multivibrator

Only very briefly in the past chapters has the effect of inter-electrode capacitance on the action of multivibrator and trigger circuits been discussed.   The sections on multivibrator wave shapes have neglected completely these capacitances, and for many circuits this will result in little error.   However, as the period of operation is decreased, a point is eventually reached where the time needed to transfer conduction from one tube to the other will become an appreciable part of the cycle.   An exact analysis of the multivibrator action during the transition period is exceedingly impractical, since two nonlinear vacuum tubes are present, along with numerous linear resistors and capacitors.   Demonstrating this complexity is the complete circuit of the basic plate-coupled multivibrator of Fig. 9-70.   The capacitors C_{pk} and C_{gk} can be considered to include any stray capacitance in the circuit.

One way an approximate solution can be made is to assume that the tubes have linear characteristics given by

$$i_p = g_m e_g \tag{9-90}$$

After considerable work, it can be shown that the time required for any given voltage wave form to complete its transition is primarily a function of the transconductance of the tubes and the total circuit

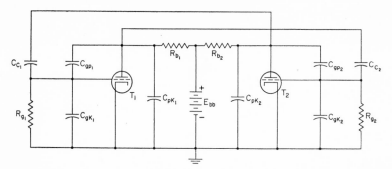

Fig. 9-70. Complete circuit of plate-coupled, free-running multivibrator.

capacitance, that is, the greater the transconductance and the smaller the capacitances, the sooner will the transition be completed.[7] Using this fact, several general statements may be made concerning the transition times.

All capacitances in the circuit should be kept as small as possible. This indicates that a choice should be made in the selection of the tube types to be used, and extreme care should also be taken in the wiring of the circuit. The output should not be taken indiscriminately from the multivibrator. Low-resistance outputs taken from a cathode will allow any connected capacitance to be charged more rapidly than from a high-resistance output. Electron-coupled outputs also tend to minimize the effects of a loading capacitance. If it is impossible to use a low-resistance or electron-coupled output, a cathode follower with its very low input capacitance may be used to obtain an output. It is also quite possible to isolate capacitance and increase the available charging current in the multivibrator by using a cathode follower to couple from plate to grid instead of by the use of the coupling capacitor alone.

A second consideration in the choice of tubes is that of the transconductance. In general, high-transconductance tubes allow the circuit capacitance to be charged more rapidly than will tubes of a lower value. For any given tube, the magnitudes of the plate load resistors can be kept as low as possible, allowing the tube to operate at higher currents and corresponding higher values of transconductance.

---

[7] See reference 81 at end of chapter.

REFERENCES

1. Abbott, A. E., "Multivibrator Design by Graphic Methods," *Electronics*, June, 1948, Vol. 21, p. 118.
2. Abbott, Wilton R., "The Design and Application of Multivibrators," *Communications*, July, 1944, Vol. 24, p. 38.
3. Abraham, H. and Bloch, E., "Notice sur les lampes-valves a 3 electrodes et leurs applications," *Publication 27 of the French Ministere de la Guerre*, April, 1918.
4. Abraham, H. and Bloch, E., "Sur la mesure en valeur absolue des periodes des oscillations electriques de haute frequence," *Compt rend.*, June, 1919, Vol. 168, p. 1105.
5. Abraham, H. and Bloch, E., "Mesure en valeur absolue des periodes des oscillations electriques de haute frequence," *Ann. Phys.*, September-October, 1919, Vol. 12, p. 237.
6. Anderson, D. E., "Frequency Division by Multivibrators," *Elec. World*, June, 1944, Vol. 121, p. 118.
7. Andrew, Victor J., "The Adjustment of the Multivibrator for Frequency Division," *Proc. IRE*, November, 1931, Vol. 19, p. 1911.
8. Andronow, A. A. and Chaikin, C. E., *Theory of Oscillations*. Princeton: Princeton University Press, 1949.
9. Applegarth, A. Rufus, "Synchronizing Generators for Electronic Television," *Proc. IRE*, March, 1946, Vol. 34, p. 128w.
10. Arguimbau, Lawrence Baker, *Vacuum-Tube Circuits*. New York: John Wiley and Sons, Inc., 1948.
11. Bailey, Robert S. and Singleton, Henry, E., "Reducing Transmission Bandwidth," *Electronics*, August, 1948, Vol. 21, p. 107.
12. Bartelink, E. H. B. and Daskam, Edward, "F-M Short Range Carrier System," *Electronics*, December, 1947, Vol. 20, p. 112.
13. Bertram, Sidney, "The Degenerative Positive Bias Multivibrator," *Proc. IRE*, February, 1948, Vol. 36, p. 277.
14. Brainerd, J. G. and Weygandt, C. N., "Unsymmetrical Self-Excited Oscillations in Simple Non-Linear Systems," *Proc. IRE*, June, 1936, Vol. 24, p. 914.
15. Brainerd, J. B.; Reich, H. J.; Koehler, G.; and Woodruff, L. F., *Ultra-High Frequency Techniques*. New York: D. Van Nostrand Company, Inc., 1942.
16. Chance, Britton; Hughes, Vernon; MacNichol, Edward F.; Sayre, David; and Williams, Frederick C., *Waveforms*. New York: McGraw-Hill Book Co., Inc., 1949.

17. Chang, W. Y. and Rosenblum, S., "A Simple Counting System for Alpha-Ray Spectra and the Energy Distribution of Po Alpha-Particles," *Phys. Rev.*, April, 1945, Vol. 67, p. 222.

18. Close, Richard and Lebenbaum, Matthew T., "Design of Phantastron Time Delay Circuits," *Electronics*, April, 1948, Vol. 21, p. 100.

19. Cole, Larry S., "Measuring and Monitoring Broadcast Frequencies," *Electronics*, July, 1946, Vol. 19, p. 111.

20. Cooke-Yarborough, E. H., "A New Pulse Amplitude-Discriminator Circuit," *J. Sci. Instruments*, March, 1949, Vol. 26, p. 96.

21. Cruft Laboratory Electronics Training Staff, *Electronic Circuits and Tubes*. New York: McGraw-Hill Book Co., Inc., 1947.

22. Curran, A. W., "Frequency Monitoring for Relay Broadcasting Stations," *Electronics*, January, 1939, Vol. 12, p. 22.

23. Davis, K. H., "Multivibrator Step-Down by Fractional Ratios," *Bell Lab. Record*, March, 1948, Vol. 26, p. 114.

24. Dietze, Theodore W., and Dickerson, Theodore M., "Electronics Applied to the Betatron," *Proc. IRE*, October, 1949, Vol. 37, p. 1171.

25. Distel, Maurice and Gross, Allan, "Single Frame TV," *Electronics*, March, 1950, Vol. 23, p. 184.

26. Duffield, S. H. and Lankes, L. R., "Testing Photographic Shutters," *Electronics*, August, 1948, Vol. 21, p. 82.

27. du Toit, S. H., "A One-Shot Multivibrator Anticoincidence and Recording Circuit," *Rev. Sci. Instruments*, January, 1947, Vol. 18, p. 31.

28. Eberhard, E.; Endres, R. O.,; and Moore, R., "Counter Circuits Using Transistors," *RCA Rev.*, December, 1949, Vol. 10, p. 459.

29. Elmore, William C. and Sands, Matthew, *Electronics-Experimental Techniques*. New York: McGraw-Hill Book Co., Inc., 1949.

30. Emery, W. L., *Ultra-High Frequency Radio Engineering*. New York: The Macmillan Company, 1944.

31. Evans, Robley D. and Alder, Robert L., "Improved Counting Rate Meter," *Rev. Sci. Instruments*, November, 1939, Vol. 10, p. 332.

32. Fenn, Willard H., "The Generation of Square-Wave Voltages at High Frequencies," *Rev. Sci. Instruments*, November, 1940, Vol. 11, p. 369.

33. Feinberg, R., "On Performance of Push-Pull Relaxation Oscillators (Multivibrators)," *Phil. Mag.*, April, 1948, Vol. 39, p. 268.

34. Feinberg, R., "Symmetrical Multivibrators," *Wireless Engr.*, May, 1949, Vol. 26, p. 153.

35. Feinberg, R., "Asymmetrical Multivibrators," *Wireless Engr.*, October, 1949, Vol. 26, p. 325.

36. Getting, I. A., "Multivibrator Geiger Counter Circuit," *Phys. Rev.*, January, 1938, Vol. 53, p. 103.

37. Gingerich, N. S.; Evans, Robley D.; and Edgerton, Herold E., "A Direct-Reading Counting Rate Meter for Random Pulses," *Rev. Sci. Instruments*, December, 1936, Vol. 7, p. 450.

38. Gordon, James F., "A New Angular-Velocity-Modulation System Employing Pulse Techniques," *Proc. IRE*, June, 1946, Vol. 34, p. 324.

39. Glegg, Keith, "Cathode-Coupled Multivibrator Operation," *Proc. IRE*, June, 1950, Vol. 38, p. 655.

40. Herr, Donald L., "Oscillations in Certain Non-Linear Systems," *Proc. IRE*, June, 1939, Vol. 27, p. 396.

41. Huntoon, R. D., "A Portable High Voltage Supply," *Rev. Sci. Instruments*, June, 1939, Vol. 10, p. 176.

42. Hull, L. M. and Clapp, J. K., "A Convenient Method for Returning Secondary Frequency Standards to a Standard Time Interval," *Proc. IRE*, February, 1929, Vol. 17, p. 252.

43. Johanson, A. E., "A Tuned Plate Multivibrator," *Bell Lab. Record*, May, 1950, Vol. 28, p. 208.

44. Johnson T. H., "Circuits for the Control of Geiger-Mueller Counters and for Scaling and Recording their Impulses," *Rev. Sci. Instruments*, July, 1938, Vol. 9, p. 218.

45. Kelley, G. G., "A High Speed Synchroscope," *Rev. Sci. Instruments*, January, 1950, Vol. 21, p. 71.

46. Kiebert, Martin V. and Inglis, Andrew F., "Multivibrator Circuits," *Proc. IRE*, August, 1945, Vol. 33, p. 534.

47. Kip, A.; Bosquet, A.; Evans, R.; and Tuttle, W., "Design and Operation of an Improved Counting Rate Meter," *Rev. Sci. Instruments*, September, 1946, Vol. 17, p. 323.

48. Lampson, C. W. and Cosby, G. R., "Electronic Switch and Square Wave Oscillator," *Rev. Sci. Instruments*, April, 1941, Vol. 12, p. 187.

49. Leslie, C. W., "Megacycle Stepping Counter," *Proc. IRE*, August, 1948, Vol. 36, p. 1030.

50. Ludman, Walter W., "Time Base Calibration," *Electronics*, September, 1945, Vol. 18, p. 117.

51. Maloff, I. G. and Epstein, D. W., *Electron Optics in Television*. New York: McGraw-Hill Book Co., Inc., 1938.

52. Mann, W. B. and Parkinson, G. B., "A Geiger-Mueller Counting Unit and External Quenching Equipment for the Estimation of C14 and Carbon Dioxide," *Rev. Sci. Instruments*, January, 1949, Vol. 20, p. 41.

53. Martin, Karl H., "60 Cycle Square Wave Generator," *Electronics*, July, 1941, Vol. 14, p. 46.

54. Martin, Thomas L., Jr., *Ultra High Frequency Engineering*. New York: Prentice-Hall, Inc., 1950.

55. Mather, Norman W., "Multivibrator Circuits," *Electronics*, October, 1946, Vol. 19, p. 136.

56. M.I.T. Radar School Staff, *Principles of Radar*. New York: McGraw-Hill Book Co., Inc., 1946.

57. Moore, John W., "Rectangular Wave Generator for Biological Studies," *Electronics*, May, 1950, Vol. 23, p. 122.

58. Nottingham, Wayne V., "An Electronic Circuit to Control Intensity and Timing of Power for Spot Welding," *Rev. Sci. Instruments*, June, 1943, Vol. 14, p. 161.

59. Orning, A. A., "A Time-Basis Proportioning Controller," *Rev. Sci. Instruments*, May, 1945, Vol. 16, p. 129.

60. Phelps, Byron E., "Motor Noise Unit for Aircraft Trainer," *Electronics*, August, 1945, Vol. 18, p. 96.

61. Pickering, W. H., "Cosmic Ray Radiosonde," *Rev. Sci. Instruments*, June, 1943, Vol. 14, p. 171.

62. Pollard, Ernest C. and Sturtevant, Julian M., *Microwaves and Radar Electronics*. New York: John Wiley and Sons, Inc., 1948.

63. Poole, M. J., "An Automatic Current Integrator," *Jour. Sci. Instruments*, April, 1949, Vol. 26, p. 113.

64. Potter, J. L., "Sweep Circuits," *Proc. IRE*, June, 1938, Vol. 26, p. 713.

65. Puckle, O. S., *Time Bases*. New York: John Wiley and Sons, Inc., 1943.

66. Pullen, Keats A., Jr., "The Cathode-Coupled Amplifier," *Proc. IRE*, June, 1946, Vol. 34, p. 402.

67. Ramsay, H. T., "Grid Current with RC Coupling," *Wireless Engr.*, April, 1949, Vol. 26, p. 113.

68. Reich, H. J., *Theory and Applications of Electron Tubes*. New York: McGraw-Hill Book Co., Inc., 1944.

69. Rich, Stanley R. and Rosen, A. H., "Sonic Navigation System," *Electronics*, November, 1948, Vol. 21, p. 92.

70. Robinson C. V., "Improved Multivibrator Quenching Circuit," *Rev. Sci. Instruments*, October, 1949, Vol. 20, p. 750.

71. Roush, R. G., "Tone Burst Generator," *Electronics*, July, 1947, Vol. 20, p. 92.

72. Roush, R. G. and Hamburger, Ferdinand, "Light-Flash Generator," *Electronics*, November, 1948, Vol. 21, p. 100.

73. Rowlands, S., "A New Method of Determining Short Half-Life Periods," *Jour. Sci. Instruments*, June, 1948, Vol. 25, p. 218.

74. Scal, Robert K. F., "Cathode Coupled Half-Shot Multivibrator," *Electronics*, September, 1947, Vol. 20, p. 199.

75. Scheuch, D. R. and Cowan, F. B., "Laboratory Pulse Generator with Variable Time Delay," *Rev. Sci. Instruments*, June, 1946, Vol. 17, p. 223.

76. Schlesinger, Kurt, "Oscillation Generator," *U.S. Patent* 2,383,822. August 28, 1945.

77. Schoenfeld, Robert L., "A Double Pulse Constant Current Stimulator," *Rev. Sci. Instruments*, November, 1949, Vol. 20, p. 827.

78. Seeley, Samuel, *Electron-Tube Circuits*. New York: McGraw-Hill Book Co., Inc., 1950.

79. Shenk, E. R., "Multivibrator-Applied Theory and Design," *Electronics*, Part I, January, 1944, Vol. 17, p. 136; Part II, February, 1944, Vol. 17, p. 140; Part III, March, 1944, Vol. 17, p. 138.

80. Silver, M. and Shadowitz, A., "High Ratio Multivibrator Frequency Divider," *Elec. Commun.*, June, 1948, Vol. 25, p. 160.

81. Snowden, S. C., "*Analysis of Multivibrator*. Ph.D. Thesis, California Institute of Technology, 1945.

82. Sowerby, G. M., "Cathode-Coupled Multivibrator," *Wireless World*, July, 1948, Vol. 54, p. 249.

83. Stansel, S. F., "Some Analysis of Waveshapes Used in Harmonic Producers," *Bell System Technical Journal*, July, 1941, Vol. 20, p. 331.

84. Sturtevant, Julian M., "A Voltage Controlled Multivibrator," *Electronics*, October, 1949, Vol. 22, p. 144.

85. Sulzer, P. G., "A Wide-Range Saw-Tooth Generator," *Rev. Sci. Instruments*, January, 1949, Vol. 20, p. 78.

86. van der Pol, Balth., "On Relaxation Oscillations," *Phil. Mag.*, November, 1926, Vol. 2, p. 978.

87. van der Pol, Balth., "Nonlinear Theory of Electric Oscillation," *Proc. IRE*, September, 1934, Vol. 22, p. 1051.

88. Vecchiacchi, F., "Meccanismo di funzionamento e frequenza del multivibratore (The Mechanism of Operation and the Frequency of the Multivibrator)," *Alta Frequenza*, December, 1940, Vol. 9, p. 745.

89. Wald, Martin, "The Relaxation Amplifier," *Wireless Engr.*, December, 1941, Vol. 18, p. 483.

90. Walker, Ronald C., "Simple High Speed Relay," *Electronics*, February, 1950, Vol. 23, p. 150.

91. Watanabe, Yasusi, "Some Remarks on the Multivibrator," *Proc. IRE*, February, 1930, Vol. 18, p. 327.

92. Watt, B. E., "High Speed Pulse Recording Circuit," *Rev. Sci. Instruments*, September, 1946, Vol. 17, p. 338.

93. Webb, H. W. and Becker, G. E., "Theory of the Multivibrator," *J. Applied Phys.*, December, 1944, Vol. 15, p. 825.

94. Webb, R. C. and Morgan, J. M., "Simplied Television for Industry," *Electronics*, June, 1950, Vol. 23, p. 70.

95. White, W. C. and Lord, H. W., "The Reciprocator—A Ring Oscillator Comprising Two One-Shot Multivibrators," *Electronics*, November, 1949, Vol. 22, p. 70.

96. Williams, F. C. and Moody, N. F., "Ranging Circuits, Linear Time Base Generators and Associated Circuits," *Proc. IEE*, Radiolocation Conv. No. 1, 1946, Vol. 93, p. 320.

PROBLEMS

9-1 What is the minimum value of R that can be used in the single-cycle

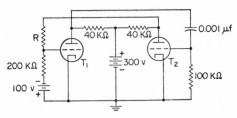

Prob. 9-1.

multivibrator shown? The tube type is a 6SN7.

9-2 The switch has been open for a long time. If it is closed at $t = ($

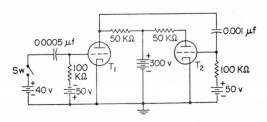

Prob. 9-2.

sketch and label the plate voltage of T_2. The tube type is a 6SN7.

9-3 In the circuit of Fig. 9-3 let $R_{g1} = R_{g2} = 250,000$ ohms, $R_{b1} = R_{b2} = 25,000$ ohms, $R_{c1} = 200,000$ ohms, $C_{c2} = 0.001$ microfarad, $E_{cc1} = -75$ volts, and $E_{bb} = 300$ volts. The tube type is a 6SN7. If a large, narrow positive pulse is applied to the grid of T_1, sketch and label a complete set of grid and plate wave forms.

9-4 Using the circuit of Fig. 9-10 and the parameters of problem 9-3, with $E_{cc2} = +150$ volts, sketch and label a complete set of grid and plate wave forms. The circuit is to be triggered by a large, narrow, positive pulse at the grid of T_1.

9-5 Using the circuit of Fig. 9-17 and the parameters of problem 9-3 where applicable, sketch and label a complete set of grid and plate wave forms. A 0.25-henry inductor is used in the grid circuit of T_2. The circuit is to be triggered by a large, narrow, positive pulse at the grid of T_1.

9-6 Using the circuit of Fig. 9-23 and the parameters of problem 9-3, sketch and label a complete set of grid and plate wave forms. The value of

R_{s2} is 250,000 ohms. The circuit is to be triggered by a large, narrow, positive pulse at the grid of T_1.

9-7 Using the circuit of Fig. 9-27 and the parameters of the example in Sec. 9-6 with the exception of R_k, plot a curve of Δt vs. R_k, for the complete operating range.

9-8 Using the circuit of Fig. 9-27 and the parameters of the example in Sec. 9-6 with the exception of R_{g2}, plot a curve of Δt vs. R_{g2}, for the complete operating range.

9-9 In the circuit of Fig. 9-40, let $R_{b1} = 20,000$ ohms, $R_{b2} = 40,000$ ohms, $C_{c1} = 0.002$ microfarad, $C_{c2} = 0.001$ microfarad, $R_{g1} = 250,000$ ohms, $R_{g2} = 50,000$ ohms, and $E_{bb} = 300$ volts. The tube type is a 6SN7. Sketch and label a complete set of plate and grid wave forms.

9-10 Repeat problem 9-9, using two type 6CB6 tubes. The suppressor grids are connected to the cathodes, and the screen grids are connected to a constant potential of 150 volts.

9-11 In the circuit of Fig. 9-49 let $R_{b1} = 50,000$ ohms, $R_{b2} = 10,000$ ohms, $R_{g1} = 250,000$ ohms, $R_{g2} = 250,000$ ohms, $C_{c2} = 0.001$ microfarad, and $E_{bb} = 300$ volts. The tube type is a 6SN7. Find the value of R_k such that the system is at the critical point between free-running and single-cycle operation.

9-12 In the circuit of Fig. 9-51 let $R_{g1} = 100,000$ ohms, $R_{b1} = 100,000$ ohms, $R_{b2} = 25,000$ ohms, $R_s = 100,000$ ohms, $C_s = 0.01$ microfarad, $R_k = 5000$ ohms, and $E_{bb} = 300$ volts. Sketch and label the grid, plate, and cathode voltages of both tubes. The tube is a 6SN7.

9-13 In the circuit of Fig. 9-53 let $R_{g1} = 50,000$ ohms, $R_{b1} = 20,000$ ohms, $R_{b2} = 100,000$ ohms, $C_{c1} = 0.01$ microfarad, $R_{g2} = 50,000$ ohms, $C_2 = 0.01$ microfarad, $R_k = 15,000$ ohms, and $E_{bb} = 300$ volts. The tube is a 6SN7. Find the minimum value of E_{cc1} which will keep the system in a nonoscillatory state.

9-14 Using the circuit of Fig. 9-53 and the parameters of problem 9-13, sketch and label the grid, plate, and cathode voltages for E_{cc1} equal to 25 per cent of the value found in problem 9-13.

9-15 A plate-coupled, free-running multivibrator is modified by addition

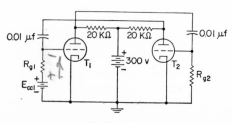

Prob. 9-15.

of a positive voltage in series with the grid resistor of one of the tubes, as shown. If this voltage is adjusted to $+250$ volts it is found that T_1 conducts exactly half as long as it does when the voltage is zero. With zero grid voltage the multivibrator is free-running at 500 cycles per second. With the $+250$-volt source connected to the grid of T_1, what is the change in plate voltage of T_2 when it starts to conduct? Assume that both tubes have a constant static conducting resistance of 10,000 ohms.

9-16 Sketch and label a complete set of plate and grid wave forms for the

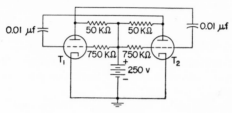

Prob. 9-16.

circuit shown. The tube is a 6SN7.

9-17 The circuit shown has been at rest for a long time. A large,

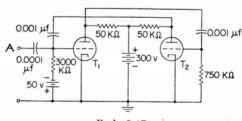

Prob. 9-17.

narrow, positive pulse is applied to A. Sketch and label a complete set of grid and plate wave forms. The tube is a 6SN7.

9-18 Sketch and label a complete set of grid and plate wave forms for

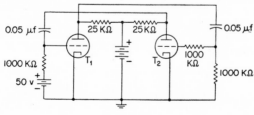

Prob. 9-18.

the circuit shown. The tube is a 6SN7.

9-19 Using the circuit of Fig. 9-54, let $R_{b1} = 40,000$ ohms, $R_{g1} = 500,000$ ohms, $E_{cc1} = 250$ volts, $C_1 = 0.01$ microfarad, $R_k = 5000$ ohms, $R_{b2} = 1000$ ohms, $R_{c2} = 22,000$ ohms, $R_{g2} = 15,000$ ohms, and $E_{bb} = 250$ volts, sketch and label the plate, grid, and cathode voltages. The tube is a 6SN7.

9-20 In the circuit of Fig. 9-55 let $R_{b1} = 20,000$ ohms, $R_{b2} = 40,000$ ohms, $C_{c1} = 0.002$ microfarad, $C_{c2} = 0.001$ microfarad, $R_{g1} = 250,000$ ohms, $R_{g2} = 50,000$ ohms, $R_k = 5000$ ohms, and $E_{bb} = 300$ volts. The tube type is a 6SN7. Sketch and label a complete set of plate, grid, and cathode wave forms.

9-21 The output of a radiation detection instrument consists of positive, rectangular pulses of 100 volts amplitude. These pulses vary in width from 25 to 175 microseconds, but the minimum time between pulses is 500 microseconds. Devise an instrument to count only those pulses which are exactly 100 microseconds in length.

9-22 Devise a system for the production testing and adjustment of delay networks. A 50-volt, 20-microsecond, positive pulse is available,

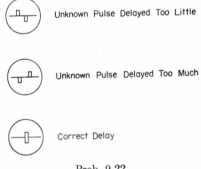

Unknown Pulse Delayed Too Little

Unknown Pulse Delayed Too Much

Correct Delay

Prob. 9-22.

which has a pulse repetition frequency of 500 pulses per second. The specifications for the system require that the same pulse be put into a standard delay network (which has a delay of 800 microseconds) and the unknown network simultaneously. The two output pulses are then to be applied to a cathode-ray tube such that the standard pulse is shown as a negative deflection, and the pulse of unknown delay as a positive deflection. The delay of the networks being tested may then be adjusted until the bases of the two pulses are coincident. Using the available input pulse give the block diagram and the schematic diagram of a circuit which will fulfill the above requirements.

9-23 Show how an oscillating system can be constructed from a series of single-cycle multivibrators.

INDEX